Chemicals for Crop Improvement

and

Pest Management

THIRD EDITION

Other titles of interest

Books

HUTZINGER *et al*:	Chlorinated Dioxins and Related Compounds
KOREN:	Environmental Health and Safety
MEETHAM *et al*:	Atmospheric Pollution, 4th edition
MERCIER:	Criteria (Dose/Effect Relationships) for Organochlorine Pesticides
SCORER:	Air Pollution
STEEDMAN *et al*:	Chemistry for the Applied Sciences
STRAUSS:	Industrial Gas Cleaning, 2nd edition

Journals*

Chemosphere

Progress in Water Technology

*Free specimen copy available on request

Chemicals for Crop Improvement
and
Pest Management

THIRD EDITION

by

M. B. GREEN

G. S. HARTLEY

and

T. F. WEST

PERGAMON PRESS

OXFORD · NEW YORK · BEIJING · FRANKFURT
SÃO PAULO · SYDNEY · TOKYO · TORONTO

U.K.	Pergamon Press, Headington Hill Hall, Oxford OX3 0BW, England
U.S.A.	Pergamon Press, Maxwell House, Fairview Park, Elmsford, New York 10523, U.S.A.
PEOPLE'S REPUBLIC OF CHINA	Pergamon Press, Room 4037, Qianmen Hotel, Beijing, People's Republic of China
FEDERAL REPUBLIC OF GERMANY	Pergamon Press, Hammerweg 6, D-6242 Kronberg, Federal Republic of Germany
BRAZIL	Pergamon Editora, Rua Eça de Queiros, 346, CEP 04011, Paraiso, São Paulo, Brazil
AUSTRALIA	Pergamon Press Australia, P.O. Box 544, Potts Point, N.S.W. 2011, Australia
JAPAN	Pergamon Press, 8th Floor, Matsuoka Central Building, 1-7-1 Nishishinjuku, Shinjuku-ku, Tokyo 160, Japan
CANADA	Pergamon Press Canada, Suite No. 271, 253 College Street, Toronto, Ontario, Canada M5T 1R5

First edition 1969
Second edition 1977
Reprinted (with corrections and additions) 1979, 1985
Third edition 1987

Library of Congress Cataloging-in-Publication Data

Green, Maurice B. (Maurice Berkeley)
Chemicals for crop improvement and pest
management.
Rev. ed. of: Chemicals for crop protection and
pest control.
Includes bibliographies and indexes.
1. Pesticides. I. Hartley, G. S. (Gilbert Spencer)
II. West, T. F. (Trustham Frederick) III. Title.
TP248.P47G74   1987   668'.65   86-25404

British Library Cataloguing in Publication Data

Green, M. B.
Chemicals for crop improvement and pest
management.—3rd ed.
1. Pesticides
I. Title II. Hartley, G. S. III. West, T. F.
IV. Green, M. B. Chemicals for crop
protection and pest control
632'.95   SBC51

ISBN 0-08-030250-5 Hardcover
ISBN 0-08-030249-1 Flexicover

Printed in Great Britain by A. Wheaton & Co. Ltd., Exeter

Preface to Third Edition

The first edition, by Hartley and West, called "Chemicals for Pest Control" was one of a series of manuals designed to introduce students to various branches of the chemical industry. In it we attempted to describe progress and problems in the development of chemical pesticides and the operational environment into which they had to be fitted.

The subject it dealt with was advancing rapidly and the book needed updating and expansion. The impact of the attitudes of the general public and of growers and the increasing importance of regulatory authorities concerned with safety had to be reassessed, and the treatment of economic aspects, in which the first edition was deficient, improved. In response to some critics, the list of chemicals, limited in the first edition to illustrative types, was extended to include most of those in commercial use. This major task of revision was undertaken by Dr M. B. Green. The current edition has been produced by the co-operative efforts of all three authors.

Some critics of the previous editions thought we had given inadequate coverage of non-chemical control measures. We ask them to accept, as we do, the limitations of our title. The *book is about chemicals*. We are well aware that chemicals cannot provide an answer to all agricultural problems and that, for many others, they may not be the best answer or may need integration with some other tactic. We do not pretend that our book is a general text on control of agricultural pests, but only on the chemicals which contribute to the total strategy. We have, however, revised chapter contents and sequence so as to explain very broadly in Chapters 1 and 2 where toxic chemicals fit in to nature and farming. We hope the book will be of some interest and use to advisers on farming problems, but it is addressed primarily to readers with some grounding in chemistry who find themselves further back in the army of scientific workers engaged in the fight for more, better and safer agricultural production. We trust that, if the book is read by field advisers or growers, it will not be their only book and we must emphasize, as was done in the publisher's preface to the Russian translation of the second edition, that any practical use of a chemical in agriculture *must* conform to the statutory regulations of the country and, *advisedly*, to local experience of soil and climate and cropping practice.

Regulations for the use of pesticides are issued from time to time by national governments. Practical guides for use in most countries are prepared under the guidance of expert committees, including government representatives, and conform to government regulations as well as keeping up to date with the science of the subject. In the U.K. the British Crop Protection

Council issues such guides. The current "Handbook of Weed Control" appears in two volumes edited by J.D. Fryer and R. Makepeace; the first volume is on Principles, the second on Recommendations. "The Handbook of Pest and Disease Control" is now edited by N. Scopes and M. Lidieu. Both books are published by Blackwell, of Oxford.

The title was extended, in the second edition, by the words "Crop Protection" to justify the inclusion of chemicals assisting growth or harvesting by means other than direct removal of competitors, predators or parasites. The word "crop" also served to indicate over-riding interest in agriculture rather than veterinary medicine or use in public health or fabric preservation.

We have now replaced "Protection" by "Improvement". The first operation to protect crops is to construct fences to prevent the untimely intrusion of livestock; but although these measures need products of the chemical industry to prevent rotting of wood, rusting of iron or shorting of electric current, no one would expect us to include them except, possibly, the first. On the other hand, many chemicals have desirable effects on crop growth or pest behaviour which, though not directly controlling, assist, are assisted by or make demands on, other methods of control. They are necessarily associated with traditional pesticides because their properties are usually revealed by the same screening techniques and their marketing is conveniently dealt with by the same teams. In assessment of risks to consumers and the environment they are dealt with by the same regulatory authorities, and, in the relevant Acts in the U.S.A., they are now actually called pesticides. We would have preferred to have avoided this extension of usage but no satisfactory word has been proposed which would include chemicals having effects on growth not necessarily lethal or harmful. If such a word existed it would properly be used in many places in this book, especially in the title of Chapter 2. Agrochemicals is an excellent all-embracing word in respect of agriculture and horticulture but, unfortunately, excludes non-agricultural uses.

Questions are often raised about the word "pests" and its extension from reference to troublesome insects or other small animals to include competing weeds and microscopic pathogens. The Oxford English Dictionary gives two meanings: (1) (rare) "a deadly epidemic disease, specially bubonic plague" (this meaning now persisting in "pestilence"); (2) "any person or thing that is noxious, destructive or troublesome". There seems less reason to restrict the word to insects than to extend it, as we do here, and as is now very general in related literature, to weeds and pathogens. Readers may be amused to note that the dictionary includes "pest-weed" meaning not a particularly bad weed but a species (butterburr, *Petasites vulgaris*) which was supposed to provide protection against the plague.

The U.S. Federal Environmental Pesticide Control Act elaborates the definition of "pest" by adding ". . . or any other form of terrestrial or aquatic plant or animal life or . . . micro-organisms which the administrator declares to be a pest". One is reminded of the executioner's song in Gilbert and Sullivan's "Mikado". We would not like to admit the right of anyone to verbal dictatorship, but, for the present, the administrator's "little list" is much the same as ours.

We have also, in the title, changed "Control" to "Management" in conformity with general practice, but although we are very much in favour of integrating chemical with other tools of management, we must repeat that this book is about the chemicals.

We should perhaps explain another choice of words in the text. "Agriculture" in many books and journals is distinguished from "Horti-culture". The former is concerned with large-scale operation on annual crops or pasture, although in some contexts, e.g. the New Zealand "A and P shows", distinction is made between "Agricultural" and "Pastoral". The latter is concerned with operations on a more intensive scale to produce vegetables for local consumption or cut flowers for export or fruit of all kinds on a very large scale. The human operators are often distinguished as graziers, farmers, market gardeners, orchardists or others. In this book we use "agriculture" and "farmer" to include the others except when referring to some specialist use or situation.

This book is primarily concerned with protective chemicals used in agriculture in this extended sense but, of course, there are other uses of pesticides which have varying degrees of interaction with agriculture. Insecticides are essential to protect public health and alleviate human suffering caused by disease-carrying insects. Except in the sense that many insecticides so used are also used in agriculture, this subject is outside our boundaries. Use against insect pests which debilitate farm animals by the irritation or tissue damage they cause is closer to use in crop protection since the crop often finds its way to the consumer, and so provides the farmer's income, in the form of animal products. Many insects and fungi attack materials of construction. These may be of crop origin — timber products, fibres and leather — and some have important use back on the farm. The crop must in most cases be stored and transported and pesticides used in various ways in post-harvest protection are included, with reference mainly in Chapters 2, 7 and 10.

This book does not aim to provide a complete catalogue of the structures and properties of all chemicals in current use as pesticides. Reference to works designed to do this are given at the end of chapters. The chemicals of which brief description has been given in this book have been selected to illustrate various aspects of the whole subject.

However, wherever possible all related compounds of a particular chemical type have been tabulated. This has been done to illustrate how a particular activity is not generally associated with one particular chemical structure but is spread over a chemical group with peaks, generally dependent on physicochemical or biophysical factors rather than on chemical nature, which represent the compounds selected for commercial development. The student entering this field should know what is set out here but if the particular chemicals on which he will find himself working are not listed here they have probably not yet been discovered or developed for commercial use.

The index of chemicals includes values of melting points of solids, vapour pressures, solubilities in water and acute oral toxicities. In the literature many compounds are listed as "insoluble", yet there may be great differences between them in absorption into leaves and roots, in translocation in the plant and in movement in and leaching from soil. It is difficult to measure small solubilities. Toxicity data should also be treated with caution as values vary with the species and sex of test animals and the solvents or suspending agents in which the compound was applied. Only major differences should be taken as significant.

Some words very familiar in agricultural and pesticide technology may be unknown in their context to students of chemistry. A short glossary has therefore been provided. Detailed references to original literature have not been given because the works referred to in the suggestions for further reading at the end of each chapter are usually textbooks or review articles which include extensive lists of references.

There is much public opposition to the use of pesticides. A large body of restrictive legislation is designed to safeguard workers in factory or farm and to protect the consumer and the environment. The associated problems are mainly discussed in Chapter 25 but some specific points are more conveniently considered in the technical chapters. There have been faults in the use of pesticides, but there have also been great achievements. There have also been faults in the opposition to pesticides, largely due to imbalance of readily available information but sometimes to uninformed prejudice. We hope this book will be of some help to sincere defenders of our environmental heritage who should be able to skip the detailed chemistry and find some value in comment from a chemist's point of view.

Contents

1

Toxic Chemicals in Nature

Chemical processes are those which rearrange the linkages between atoms to form different molecules and result in tangible changes in the matter which the molecules make up. The material changes are evident — solid to liquid, liquid to gas, cold to hot, sour to sweet, scented to stinking — the underlying chemical processes are not. Our knowledge of them, often firmly established and precise but always incomplete, is inductive.

The student of chemistry well knows that more, and more varied, chemical processes go on in his body than in his laboratory or factory, but most men and women tend to regard the subject and processes as fabrications of man, if not indeed of the devil. They fear and distrust the unseen. The first step towards overcoming this is to appreciate that all the pleasant changes in the world around us arise just as much from chemical reactions as the unpleasant. We cannot, however, in this limited book, discuss the chemistry of the wonderfully elaborate structures of normal living organisms. Our subject is the apparently darker side of the effect of chemistry on life — and death. We must undertake the difficult task of introducing some balance — a word often used in other contexts in this subject — into the place of poisonous chemicals in agriculture. Our first step is to look briefly at poisonous chemicals in nature.

The struggle between prey and predators, hosts and parasites is as old as life itself. It is not surprising that the natural chemical weapon has evolved along with others. Probably it was at first an offensive weapon used by less mobile animals to prey upon more mobile ones — as in the poisoned tips of the tentacles of the primitive sea anemones. It is now, however, just as often used in defence, or even as a deterrent. Thus the plant deadly nightshade is highly toxic to most animals, but these have learned (in the evolutionary sense) to avoid it.

Examples could be quoted, from every major class of living organisms, of species which in nature poison other species. Some of the most toxic of known chemicals are of natural origin — strychnine, curare, snake-venoms and many others — a fact often forgotten by those who condemn the chemical pesticides industry for "unnatural" practices.

The generating species may use the poison to teach the potential consumer "if you eat me you will be sick". It may use it to kill in self-defence or to kill or only immobilize as a preliminary to eating. The operations are necessary for survival but we humans tend to regard the tooth and claw as "clean" weapons and the poison as "dirty". We regret the "necessity" of

1

mechanical warfare but regard chemical warfare as totally abhorrent. In reality the contrast is not so clear. The long-term consequences of mechanical injury are often more serious than those of near-lethal poisoning. The butcher bird, which impales its living prey on sharp thorns to await consumption, compares very unfavourably, on humanitarian standards, with the parasitic wasp which anaesthetizes its prey before inserting its eggs.

A great many lethal, warning or repellent chemicals are produced by green plants. These are far the most versatile of chemical operators. We say "green" plants, although we should include bacteria and fungi, to distinguish from the large industrial erections of glass and steel and other artificial fabrics which, in other contexts, we should call "chemical plants". (This dual use of the word can give rise to confusion in this subject. In this chapter "plant" means a living organism of the vegetable kingdom.)

There has been a long history of the use of plant poisons to help food collection. Curare is the poison favoured by jungle dwellers to anoint the tips of blow-darts when hunting. Dried and powdered leaves of species of Derris and Lonchocarpus are spread on rivers in tropical East Asia and South America to stupefy fish, causing them to float idly on the surface. The Chinese have for many centuries used Derris as an insecticide. The Romans used false hellebore (*Schoenocaulon*, formerly called *Veratrum*, species) to kill both insects and rodents. Nicotine was used as an insecticide, certainly before 1690, in France. Pyrethrum powder has long been used and extraction of the active insecticide began around 1850. Several other vegetable products have had local uses. Two have recently created renewed interest since the active principles have been isolated. Azidirachtin is obtained from two related species of the Mahogany family, the neem tree and Chinaberry, the berries, leaves and stems of which have long been used as repellents and insecticides in India. If, despite the repellency, caterpillars feed on the leaves, the compound interferes with the cycle of moults, slows down their growth and eventually kills them. Myristicin, an essential oil from nutmeg, has recently been found in the edible root of parsnip: it is moderately insecticidal and strongly synergistic with pyrethrins.

Several thousand species of plants have been tested in the laboratory against representative insects but the only natural insecticides of present commercial importance are nicotine, rotenone (Derris), ryanodine and pyrethrum. The last named is, of course, the most widely used and the only one which has been successfully — and very successfully — taken as a model for synthetic analogues. It is therefore considered in a separate chapter.

Natural compounds are not, in general, less poisonous to man than synthetic chemicals, except in that only those of low toxicity have been exploited. Even in this choice, however, some illogical bias in favour of natural chemicals exists. Sabadilla, the insecticide in false hellebore mentioned above, was at one time approved without question as a natural product. It was discarded because it was not effective enough, but a close relative of the species from which it was obtained was later found to be responsible for severe deformities in lambs born to ewes which had consumed it. Of the four "botanicals" still in use, only nicotine is a powerful mammalian poison and it came into use as an insecticide after tobacco-smoking had become a widely accepted practice. The others have very low mammalian toxicity, especially pyrethrum. Ryanodin is more selective among orchard pests than the others. Derris is, of course, a very potent fish poison. It would be very unwise to assume that, because a chemical generated by a plant helps its defence against natural predators and parasites, it obligingly leaves man alone.

Only if the generating plant is one which has a long history of harmless consumption by man is the assumption of safety valid. Any candidate pesticide would have an easier passage through the safety tests and regulations if it could be shown to be a normal constituent of an accepted foodstuff, because, although positive physiological effect of a compound in relatively high dose can be established, the *absence* of *any* effect following prolonged consumption of trace amounts is always subject to question. This encourages the chemical search among plants which have long been consumed by man and experiments were conducted at the University of Wisconsin on many plants grown in soil completely free from known pesticides. The finding of myristicin (5-allyl-1-methoxy-2,3-methylene-dioxybenzene) in parsnip and 2-phenylethyl isothiocyanate in brassica (cabbage, etc.) species, both insecticidal, was one result. The latter compound, and the well-known mustard oils (allyl and other isothiocyanates) are toxic in high dosage. Brassicas in excessive amount (equivalent to a daily consumption of about 5 kg by man) are known to produce severe anaemia in cattle, but any doubt about long-term effects in man is resolved by knowledge that our ancestors have eaten the food regularly through their long lives.

So far, however, no commercially useful insecticide has been derived from research on normal foodstuffs. Research on these lines by the chemical industry is rather inhibited by the uncertainty of valid patent registration which would be necessary to recover costs. The industry is more interested in using the structures of natural toxicants as models for synthesis of new compounds. There have been several developments on these lines in addition to the outstanding pyrethroids, but the natural sources of the original compounds were not accepted major foodstuffs and, in one case, nereistoxin, came from an annelid, *Lumbriconeresis heteropoda*, used in Japan as a fish bait.

Potent insecticidal compounds have been isolated from extracts of the fern *Aspidium filix-mas* and Japanese work on *piericidin* indicated that common fungi such as streptomyces species also may produce new types of insecticides. The large number of microbial cultures under examination for antifungal and antibacterial activity may provide many new leads for synthetic pesticides.

Development of resistance to synthetic insecticides in species which were at first susceptible has been a serious problem. The subject is considered more fully in Chapter 24, but we must here note that resistance is not confined to the synthetics. In Nature it appears to take a different form as a result of the generation of natural insecticides being localized, of preference of laying females for particular plant species, and of the very long history of interaction. Species of insects have adapted in the course of evolution to avoid plant species toxic to them *or* have developed a special biochemical mechanism of immunity. The avoiders have no need of resistance. The resistors have no need of avoidance: indeed they gain the advantage of an unpopular food source.

The caterpillar of the monarch butterfly, for example, feeds exclusively on some members of the family Asclepiadaceae, most of which contain a powerful poison. The tobacco plant contains nicotine, a very general poison used to some extent as a commercial insecticide, but some species of insect, e.g. the tobacco hornworm, feed on it with impunity. There are broadly two types of biochemical resistance mechanisms. Some nominal poisons are not reactive at the toxic site but need conversion by some normal metabolism to the active toxicant, a process which Sir Rudolph Peters called "lethal synthesis". If this conversion is blocked, the insect can avoid being harmed and even accumulate the poison and, as in the monarch caterpillar, pass the toxicity on to the pupa and butterfly where it protects them against predatory birds. It takes more than one insect to kill, but the bird is made painfully sick, a better strategy for the monarch, as a species, because the birds learn to avoid the characteristic strong colour and pattern of the insects. They avoid them even when the caterpillar has fed on a much less poisonous asclepiad. They even avoid another species of insect, aptly called the viceroy, which is quite harmless but has imitated the monarch's appearance.

In the other main mechanism of biochemical resistance, more usual and more diverse in detail, some alternative "detoxifying" reaction is developed in the resistant species which greatly reduces the amount of the toxicant that can reach the vulnerable site. Such detoxification can be achieved by specialized enzymes, by increase in content of a normal enzyme or change of accessibility through cuticles and membranes.

This diversification into different extremes of response has taken a very long time to evolve and could only have evolved in a complex population of interacting species with specific mechanisms of synthesis and preferences. Evolution of species producing and adapting to poisons among other weapons has been going on for many million times longer than our use of synthetic insecticides. We do not know how many potential hosts and parasites have become extinct because they have failed in development of toxic attack or defence.

There is now left a moderately stable balance but subject to drastic changes which are not satisfactorily explained — irregularly periodic plagues of mice or caterpillars and occasional almost complete extinction of some established tree species such as the sweet chestnut in the U.S.A. and, in 1976, the elm in the U.K. Certainly synthetic chemicals are not the only disturbers. When pyrethrins are extracted from their natural situation in the leaves and flowers of chrysanthemum species and sprayed inside houses the mosquitos are faced with a new menace and have responded by selection of more resistant strains, though not as effectively as to DDT. The latter probably produced more extreme response because it is much more persistent and was, for a period, much more widely used.

A compound which nicely illustrates the absurdity of making sweeping distinctions between natural and synthetic chemicals is monofluoroacetic acid. Synthesized during World War II, it was found to be a powerful poison of a novel kind. It behaved as a good insecticide systemic in plants but was considered too toxic to mammals to be safe. Its synthesis required drastic conditions, but, once formed, it was very stable and expected to be too persistent in the environment. At the time of its discovery, but with no cross-knowledge because of wartime restrictions, it was found to be the natural poison responsible for many deaths of cattle eating the flush growth of a localized weed of rangeland in South Africa. The land itself was not poisoned. The compound, made by normal temperature biochemistry in the aqueous tissues of the plant, was vulnerable to biochemical destruction, even in plants which did not make it and by soil microflora, especially *pseudomonas* species. The compound was at one time widely used as a rodenticide and this use in extensive hill pasture against rabbits and opossums continues in New Zealand where there is now some suspicion of resistance. It has been found in several wild legumes in isolated semi-arid areas of Australia and the local opossums have been found to survive up to ten times the normal dosage. This degree of resistance is sufficient in regions where the toxic plant contributes only part of the diet.

Toxic compounds are produced in plants not only to warn or kill would-be animal consumers but also for protection against parasitic fungi and even as weapons of competition with other plants. The parasitic fungi responsible for much crop loss are mostly very host-specific. The mechanism, in most cases where research to elucidate it has been successful, is the generation by the resistant species of a chemical fungicide. These have been isolated and identified in Australia from the pea. *Pisum sativum*, and in the U.K. from the broad bean, *Vicia faba*. Several other examples could be quoted. None of the extracts has been found commercially successful when applied to other plants. The compounds are unstable and successful only in their natural host because locally produced in response to the attempted invasion by the parasite, and often to other local injury. They are not, of course, successful against the successful parasite. The objective in this research is to find some natural fungicide in species A, which will, extracted or synthesized and applied externally to species B, protect the latter against its own specific parasite.

Rather more progress has resulted from examining more general fungicides produced in some tree species, which help to preserve the dead-cell heartwood, necessary for mechanical strength in the growing tree and converted timber. The heartwood of some species is outstandingly resistant to saprophytic fungi and wood-boring insects which use fungi to pre-digest their food. The resistance is partly mechanical, the structure being more dense in resistant woods and the cellulose fibres being more tightly enclosed in polymeric lignin. The polymerizing monomers are phenolic-substituted unsaturated alcohols, chiefly 3-(3-methoxy-4-hydroxyphenyl) allyl alcohol. Associated polyphenols and quinones are generally fungicidal in high concentration. Such compounds, released at high temperature when the practice of burning the ends of oak roof beams was common, were probably responsible for the protection against rot. The later practice of increasing strength and durability of wood for special purposes by impregnation with polymerizing phenol-formaldehyde resins can be regarded as continuing a process where nature left off. Resin-enclosed fibre-glass has now, of course, largely replaced such products. Impregnation of less durable timbers for outside use by coal-tar creosote is still much used and is semi-natural, but longer durability is obtained by borates and arsenates of chromium and copper.

There is a wealth of empirical knowledge among practical growers about desirable and undesirable crop sequences and intercropping. Management considerations play an important part and effects are often associated with pest build-up in the soil and with nutrient demand, but there is evidence in many cases that one crop or weed species has adverse effect on another close neighbour by a chemical effect of root exudation or even vapour transfer. Many plants, where grown in water culture, liberate compounds active on seedlings even when the root medium has been diluted with fresh nutrient solution. Suppression or delay of germination of seeds is the most frequent response, but early growth is often reduced or in some way abnormal. The advantage for an established or early-germinating plant is obvious but poisoning of competitors — allelopathy, as it has been called — is less clearly demonstrated under field conditions. Other factors are usually operative in competition and the chemical effect is reduced by adsorption on soil colloids and decomposition by microflora, but there is no doubt that the severe depression of cereal yields by many grass weeds is much greater than by apparently comparable growth of many other weeds and that phytotoxic chemicals are responsible. Quitch grass, wild oat and Italian ryegrass are particularly suppressive, but so far no herbicides useful by spray application or directly suggestive of exploitable synthetic analogues have been found. The natural compounds have been too unstable, but a transient effect can be very useful in natural competition if it delays seed germination until the chemical producer is sufficiently established for competition for water, nutrients and light to take over. Also the transient compound is continually produced: a spray is desirably applied only once in a season. Tetronic acid $(CH_3.CO.O.CH:CO)$ is implicated in Italian ryegrass but is not the sole agent. An American range-shrub, *Encelia farinosa*, appears to keep its territory clear of weed seedlings by 3-acetyl-6-methoxybenzaldehyde washed off the leaves. This might be considered a more feeble and unstable analogue of more active chlorobenzoic acids.

Seeds developed in fleshy fruits are usually associated with a chemical inhibitor of germination so that they germinate only after becoming free and subject to rain washing. Often some other mechanism is involved to ensure germination only after winter rest. A period of freezing may be sufficient, but, in many of the most troublesome weeds of cultivation, a rather elaborate microclimate sequence is necessary and the seeds are able to remain dormant during pre-crop cultivation, germinating only after the crop is present and future mechanical removal difficult. A trick developed by some obligate parasitic plants, various *Orobranche* and *Striga* species, is to require the presence of a "trigger" compound exuded by the roots of the host plant. In the case of *Striga*, a troublesome parasite of maize in the semi-tropics the exudate is a mixture of stereospecific tricyclic sugars. Application of aqueous extracts of maize seed to the land before sowing in the hope of initiating germination so that the prematurely emerged parasite can be killed have not been practicable.

Natural chemicals are also used by parasitic fungi and insects to modify the growth of plants to their advantage. Some, injected by insects, cause expanded leaves to curl so enclosing the pest and protecting it from predators or causing galls of modified plant tissue to develop within which the larval form can feed in complete seclusion. Elucidation of the chemistry of such abnormal growth might lead to modification exploitable in our own interest. This has already happened in examination of the effect of a fungal parasite of rice which causes elongation of the stem between nodes. Gibberellins produced by the fungus in artificial media are used to increase peduncle length in grapes and flowers and their closer study has helped in discovery of compounds having the opposite effect.

We may summarize this brief exemplification of the use of poisons in nature by repeating that Nature, as usually understood, is the inter-related totality of plants and animals. All these living creatures are chemical factories of varied size and very great complexity. They have to be to live. Most of their chemical processes are used directly for their own growth and life, but many are used for attack and defence in their fight for survival. Man's use of chemical pesticides is only an extension of ancient techniques. It is usually much less precise, but is no less natural than the replacement of the digging stick by the steel plough.

Further Reading

Crosby, D. G. *Natural Pest Control Agents*, American Chemical Society, Washington, D.C., 1976.

Feuell, A. J. *Insecticides*, vol. 4. In *Die Rohstoffe des Pflanzenreich*, ed. J. von Wiesner, Verlag von Cramer, Weinheim, 1965.

Green, M. B. and Hedin, P. A. (Eds.) *Natural Resistance of Plants to Pests*, A.C.S. Symposium Series No. 296, American Chemical Soceity, Washington, D.C., 1986.

Liener, I. E. (Ed.) *Toxic Constituents of Plant Foodstuffs*, Academic Press, New York and London, 1969.

National Academy of Science Research Council. Publication No. 1354, Washington, D.C., 1966.

2
Pesticides in Agriculture

The Universal Providers

Nearly all life on earth relies, directly or indirectly, on the green plant for its substance and sustenance. The essential process of the reduction of the final product of carbon metabolism — carbon dioxide — is carried out in the chlorophyll-loaded chloroplasts inside the cells of green leaves, using the energy of sunlight. The process is very inefficient, only a few percent at best of the incident energy being stored in the carbohydrates produced, but it is more efficient than any present device of laboratory or industrial chemistry. Subsequent chemical processes in the plant and all those in other forms of life use oxidation of the products of photosynthesis as their energy source.

Another very vital act of fundamental chemistry, occurring in some bacteria associated with green plants or themselves containing chlorophyll, is the "fixation" of nitrogen. This most abundant element in the atmosphere is, in that form, very unreactive. Only after an initial step of oxidation or reduction is it capable of reacting with carbon compounds to enter into the most characteristic components of living matter, the proteins and genetic material. By "fixation" we mean the capturing of molecules of elementary nitrogen and holding them down on the chemical operating table in the living cell. This process also is very inefficient and much of the transiently fixed nitrogen slips back into the stable elementary form. Industrial chemistry can fix nitrogen as ammonia or nitrates more efficiently and can therefore help agricultural synthesis of more complex compounds. The industrial reactions, however, require high pressures and temperature and study of the complex vital process occurring in dilute solution at ordinary temperatures is an active field of research.

Competition for the Material Provided

Plant species compete with one another for space, light, water and mineral nutrients. Animals chew them, suck their juices, burrow into them and use their dry skeletons for shelter. We humans compete with other animals. If they can be hunted or domesticated we make use of them. If they are small and numerous and consume what we want to use we call them pests. In this sense, pests are inevitable and totally natural. If there are none on some

9

remote atoll it is only because no inhabitant can speak our language.

It is often said that chemical pest control defeats its own object by upsetting the beneficial balance of nature. Every species upsets this balance in the sense that the balance of other populations would be altered if the selected species were removed. If a large area of stable, managed farmland in temperate latitude were fenced off from all human activity it would for a long time become less balanced. The species which at first increased most rapidly would be displaced by slower, stronger competitors, using chemicals among other weapons. After a long period of scrambling warfare amongst the succession species there would eventually be established a permanent forest of more limited species — the local "climax" type. Permanently, that is, until man removed the fences or some natural catastrophe, earthquake, fire or flood brought the region back to a new start.

The climax vegetation would be quite unsuitable to feed a dense human population. Every species is striving to increase its population. Man differs mainly in being more successful than others. He modifies his environment more; he digs bigger holes than the rabbit; he builds bigger dams than the beaver and bigger houses than the termites; he makes more clever tools than does the monkey; he has flown further than the bird. He makes bigger mistakes than most, but, at his best, he is a better cultivator than any. His operations are at best well balanced, but the balance is not natural, no more than is any other form of culture. A learned biologist aptly described the objective of good farming as finding "how we can most safely disturb the balance of nature to our own advantage".

A contrast is often made between the "unnatural" life of the city and the "natural" life of the countryside. Yet, there is nothing "natural" about the modern countryside. Agricultural is a totally "unnatural" technology and has to be maintained by "unnatural" means. It is difficult to see that a pesticide is more "unnatural" than a plough. The good farmer must use many weapons but must use them all wisely—steel digging and scraping tools, plastic water carrying tubes, electric fencing, selection of the best crop seed and livestock. It is unreasonable to raise the cry of "disturbing the balance of nature" only when his heavy tractor returns his multi-furrow plough to the yard and he hitches up a spraying machine.

Problems of Monoculture

Nomadic man took his vegetable food where he found it and followed his herds. The pastoral farmer organized the grazing of his animals and restricted his pastures in varying degrees to the more nutritious species. The arable farmer devoted manageable-sized areas to single chosen cash crops, although his more intensive market garden friend would do some selective inter-cropping, growing, for example, a quick crop of lettuce between later-sown beans. On a farming scale a mixed crop of wheat, cabbage and sugar beet would be absurdly unmanageable.

A workable area devoted to a single crop is called a monoculture but the word is sometimes used only where the same crop is repeated year after year and even over whole regions including many farms. Problems inherent in monoculture increase with extension of one species in time and space. Following one crop with another over a cycle of a few years is called crop rotation and can help to avoid the build-up of pests. There is also a management advantage in that labour can be more uniformly employed if the chosen crops require most attention at different times of the year. Extension of the areas of single-species cultivation has been encouraged by the development of cultivating, harvesting and transport machinery. Giant machines eat up land and crop at great speed but need more turning space than their modest predecessors and greater areas over which to spread their capital cost.

Most insects, fungi and bacteria have evolved to live specifically on one source of food and to infest one particular type of plant or animal. In a natural environment, any plant which can be a host for one organism will be surrounded by other types of plants which cannot and so, for any particular organism, the supply of food will be limited and this, together with the presence of natural enemies of the organism (predators) limits reproduction and population growth. A large area covered by plants of the same kind standing close together offers abundant food and no barriers to inhibit movement of any pest or disease for which that type of plant can be a host. The attacks can therefore build up exponentially throughout the whole crop. The same is true for large stores of a commodity such as grain, the existence of which can enormously increase rodent populations, or for large herds of animals or massive populations of men jammed into cities. These all provide conditions under which infestations and epidemics can run riot.

The danger of disastrous pest damage when large areas are devoted to one crop is greatest when air-borne parasitic fungi are the agents. Until the introduction of fungicides and bactericides, mankind had been singularly unsuccessful in controlling plant diseases which were often the cause of total loss of crops and consequent famine. This crop loss still occurs in developing countries and, even as recently as 1970, 800 million bushels of corn were lost in the U.S.A. in an epidemic of Southern corn blight. This was an example of the damage which can be caused to susceptible varieties grown over large areas when weather conditions favour rapid spread of a virulent fungus. The total financial loss of about $2 thousand million was paid by the consumers of corn products since the price of corn rose from $1.28 per bushel to $1.60 per bushel as a result of the epidemic.

Monoculture is particularly suitable for chemical methods of pest control. Spraying of herbicides must be restricted when a selective herbicide is used on a small area of resistant crop if drift on to a neighbouring sensitive crop is to be avoided. Insecticides can also pose drift problems if insects are damaging one crop while a neighbouring crop needs bees for pollination. An interesting problem is posed in southern Asiatic Russia by the use of mulberry trees — fodder for the natural silk industry — as shelter for the cotton fields. In this case the problem cannot be reduced by increasing the size of monocultures since windbreaking would no longer be effective. The most difficult layout for effective chemical pest control is the suburban garden, if a mixture of ornamentals, fruit and vegetables is grown and a fishpond is included. Very localized application is needed. Large mono-cultures may make crops more subject to pest attack but they also make chemical spraying safer and more convenient.

As with other machinery, increase of size, sophistication and speed of spray equipment biases the farmer in favour of bigger monoculture areas. There is no simple general answer. Chemicals must be regarded as providing the good farmer with more tools to be used with his best — if fallible — judgement. Where chemicals have earned some bad repute is where they have been used to rescue bad farming rather than assist good farming.

Aliens

Mechanical advances, particularly of speed, have tended to increase the areas of monoculture, but have also had an adverse effect in providing more rapid spread of weeds and diseases and, especially, by air transport, of insects. Alien species brought into cultivated areas by long distance transport often become more serious pests than in their native land if, as is often the case, they have left their parasites and predators behind. Europe, having a very long history of agriculture, has received most pests able to survive there but the potato arrived in the sixteenth century from South America without its worst disease. When *Phytophthora* followed it around 1840 the result in Ireland was disastrous. The *Phylloxera* aphis arrived from North America around 1860 and wrought havoc in the French vineyards until the resistant American rootstock was brought over. *Galinsoga*, an annual weed of the Compositae family, is a fairly recent South American introduction and has spread widely. American agriculture, much younger than European, and started mainly by European immigrants, has naturally suffered more from alien pests: Australasia even more. Most of the serious weeds of arable land and even of pasture in New Zealand are species introduced from Europe or America, the rich native flora never having had to survive European type cultivation though some few have adapted successfully. Some Australasian species have travelled the other way, mostly as garden introductions, but a few, e.g. the burr-seeded *Acaena*, was introduced with wool and became naturalized.

The first safeguard against introduction of alien species is the implementation of quarantine regulations. Their success is necessarily limited. It would be impossible to make complete examination of all personal luggage and clothing without greatly increased staff and serious discouragement of desirable trade and tourist exchange. Quarantine is most successful in stopping introduction of specific animal diseases which could enter only on farm stock and related animals. Livestock is subjected to retention in isolation, preferably on small islands, under expert supervision before release to commercial farming. Import of meat is closely regulated involving inspection by veterinarians from the importing country of slaughter and transport methods in the exporting country. While it is impossible to prevent some accidental, careless or deliberate importation of small seeds or spores on personal clothing, commercially imported seed or live plants can be held for close inspection.

Pest-controlling chemicals have an important part to play in quarantine procedures. Dead animals or vegetable products such as skins, wool and cotton can be fumigated and evidence can be demanded of approved treatment of timber in the country of origin. Even imported fruit and live plants can be fumigated although in their treatment the range of permissible chemicals is reduced and more risk of damage is involved.

Unfortunately many introductions were made before there was awareness of the general risk or evidence of particular danger. Quarantine procedures were then too late. The journals of the eighteenth-century voyages of the great navigator James Cook and, on the first voyage, of the wealthy amateur Joseph Banks, later to become the longest serving president of the Royal Society, make interesting reading. Northern hemisphere seeds and livestock were left on South Sea islands with a recklessness which would now be held to be wildly irresponsible. One of Cook's outstanding achievements was to complete a very long journey with no incidence of scurvy among men crowded into very cramped quarters; but he left behind a legacy of venereal disease and environmental disturbance. Later, the first deer arrived in New Zealand as a present from Queen Victoria, then, as no English gentleman could be expected to farm without a sporting gun, the rabbit was introduced: then the cat and the stoat to keep the rabbit pest down, but these were more successful against the flightless native birds. The natural balance of an environment has nowhere ever been disturbed to this extent by chemicals.

Biological Control

The ravages produced by uninhibited alien pests, mainly in America and Australasia, led to the deliberate introduction of parasites or predators, under safeguards which were so irresponsibly absent when the cat followed the rabbit to New Zealand. Two very successful operations have been the reduction to unimportant levels of two introduced weeds by introduced insects. The prickly pear (*Opuntia* spp) in Australia and the perforate St John's wort (Klamath weed, *Hypericum*) in western U.S.A. and Australia had spread rapidly in rangeland, virtually denying usefulness for grazing of more than a million acres, the cactus by its spiny armour, the edible weed by sensitizing sheep to lethal sunburn. After several importations of insects and rigorous starvation tests to ensure that they would not adapt to other and useful hosts, two released species in each case became established. There have been other successes, but few so spectacular, and also many failures.

There have been several successes against insects. One of the earliest applications of this technique was the control in 1889 of the cottony cushion scale on citrus trees in California by the Australian ladybird beetle, *Vedalia cardinalis*. This method was highly successful. It has been suggested that birds might be used for biological control of insects, since they naturally devour large quantities of insects and insect larvae, but this idea has never been practically developed. An attempt was made in the U.S.A to use bats to control codling moth but, by and large, control of insects has been by other insects. Most success has been with the use of imported predators or parasites to control imported pests, particularly in Australia, and difficulties are often encountered when attempts are made to control an indigenous pest.

The method has had some success in southern Europe but none at all in Northern Europe. In the U.K. the only examples of successful control have been in the highly controllable environment of the glasshouse. In the U.S.A. up to 1956, 485 biological agents had been released against 77 species of pests. Of these agents, 95 became established and exerted some control over 22 of the pest species. Very large numbers of the predators or parasites are required. Thus, in Canada, between 1916 and 1956, one thousand million specimens of 220 species of parasites and predators were liberated against 68 pest species. Production of these numbers presents considerable difficulties, particularly if the parasite has to be reared on the host plants.

A related technique is the use of pathogens, that is, fungi, bacteria or viruses or their toxins which infect or poison the insect and cause its death. This is not an easy method to use since it is very susceptible to changes in external factors such as weather conditions. One of the most successfully used pathogens is *Bacillus thuringiensis*, which has proved effective against a number of species of caterpillar.

Control of insects by predators, parasites or pathogens can, if successful, be a cheap method of crop protection. Biological control agents also have the advantage of being highly specific in that they affect only the target pest and have no direct effects on non-target species. This can, however, be a disadvantage when certain minor pests which are controlled incidentally by chemical pesticides used against major pests become major pests themselves when competition is removed by biological agents highly specific to the original major pests. This is an example of Nature's tendency to fill any available ecological niche.

Difficulty also arises when more than one insect is attacking a crop but only one is controlled by the specific biological agent. If a chemical is used to control the other pests it is likely to kill the biological agent. An answer to one such problem presented itself in a New Zealand orchard. The predatory mite, *Typhlodromus pyri*, controlling the two-spotted phytophagous mite *Tetranichus urticae*, developed a strain resistant to the organophosphorus insecticides used to control other pests. This resistant predator has, of course, been encouraged, spread and exported. There are interesting possibilities of deliberate breeding of resistant strains of other predators and parasites.

Use of biological control agents requires a great deal of care and extensive background studies. It is also a technique for use by specialist operators and not one which can easily be applied by the average farmer. It is applicable to large regions rather than individual farms and is a long-term measure which cannot be used to give rapid control of an unexpected infestation. It is not usually effective at low population densities of the pest, so it is normally necessary to maintain the pest population at a minimum level by artificial infestations to prevent the biological control agents from dying out. Expert judgements and constant observation are required to ensure that the right balance is maintained and this is very difficult to achieve in regions with unpredictable weather patterns.

Biological control is not without the possibility of environmental risk, since introduction of an alien life-form into an established environment is bound to have some effect on the equilibrium of species in that area. The possibility always exists that an introduced insect might become a pest of some economic crop. Thus, the larvae of blister beetles imported into the Philippines to control louse eggs gave adult insects which attacked lucerne. An introduced pathogen might change and become infectious to man or animals. It is therefore essential to undertake extensive studies before any new system of biological control is introduced, just as it is with a pesticide.

Desirable selectivity in favour of predators can be helped by the use of systemic insecticides, i.e. those which enter the tissues and conducting vessels of the plant, because the compounds remain available to the feeding or sucking insect but, since they disappear from the outer leaf surface, they become less available to walking predators. The predator can, of course, consume insecticide along with its prey, but in many cases considerable biochemical degradation to harmless products will have occurred. Also it is probable that moribund prey tends to be avoided.

Systemic insecticides and resistant strains of predators are ways in which chemical and biological controls can co-operate.

Crop Breeding

Pest damage to a crop can be reduced by selection of strains which are in some degree resistant or repellent to the pest. They must, of course, if annual, breed true from seed, but resistant perennials can be vegetatively propagated. There is a long history of breeding wheat varieties resistant to the yellow rust fungus, but there are many other examples. Advances in breeding technique, including genetic engineering, will make this approach to pest avoidance increasingly important.

In the past, resistance of a plant variety to a certain disease has generally depended on one gene. Sometimes this is sufficient to give a permanent solution to a particular disease problem. Resistance of potatoes to wart disease depends on a single genetic factor and the disease has been diminished in the U.K. by legal restrictions on cultivation of susceptible varieties. More usually, however, the disease develops new strains which break down the resistance of the plant, often quite quickly and suddenly. In most natural disease populations there are strains capable of overcoming inbred resistance in plants and it is, generally, only a matter of time before these strains become dominant. For instance, the yellow rust of wheat has continually developed new strains which have successively overcome the resistance of a range of new varieties. Resistance can also be broken down by external factors, e.g. if the plants are transferred to different soil or climatic conditions. This widespread failure of major gene resistance has led plant breeders to turn from using race-specific resistance ("vertical" resistance) to non-race-specific resistance ("horizontal" resistance). This approach, coupled with developing knowledge of "genetic engineering", offers more hope for the future, and plant breeding will certainly have an important future contribution to disease control. If this is to be achieved, it is necessary that as many varieties as possible of the major crops of the world and of their wild progenitors shall be collected and conserved in "gene banks" to give the breeders sufficient basic material to work with.

As it is unlikely that a plant bred to be resistant to one particular disease will be immune to other pests and diseases, there are obvious limitations if the crop is likely to be attacked by a variety of these. In the process of natural selection varieties evolve which have a good average resistance, since the plant has to fight not only one but many enemies. Another difficulty is that often the variety which has the greatest resistance to disease turns out not to give the greatest yields or best quality. Where this is the case, cost-benefit considerations may make it more advantageous to the farmer to grow the variety which gives the biggest yield and to protect it, if need be, by fungicides. It may take 12 years, or more, to develop a new variety for commercial use and a variety which had been bred during this time specifically for resistance to disease may have to compete with other new varieties bred during the same period for improved yield and quality.

Breeding of varieties of crop plants resistant to or tolerant of certain animal pests has not been as well exploited or as successful as breeding for resistance to diseases, so there is considerable scope for future developments. It is believed that many plants, such as the yew and laurel, are naturally resistant to a variety of pests, because they contain natural repellent chemical substances. This offers the possibility of a new type of chemical approach to control.

A rather general reason for the lack of success with animal pests is the similarity with humans in nutrition and appetite. A cabbage variety which rabbits would not eat might not be sold twice to the same housewife! Insect preferences are basically different and there is evidence that laying females prefer some cultivars to others. One example is that the common cabbage white butterfly is rarely found in the caterpillar stage on the very wrinkled leaf of curly or "Scotch" kale. Whether a tactile or olfactory reaction is responsible is not known. Insect choice, where not absolute, could well be supported by insecticide use. A few rows of a non-preferred cultivar intended for market, separated by single rows of preferred cultivar heavily treated with a non-repellent insecticide and intended for destruction could increase the yield of unblemished produce. The psychology behind the absence, at least in European languages, of a strict opposite to "prefer" may also be behind the non-use of such practice in modern horticulture. Trap-cropping was, of course, exploited in older nursery practice, e.g. rows of wheat, later to be poisoned, to attract wireworms from inter-planted tomatoes.

The more general collaboration of the plant breeder and pesticide chemist has already been mentioned — the use of pesticide enabling a good crop to be obtained from a cultivar of improved yield or quality when the selection for these has resulted in poorer competition with weeds or increased vulnerability to pests. Weed control by chemicals is now very widely practised and the cost of production of many crops would be increased if the practice were abandoned. The need has arisen for closer discrimination between species, e.g. removal of weed grasses from wheat and barley, and therefore for the use of chemicals which are not so completely safe to the crop. Differences in susceptibility of cultivars become important and tests for susceptibility to some chemical herbicides are now routine in the search for new varieties.

Special chemicals are, of course, used further back in the technology of plant breeding, to induce mutations or, by the response of seedlings, to act as genetic markers; but such use, and indeed the whole advancing technology of breeding, is outside the scope of this book. One may mention, however, that marker characters can sometimes be disclosed by pesticide trials. One well-known example is that the insecticide DDT, quite harmless to most plants, including barley, was found to be lethal to barley varieties carrying a specific gene.

Induced Sterility

The idea of arresting the propagation of weeds by chemical treatment is an attractive one but so far without hope of implementation. If a chemical were found which could stop the development of fertile seed without other effect it would have important uses. Sprayed over a weedy crop it would reduce the seed supply for the following season. This would be unimportant for a crop grown for its leaves or roots since next season's seeds would normally come from a different area and indeed it might be an advantage in leading to greater vegetative growth. For the weeds it could lead to their almost complete elimination over a few years. Unfortunately the seed is usually the last organ to be damaged and a starved or injured plant will often set seed prematurely, thus safeguarding the species at the expense of the individual.

A heavy local dose of some herbicides can, of course, render seeds non-viable. This has been used in the form of the "chemical glove", trickle fed with dalapon solution, to rogue out wild oat flower spikes from a cereal seed crop. The method has even been used by diligent farmers to stop, in its early stage, invasion of wild oat in cereals grown for the food market. Such use of a chemical is more economic than waiting for an invasion to increase to the extent where it needs overall spraying for several successive seasons. Roguing by chemical stroking has two practical advantages over pulling out the plants: the worker does not have to carry loads off the field and the disturbance of crop roots by uprooting of the weeds is avoided.

Sterilization can be used against some insects in an entirely different way. The technique involves the culture and release of millions of male insects which have been sterilized either by radiation or by treatment with suitable chemicals so that they compete with normal males for mates but fail to fertilize the females, thus the pest population diminishes. World progress on application of this technique has been disappointing. One problem is the prodigious number of male insects required. It has been calculated that, if there is a natural population of one million virgin females in an area, then release of two million sterile males in each of four successive generations will theoretically reduce the population substantially to zero. This is obviously not a method which can be applied on a single farm, but must be applied to the total region in which the insect occurs, or to an area which can be geographically protected against an inflow from outside. Thus, it had a spectacular success in eradication of the screw-worm from the island of Curaçao. The campaign against the Mexican screw-worm in the south-west U.S.A. necessitated release of four thousand million sterile males over an area of 850,000 square miles. It is a long-term technique that cannot be used for rapid control of a sudden infestation. Also it is most effective at low pest population levels and cannot deal with major attacks.

The method can only work with a species where the female is satisfied with the act of mating rather than the fact of pregnancy, but, where this condition is fulfilled it has the great advantage of extreme specificity. The screw-worm is an unusually suitable target. It is a flesh eating parasite of sheep, although its specific name of *hominivorax* recognizes other hosts, including man, and it can be reared in vast numbers on factory lines on slaughter house by-products.

If used against phytophagous pests, their reproductive habits would have to be thoroughly researched and a suitable processed food developed. It has been estimated that, in the Mediterranean area, rearing of sufficient olive fruit flies to provide effective control of the natural pest population would require a substantial proportion of all the olive trees in the area to be devoted to this purpose. It is therefore unlikely that the sterile male technique will be used on its own in the future. It is more likely that infestations will first be reduced to low levels by conventional insecticide treatments and then kept under control by sterile males.

Control of Insects by Diseases

Insects, like animals, suffer from a variety of diseases caused by micro-organisms such as fungi, protozoa, bacteria, rickettsia and viruses. It is an attractive idea to control insects by artificially spreading diseases to which they are prone. Any micro-organism which is to be used for insect control should be highly virulent and show no tendency to become attenuated in this respect; it should be specific to the target pest and harmless to other living organisms; it should be economical to produce and stable in storage; it should act rapidly to minimize crop damage. In particular, there must be no possibility that the organism might develop mutant forms pathogenic to men and animals because the adverse effects of a self-reproducing micro-organism released into an environment if it took a "wrong turn" could be far more horrifying than the effects of any chemical substance.

There are over 400 species of fungi which infect insects but they rarely reduce insect populations below the levels at which they cause economic damage to crops, and it is not thought that they offer much prospect for practical pest control. Protozoa are, in general, not highly virulent nor do they cause rapid death, so are also not regarded as candidates for control methods. The rickettsia likewise do not kill rapidly and it is suspected that they may be, or could easily become, dangerous to men and animals.

The bacteria offer much more possibilities and one in particular, *Bacillus thuringiensis*, has found widespread commercial use. It is easily produced on artificial media and the dried spores store well and remain potent for many years. It appears to be completely non-toxic to men and animals, and specific to lepidopterous larvae. The spore case (sporangium) of the bacteria contains, as well as the spore, a protein which rapidly paralyzes the gut of the insect and causes cessation of feeding a few minutes after injection, so it is very fast-acting.

For the future, it is probably the viruses which have the greatest potential for insect control, particularly the nuclear polyhedral viruses. They are very specific and highly virulent and can survive for years because of an inert protective coating. The ruptured body of one infected insect can release vast numbers of virus particles into the environment to infect other insects. Viruses have already been used on a number of occasions for highly successful pest control, for example, on the spruce sawfly in Canada and on the pine moth in France. The major obstacle to practical use of viruses has been the difficulty of their commercial production. They can be reared only on living insects and this is costly to do as the required insects may be available for only short periods during the year and have to be fed on fresh foliage which is also available only in limited amounts for a limited time. In recent years great developments have been made in mass rearing of insects on artificial media all the year round. As a result, viruses may become practical and economical means of pest control. Experimental products are already available for use against cotton bollworm, tobacco budworm, cabbage looper and tussock moth.

Use of these disease agents could be integrated with the use of synthetic pesticides with advantage if, for instance, the disease, by dealing with one difficult pest, could allow a pesticide less harmful to predators to be used against others. There could, of course, be some conflict if a chemical pesticide, by killing carriers of disease more quickly, reduced the rate of infection. Successful treatment is therefore most likely to be by disease *or* synthetic chemical. In the case of *Bacillus thuringiensis* the disease kills by the chemical it generates. The culture of a virus or bacterium on sufficient scale to be distributed as a pest-controlling agent is a process demanding chemical engineering development. The application of the product needs equipment similar to that for the application of orthodox pesticides. It is easy to foresee that, with the extension of these methods, the production and distribution will tend to be undertaken by the pesticide chemical industry, just as other microbiological processes have been adopted in other branches of the industry.

Chemicals and Cultivation

The traditional, ancient practices of digging, first with primitive tools such as a pointed stick or an animal's horn or jaw bone, evolving through the steel spade and fork to the multi-furrow plough, drag-harrows and rollers, had the function of loosening top soil to provide access to roots and breaking down matted stubble of a previous crop or natural cover. The operations were equally important in reducing weed populations by uprooting perennials and burying seeds too deep for germination. More superficial mechanical processes, hoeing and hand-pulling, are mainly directed to weed control.

They are probably still, the world over, the main means of weed control, but selective herbicides have taken over this function in the more developed countries in close-planted crops like the cereals, in which, at an early stage of growth, hand cultivation becomes impossible. Labour costs favour cheaper chemical control, where technically possible, in many other crops. Chemical weed control is not only more economic but has important technical advantages. If a sufficiently selective chemical is available, it can eliminate annual weeds growing intimately close to the crop seedlings and therefore the ones most important in competition. It causes less root disturbance than mechanical hoeing and brings fewer weed seeds up from depths where they lie dormant. It can kill many overwintering weeds which, when cut off by a hoe, can regrow in a more branched form.

A very important development has been the use of chemicals having a very general lethal effect on vegetation when sprayed on to foliage but having little or no effect via the soil. Such chemicals, described in the herbicide chapters, can kill off crop stubble, weeds surviving after harvest and even worn-out or short-term pasture, leaving a dense dead organic mat in which a new crop can be started with minimum mechanical disturbance. This technique, known as "minimum tillage", "no cultivation", "chemical ploughing" or "direct drilling", is now used on millions of hectares the world over. None of these names is satisfactory. The first two are negatives and could mean that nothing is done to prepare the ground for the next crop. "Ploughing" has for centuries meant the mechanical act of inverting the top soil layer. "Direct drilling" is, like the first two, negative in the sense that it implies that nothing is done between harvest and drilling of the seed: moreover it is sometimes used for an entirely different technique — sowing seed in the field where the crop, e.g. tomatoes, is later, after pulling out of excess plants, to mature, as distinct from raising young plants in a nursery and then planting out.

Many agriculturists, for years before the killing of an undisturbed sward became practicable, argued against the reverence in which ploughing had long been held. The opponents of ploughing held that the organic rich layer of the soil should be kept in its natural place, above the mineral rich; that the inversion had an adverse effect on the microflora and fauna of the soil; that high wind and heavy rain can blow or wash off both surface soil and seedlings; and that the plough mechanism, while loosening the top soil, necessarily compresses the soil under the plough sole creating a "plough pan" impervious to water and roots. All four objections are valid for some crops in some soils and in some climates but their importance varies greatly. Destruction of the last crop and weed stubble by chemicals, considered as a strict alternative, is again not universally satisfactory. Heavy clay soils do need some mechanical loosening in the surface and occasional break-up in depth with a mechanical subsoiler. The dense fibrous mat left by killed grass sward needs a specially designed seed drill and is even then a rather hostile medium for some seeds. Plant residues in an early stage of breakdown can generate some chemical compounds which suppress germination or early growth.

Chemical preparation for seed sowing is sufficiently successful to have demanded the design and production of new machinery for drilling into a fibrous mat. It is certainly one of the more important recent advances in crop production but is best considered as another weapon in the hands of the farmer who wants to get from the land the crops which the other members of his species need. It has a very important part to play in combined good management. It may well have an increasingly important part to play in getting an early start for suitable crops in areas where the land is too wet, at the preferred sowing time, to carry wheeled machinery. The chemical preparation and sowing of suitable pelleted seed can be carried out from the air, leaving harvest as the only ground-based operation.

Further Reading

Apple, J. L. and Smith, R. F. (Eds.) *Integrated Pest Management*, Plenum, New York, 1977.

Baker, K. F. and Cook, R. J. *Biological Control of Plant Pathogens*, W. H. Freeman, San Francisco, 1974.

Brown, A. W. A. *Ecology of Pesticides*, Wiley, Chichester, 1978.

de Bach, P. (Ed.) *Biological Control of Insect Pests and Weeds*, Chapman Hall, London, 1970.

Chapman, B. and Penman, D. *Natural Pest Control*, Reed Methuen, Auckland, 1986.

Fryer, J. D. and Matsunaka, S. (Eds.) *Integrated Control of Weeds*, Tokyo University, 1977.

Huffaker, C. B. (Ed.) *Biological Control*, Plenum, New York, 1977.

McEwen, F. L. and Stephenson, G. R. *The Use and Significance of Pesticides in the Environment*, Wiley, Chichester, 1979.

Martin, Hubert. *Scientific Principles of Crop Protection*, 1st edition 1928 and successive to 6th 1973; 7th revised by D. Woodcock, Arnold, London, 1983.

Ordish, G. *Untaken Harvest*, Constable, London, 1952.

Price-Jones, D. and Solomon, M. E. (Eds.) *Biology in Pest and Disease Control*, Blackwell, Oxford, 1974.

3

The Shape of the Industry

A Convergent Industry

As the title suggests, this book is about chemicals for crop improvement and pest management, considered as products of manufacture and trade by a section of the chemical industry.

Within this trade, these products are often referred to as agrochemicals. The trade association in Britain, which began as the Association of British Insecticide Manufacturers, is now known as the British Agrochemicals Association because its members realized that a major part of their trade was in herbicides and that fungicides should also logically be included. It is accepted by the association that the term 'agrochemicals' does not include the large-tonnage fertilizers — inorganic salts supplying ammonium, potassium, nitrate and phosphate ions for major crop nutrition, although it is sometimes held to include more specialized nutrient products, such as organic chelates of iron and manganese, aimed at curing deficiency "diseases" of plants. It also includes compounds having some other ancillary use in crop production, such as the encouragement of rooting of cuttings or of setting of fruit. Agrochemicals could not logically be held to include compounds used for control of non-agricultural pests, but it would, of course, be absurd either in the organization of the industry or of this book, to include DDT if used for killing pea-moth and not DDT if used for killing bed-bugs. It would be equally absurd to include simazine if used as a selective herbicide in the maize crop but not if used at a higher rate to keep all vegetation out of a railway siding.

The title of the previous edition, "Chemicals for Crop Protection and Pest Control", was originally chosen as most comprehensive and least likely to convey a wrong impression outside the trade. Fertilizers were excluded but chemicals having functions in the maintenance of crop health other than the control of visible pests were included. Competing plant species — weeds — were classed as pests as were the often unseen micro-organisms responsible for plant diseases. However, times change, and chemicals are being increasingly used not just to protect crops from competition from other plant species and from infection by plant pathogens but also systemically to cure such infections after they have occurred and to increase the yields and qualities of those part of the plants that constitute the crop and to make them easier to harvest. The practice of pest control in which the aim was to kill as many as possible of the offending species has been replaced by the concept of pest management in which the infestation is kept merely to the economic threshold of crop damage and thus an ecological balance of pests, predators and parasites is maintained. To reflect these changes the title "Chemicals for Crop Improvement and Pest Management' has been chosen for this new edition.

Chemicals for crop improvement and pest management include a very wide range of structures and their manufacture requires a wide range of processes. The industry is not unified at the stage of chemical production. Technically, it is unified, not by common starting materials or processes, but by the manner and purpose of use of the end products. Commercially, it is unified more by its sales organization than by its production organization. This structure is dictated by the need for a highly technical sales force which must deal with a very large number of technical customers. On both sides, however, the need is for expertise in pest or agricultural technology rather than chemical technology. If single descriptive words are wanted, one can most suitably call the pesticide industry a convergent one, which brings products from a variety of sources on to a group of closely related targets. These targets are related biologically and economically, not chemically.

The heavy chemical industry provides a marked contrast. It must be organized on lines dictated by its major processes. A chlorine plant which discarded its simultaneously produced alkali could not be economic. The integration of the related processes of the early "LeBlanc complex" is described in "A History of the Modern British Chemical Industry". Such industry might fairly be called divergent. A good example was the form of the Albright and Wilson Company up to the time of recent acquisitions and diversification. This company was based on the processing of a single difficult and important element — phosphorus. The only practicable way, for a long time, to obtain most phosphorus compounds in adequate purity was via elementary phosphorus. This was a difficult substance to produce and demanded special methods of handling. It was a natural step, economically, to harness as many orthodox secondary processes as possible to this highly specialized primary process.

The pesticide industry is often described as "research intensive". There are still many pest problems not solved by any existing chemicals. Requirements in agricultural pest control are constantly changing owing to the impact of changes in cultural methods (including pesticide use) on pest problems. The development of strains of insects resistant to insecticides is a serious problem in both agriculture and public health. The requirements of governmental registration authorities for safety to the consumer and to the environment have become much more stringent. The research chemist is therefore always seeking new structures and the research biologist new tactics and strategy. It is rather unusual for a compound to command a large share of the market for a long time. The compound may therefore cease to be commercially viable before means for its most economic production have been worked out.

Fertilizer production provides an informative contrast. Crops will always need available nitrogen, phosphate and potash (NPK). Compounds which are worth considering to supply this need are very limited. Research on the economics of packaging and transport and the problems of serviceability at the user end are, of course, common to all industries producing consumer goods, but whereas a large proportion of fertilizer research effort must go into minimizing cost of production, the need in the pesticide industry is to get down to an acceptable cost quickly rather than to the lowest possible cost eventually.

Another contrast with the fertilizer industry illustrates a further important point. Not only will NPK always be needed by plants of any kind known to man throughout history, but will also be needed by crop producers every season in not very variable amount. The farmer, however, always hopes that he will not need pesticides, sales of which are, in consequence, subject to wide variation from one season to the next. In the phenomenally wet summer of 1958 in the U.K., the industry completely exhausted its supplies of copper fungicides for use against potato blight, but, in the following, phenomenally dry, summer, such products could hardly be given away. Both the farmer and the manufacturer are reluctant to tie up capital in stock-piling. It is therefore a very desirable feature of pesticide production processes that they be elastic with regard to rate of output.

The products of the pesticides industry are toxic to some living species and are valued for just this reason. Few are so highly selective that their ingestion in accidental amounts would be quite without significance in man or farmstock. Indeed a comprehensive term for these products, often used in the U.S.A., is "economic poisons", which conveniently emphasizes both their value and the hazards latent in their use. During the last 20 years an increasing effort has been put into the study of these hazards and of means to reduce them and many countries have introduced elaborate legislation to control the use of pesticides. This legislation now imposes on the industry an expensive burden of closely specified and expert investigation which will be described later. This public responsibility of the industry is another powerful reason why it is unified at the using, rather than the manufacturing end.

Production of a multiplicity of complex chemical products, mostly on a comparatively small scale, poses considerable economic problems, and, for this reason, few chemical companies are in the pesticide manufacturing business alone. The general tendency of large financial groups to ensure their future stability by diversification of interests is therefore strengthened.

Association with other manufacturing facilities enables the pesticide section of a large company to concentrate on the peculiar problems of its multi-customer, highly technical market, while leaving some of the basic production to be integrated with other production for quite different markets. Association with groups having other interests in research on new chemicals enables the expert "screening" facilities of the pesticide group to have a larger number of speculative new chemicals to test for activity in its own field.

Although the processes of manufacture of active compounds are diverse, the types of "formulation" in which they are offered to the user are more limited and characteristic of the industry and the market it supplies. The properties of the active compound may restrict the choice of formulation, but what is desirable at the user end is determined by considerations of packaging, transport, application and biological efficiency and has little in common with the formulation of cosmetics and pharmaceuticals. Technical aspects of formulation of pesticides are dealt with in a later chapter, but it should be pointed out here that one result of the diversity of active compounds and the close association of formulation with market requirements is a tendency for formulation to be carried out in local small units, taking their active and ancillary compounds from different sources. This tendency is much greater in countries such as the U.S.A., Africa and South America, where long transport hauls must be made from the manufacturing bases, than in small and industrialized agricultural countries like the U.K. There are two reasons for this. Firstly, many formulations require dilution of the active compound with water, solvents or powdered minerals, and economics dictate that these diluents be added locally. Secondly, various factors in local conditions, including customer preferences and compatibility with other locally used products, have a big influence on choice of formulation. As the larger land units are more diverse in climate and agricultural practice, the local formulator, with his knowledge of local factors, is better able to meet the requirements than a remote manufacturer.

Many manufacturers have their own formulation branch factories in important regions. Others may supply their active chemical products to a local formulator. The parties will, of course, find it desirable to protect their interests by some specification agreement, the formulator to protect himself against difficulties due to variation in the technical product, the manufacturer to avoid his product coming into disrepute through bad formulation. Where the active compound has ceased to be protected by patents, manufacture may pass into the hands of general chemical companies who may have little knowledge of agriculture or pest control but have facilities for cheap production of the compound. Some pesticides have in this way become commodity products.

The companies developing and manufacturing new pesticides carry very heavy costs for discovery and development and for research into safety and use problems, about which more is said below. There is no possibility of recouping these costs if the product can be made and sold freely by a purely manufacturing company incurring only process research costs. Pesticide companies are therefore very concerned to exploit patented products. They may formulate commodity items in order to complete their sales range, but if adequate control of quality can be exercised, will buy in these products from a commodity manufacturer. They may therefore be strongly competitive in their exclusive products but buy other products from one another.

Relation with Pharmaceutical Industry

The problems of production raised by the great multiplicity of chemical structures are in large measure shared by the pharmaceutical industry, except that the latter generally confines its interests to more complex and expensive compounds, used medicinally. The technology of chemicals for pest control is often called, especially in France, "phytopharmacy" but it covers a wider field than attack on diseases produced by internal micro-organisms. The mechanical advance of civilization has reduced the significance for human health of many predators and vectors of disease. In remote communities where war must be waged on the leopard or the wolf, the part played by the chemical industry is to provide propellents for bullets rather than poisons. If attack must be made on the malaria-carrying mosquito or the typhus-carrying body louse, the necessary chemicals are obtained from the pesticide rather than the pharmaceutical industry.

Human pharmacy and plant pharmacy are not therefore, in practice, fully comparable. Plant pharmacy is much more concerned with gross parasitism and predation than with diseases in the generally accepted sense, while in human pharmacy the relative importance is reversed. One should not conclude that plant diseases produced by microscopic or submicroscopic parasites are either unimportant or unrecognized. Historically, the first diseases to be clearly attributed to the growth of micro-organisms were fungal diseases of plants — blight of potatoes, rust of wheat, clubroot of cabbage. The discovery of bacteria took place only a few years later, the first disease to be shown to be caused by bacteria being anthrax in sheep, followed rapidly, by a "vegetable anthrax" — fire blight in pears. That filter-passing, proliferating substances, later called viruses, were responsible for some diseases was discovered almost simultaneously in plants (tobacco mosaic) and cattle (foot and mouth disease). One can say broadly that, in the 50 years from 1860 to 1910, man's knowledge of the causes of disease of plants and animals developed from vague ideas about miasmas and murrains to the sound foundations on which an extensive detailed structure has since been built.

Prevention, amelioration and cure of the true diseases have made much more rapid progress in animal, and especially human, pharmacy than in plant pharmacy. The reasons, biological, sociological and economic, are outside the scope of this book, but it is well to be reminded that, as agriculture increases control over competition by weeds and consumption and damage by insects, then, in the treatment of true diseases, delay of invasion and control of insect vectors may be replaced by curative treatments of which much could be learnt from human medicine. The development of systemic fungicides (see chapter 17) is an example of this progression.

The science and industry of veterinary chemicals is rather naturally intermediate between that of agricultural pest control and human medicine. There is more concern with cure of animal sickness than of plant sickness, but more concern than in human medicine with control of the larger parasites. By the larger parasites are meant insect and acarid "*ecto*"-parasites, such as blowflies, lice and ticks, and helminth and insect "*endo*"-parasites, such as lung worms, intestinal worms and warble-fly larvae.

There are obvious advantages in the integration of the pest control and pharmaceutical branches of the chemical industry and the majority of companies with an interest in the one have association of some sort with a company interested in the other. Experimentation on veterinary medicines has obviously a great deal in common with that on human medicines, but a sales channel for a successful compound may be opened more easily in the agriculturally oriented sister company. Preparation of speculative new chemicals may be intended to provide a cure for the common cold but may show, instead, a useful action against an agricultural pest if tested for this purpose. Occasionally there may be an exploitable activity in both fields, a classic example being warfarin which is used both curatively in humans suffering from thrombosis and as an effective poison for rats.

In the field of human medicine, more is known about the biochemistry of pathological conditions and the mode of action of curative drugs than in the much wider and less intensively studied field of pest control. There is more possibility for chemical logic in the design of new molecules, but even here the logic has in most cases to be confined to minor changes on an established structure. In the field of pest control, almost every "break-through" into an entirely new type of active structure has come from wide-range hit-and-miss research by teams of organic chemists and biological "screeners". One could perhaps claim as a partial exception the discovery of 2,4-D and MCPA as suggested by natural plant hormones and consider that Wain's finding of more selective herbicidal action in the 4-phenoxybutyric than in the phenoxyacetic compounds was neither minor nor accidental. While it is at present true that successful wholly new structures have been found by serendipity and that, if anything is known of the biochemistry of the toxic action, the knowledge has come after the event, predictive biochemistry is likely to become increasingly important. Increasing effort is therefore going into the study of biochemical mechanisms in both academic and industrial research.

Research Collaboration

Until predictive biochemistry takes over, the present strategy of synthesis of new compounds in wide variety is likely to be maintained for some years to come. It is therefore an obvious advantage for the pesticide manufacturer to have close association, at the compound-testing stage, not only with a company working in the related pharmaceutical field, but also with any company producing a wide variety of chemical compounds which may be of interest directly or as intermediates. The dyestuffs industry is a useful ally since it must produce compounds in great variety, (a) to meet the whims of fashion and (b) to solve the problems set by advances in synthetic fibres. There is little doubt that the early development of dinitrophenol compounds, and much later, of the substituted diamino-s-triazines, was initiated by availability of compounds from the associated dyestuffs industry. Amino-triazole was an intermediate in colour-photographic dye production before it was known as a herbicide.

Other technologies have contributed. The dithiocarbamate fungicides were first produced as ancillary compounds in rubber processing. Organotin compounds had their origin in purely chemical exploration of the combining properties of tin. Their first exploitation was for stabilization of polyvinyl-chloride against photochemical attack.

At the research stage in the industry, therefore, diversity of chemical synthesis is an important characteristic, often augmented through compound-exchange and collaboration with other laboratories. An efficient biological screening department is an equal necessity. It must be able to test compounds on a small scale, quickly and all the year round, for activity on a representative range of plant and pest species. If, perhaps, two or three compounds in a thousand show some preliminary promise, they must be tested under more varied and realistic conditions and a start made on the eventually extensive investigations on all aspects of safety, including means of quantitative estimation in trace quantities on crops. For these extended investigations the chemist must meet the problem of preparation on a scale exceeding that convenient in ordinary laboratory practice. Most of these first-selection compounds will fail to meet one or another requirement for commercial success. One commercially successful compound out of 15,000 must be regarded as satisfactory. To avoid expensive waste of effort it is therefore necessary that all the steps in the follow-up research on a candidate compound be closely co-ordinated and further work stopped as soon as failure is certain.

It is in the important exploration of detailed chemical variations on a promising new theme — a "lead" as it is always called in the trade — that physicochemical and biophysical logic can play a part. Observation of the effects of changes in parameters, such as acidity of a molecule and its oil-water partition coefficients, on biological activity within a particular chemical group can facilitate prediction of the structure of the most active compound within that group. The advent of the computer has made it possible to handle the considerable amount of data needed, to calculate the required parameters for thousands of possible compounds, and to home in on the optimum combination of those parameters. Nevertheless, physical parameter/biological activity relationships are not yet so certain that the best compound can be indentified unequivocally; the field of search can be greatly narrowed but rapid biological testing, without limitations of season, in an efficient screening department working closely in association with the synthetic chemists, is still an important requisite to identify the compound which has the best chance of commercial success.

One great difficulty in identifying the potential commercial "winner" at an early stage in research and discarding the "loser" before a great deal of money has been spent on its development is the frequent lack of correlation between performance in the glasshouse and performance in the field. The reason for this is that the glasshouse is a limited controlled environment whereas the field is an open environment in which many variable factors can affect the performance of a pesticide. Screening tests are conducted by technical experts under controlled conditions but a compound for commercial use must perform effectively in the hands of non-experts under a wide range of conditions of soil and climate. For this reason the current tendency is to take a promising compound into the field in a number of localities as rapidly as possible.

The industry, no doubt in common with many others, is facing changing problems. Some, such as arise from diversity of chemical processes, it must sort out for itself. Others may require increasing collaboration with research organized by governments, with agricultural trade organizations or with other bodies outside the chemical industry.

Further Reading

Bradbury, F. R. and Dutton, B. G. *Chemical Industry: Social and Economic Aspects*, Butterworths, London, 1972.

Gregory, J. G. (Ed.) *Modern Chemistry in Industry*, Society of Chemical Industry, London, 1968.

Jones, D. G. (Ed.) *Chemistry and Industry*, Clarendon Press, Oxford, 1967.

National Agrochemicals Chemicals Association, Pesticide Industry Profile Study, Washington, D. C., 1971.

Shreve, R. N. *Chemical Process Industries*, McGraw-Hill, London and New York, 1967.

Williams, T. I. *The Chemical Industry*, Pergamon Press, London, 1953.

4

Technological Economics of Pesticides

So great has been the increase of agricultural productivity under the influence of applied science that the nineteenth-century warnings by Malthus about the limited feeding capacity of the world seemed for a time unimportant. The control of crop pests has, however, been matched by control of human disease. The increase of crop productivity has been matched by that of human population. There can be no relaxation in the development of pest control methods while mankind is solving the enormous problem created by his own increase.

Man must eat throughout the year. Most staple foods are gathered in a short harvest period and must therefore be held in store for several months. A great deal of stored foodstuff can be lost to pests. A fair estimate, the world over, is that pests take one quarter of the crop before harvest and another quarter in storage. A proportion of pesticides goes on to stored food or its containers. Much less, however, is used in this way than on growing crops, for two reasons.

Firstly, the toxic residue problem is more critical on stored grain because the compound is protected from weathering and, being applied to a dry and dormant plant organ, is less subject to biological destruction. Moreover it is applied directly to the edible portion of the crop, while most field-applied pesticides are applied before the harvested organs are accessible. These considerations impose severe limits on the number and quantity of pesticides which can be used on stored products, although the fact of their storage in closed spaces permits the use of fumigants which are of little use in open agriculture.

Secondly, non-chemical alternative means of protection are much more effective in the case of stored products. High value foods such as meat and fruit and vegetables can be stored in sealed cans or deep-frozen. Grain can be stored in rat-proof buildings and pests in it destroyed by low temperature or anaerobic conditions. Most of the heavy losses of stored grain in under-developed countries could be prevented by impermeable (but more expensive) containers and better organization.

Not only foods, but also structural materials, are vulnerable to damage by insects and fungi. It might be thought that the most important contribution

31

of the chemical industry to this problem is the provision of synthetic structural materials. It would be unwise, however, to underestimate the ability of insects, fungi and micro-organisms to evolve strains adapted to wholly new nutrients. Cases are already known of "biodeterioration" of synthetic materials. It must also be appreciated that replacement of natural structural materials has still not gone very far. Annual world production of timber is about 400 million tonnes. This is about equal to the tonnage of wheat. Of this, over 80% is used as structural timber, the rest being processed in various ways into composition boards, paper and fibres. Cotton, with a world production of 16 million tonnes is still by far the most used fibre. Truly man-made fibres have only recently exceeded the production of sheep-made wool. Economic loss and danger to life can result from attack on structural materials by a wide range of organisms, from rotting of wood and textiles by fungi, collapse of wooden buildings tunnelled by termites, fires started by rupture of gas mains by sulphuric acid produced by anaerobic bacteria or by rodents gnawing through the insulation of electric cables.

When a successful method of control of some agricultural pest is known, comparisons can be made of the yields from similar treated and untreated plots and a reasonable estimate of economic return can be made. Often the value of the extra yield is many times the expenditure on pesticide. The economics are often difficult to assess. The gain from treatment of one crop in one season may be reaped mainly in a succeeding crop in the next season. The true loss may be hidden because an uncontrollable pest, or, more usually, a disease, may necessitate replacement of a preferred crop, in a region where soil and climate seem suitable, by a less valuable alternative.

Subject to these reservations we can now summarize the directly assessable savings and expenditure for major crops and pesticides.

Economics of Pesticides for the Manufacturer

The modern development of crop protection chemicals came almost entirely from the chemical industry. In this respect it differed from many technologies which evolved from initial discoveries made during the scientific pursuit of knowledge in universities and other academic institutions. The object of research in industrial companies is not, as in universities, to increase scientific knowledge for its own sake, but to find new ways in which the company can increase its business and earn profits. The chemical industry has no obligation to discover, develop and manufacture new pesticides. It has done so because it has proved to be an acceptably profitable investment for new capital. It will continue to do so only so long as it is more profitable to do so than to invest available money in discovery, development and manufacture in other commercial areas such as plastics, pharmaceuticals, cosmetics, synthetic fibres and similar technologies.

The pesticides industry in the modern fine-chemical sense dates from World War II. Before that pesticides were mainly inorganic materials, for example, sulphur or lead arsenate, together with a few naturally occurring organic materials, such as nicotine and pyrethrum. The advances made in the science of organic chemistry during the latter half of the nineteenth century led, in the first half of the twentieth century, to commercial exploitation of organic chemicals, first in dyestuffs, and then in pharmaceuticals. Before World War II a number of chemical companies were considering the possibility of using organic chemicals to control the pests and diseases of plants. However, in the 1930s, farming was in a depressed state in the U.S.A. and Europe and it did not seem likely that farmers would be willing to pay the high prices which seemed likely to be needed for such chemicals. Nor was it clear, at that time, that any organic chemicals could, in fact, be discovered which would be useful in treating horticultural and agricultural pests and diseases. So it appeared, at that time, to be a highly risky and uncertain undertaking for the chemical industry to invest money in research and development in this area.

After World War II, the picture had changed. Food prices had increased considerably, standards of living in developed countries were rising rapidly and farming was becoming a much more profitable occupation. The discoveries of DDT in Switzerland, of the organophosphorus insecticides in Germany and of the phenoxyacetic herbicides in the U.K. had all demonstrated that useful crop protection products could, in fact, be discovered and that these need not necessarily be costly to produce. The organic chemical industry now saw pesticides as a profitable diversification of their manufactures, and so the pesticides industry had a phenomenal growth rate during the period 1945 to 1975, as illustrated in Table 4.1.

TABLE 4.1

Growth of world pesticides industry (thousands of tonnes)				
	1945	1955	1965	1970	1975
World output	100	400	1,000	1,500	1,800

This remarkable growth was augmented by the fact that the new post-war petro-chemicals industry was producing all kinds of novel organic starting materials from oil, and many of the larger manufacturers of primary petro-chemicals therefore came into crop protection and pest control as an outlet for their products. However, it cannot be too strongly stressed that the fact that the first effective organic pesticides which were discovered were cheap and easy to manufacture led to acceptance by farmers of much more expensive products and was a major factor in the rapid growth of the industry. The post-war development of the pesticides industry is a good example of the recipe for commercial success — "the right product in the right place at the right time at the right price" — and illustrates how successful innovation depends on technological, economic and social factors all being favourable. If the phenoxyacetic herbicides had been discovered in 1930 it is doubtful whether their commercial impact on agriculture at that time would have been very substantial.

Pesticides have always been a high risk investment. Development of a new crop protection chemical is a long and expensive business. Many compounds have to be synthesized and screened before a "lead" is discovered and extensive synthetic work has then to be undertaken to locate the most suitable compound in the "lead" area for commercial development. This selected compound has then to be evaluated world-wide on a range of crops, soils, climates and environments and, concurrently, far-reaching toxicological, residue and environmental studies have to be carried out. Economical processes of manufacture have to be discovered, pilot quantities produced and full-scale manufacturing plant designed, constructed and commissioned. The way in which development costs build up is shown in Table 4.2.

The type of cash flow which this produces is shown in Figure 4.1. This is the cash flow for a typical successful pesticide which shows the cumulative difference between money laid out and money coming in, adjusted to take account of the fact that the value of money several years hence is considerably less than the value of money now. This is what is called a "discounted cash

TABLE 4.2   *Estimate of typical development costs of a pesticide in 1985*

Year		No of compounds	Cost per compound	Total cost
			$	$,000's
1	Synthesis	16,000	700	
	Screening		325	16,400
	Survival rate 1:100			
2	Glasshouse trials	160	25,000	
	Initial field trials			4,000
	Survival rate 1:5			
3	Field trials	32	50,000	
	Initial toxicology		20,000	
	Survival rate 1:4			2,240
4	Field evaluation		250,000	
	Toxicology	8	100,000	4,800
	Formulation and process		250,000	
	Survival rate 1:2			
5	World-wide evaluation		2,500,000	
	Toxicology, environment, ecology		2,350,000	
	Formulation and process	2	1,000,000	15,700
	Production		1,000,000	
	Registration and patent		1,000,000	
	Survival rate 1:2			
			Total cost	43,140

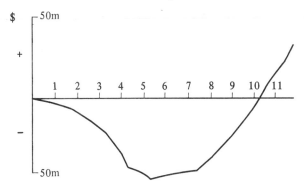

FIGURE 4.1   Discounted cash flow of successful pesticide

flow" and is a good guide to the profitability and risk of any proposed investment.

The cash flow in Figure 4.1. illustrates both the risk and uncertainty of development of new pesticides as a commercial investment. It goes $50m into the "red" and breaks even only after 10 to 11 years. It is only after this "break-even" point that profit is made but, by then, there remain only a few years out of the total life of the patent (20 years in the U.K.) before competitors who have had to bear none of the heavy development costs can come in and force down prices. This is because the patent will almost certainly have been taken out when the original discovery was made. The cash flow shown in Figure 4.1. is that of a commercial "winner", the development of which has gone smoothly and without major setbacks. Performance in the field which is not consistent over a wide range of soils and climates, unexpected toxicological or environmental effects, discovery by competitors of cheaper or more effective alternatives, development of resistant strains of the pest or disease, could all "kill" a promising new product, often after a considerable amount of money has been spent abortively on its development.

The total cost of development of a new pesticide in 1969 was $5.5m, but the chance that sales would ever exceed $5m per year was estimated in that year to be about 10 to 1 against. Of all the pesticides introduced to western Europe between 1960 and 1969 only 12 achieved annual sales in western Europe greater than $2.5m. To put large sums of money at high risk for long periods in the hope of eventual profit is acceptable only to the largest chemical manufacturers who have a great liquidity of assets and a diversity of interests to buffer them against misfortune. This is why the number of firms engaged in discovery and development of new pesticides is comparatively small and why these are the large diversified international chemical organisations.

Such companies have a responsibility to their shareholders to invest their money wisely and to their employees to maintain viable businesses so, if pesticides cease to be an acceptable financial risk, discovery and manufacture of them will cease. It has already been pointed out that, before World War II, the risk was not an acceptable one. From 1940 to 1980 the risk was still there but it was now acceptable because the profits to be made from a successful product were very large. Nevertheless, it is interesting to note that such highly profitable major products are few and far between and that each major producer of pesticides in the world has two, or, at the most, three such products to his name which supply most of the profit for his pesticide business, augmented by a number of minor products which help to maintain an acceptable cash flow. The interesting question whether discovery and development of new pesticides is once again becoming an unacceptably risky investment is currently being hotly debated in the industry.

We have seen that after World War II, everything was right for the developing pesticides industry. Farming was becoming a prosperous occupation, agricultural land prices were rising rapidly and agricultural labour was becoming scarce and expensive so there was great incentive to improve yields per hectare. Food prices were rising and the populations of developed countries were increasing in number and becoming more affluent and able, therefore, to demand and pay for a wider variety of more expensive foods. Marketing methods and food processing both called for fruit and vegetables with no visible signs of pest or disease damage. Why, then, should there now be difficulties for the pesticide industry?

Firstly, the costs of discovery and development of new pesticides are rising rapidly, as shown in Table 4.3. The percentage of sales income spent on research, and the time needed for development of a new product are both increasing, as shown in Table 4.4. At the same time the number of candidate compounds which have to be screened to obtain one commercial product is increasing, as shown in Table 4.3. and the success rate is falling.

TABLE 4.3   *Increase in development costs of a pesticide*

Year of estimate	1956	1964	1969	1973	1979	1985
Cost of development ($ millions)	1.2	2.9	5.5	10.0	21.0	43.0
Number of compounds screened per marketed product	1,800	3,600	5,500	10,000	13,000	16,000

Secondly, the requirements for toxicological and environmental testing have become much more stringent in recent years, as shown in Table 4.5, and are likely to become even more demanding — and, therefore, more expensive — in the future. The cost of providing the necessary evidence of safety falls entirely on the company which wishes to market the new product, and may amount to $5m. This cost has to be recouped from the profits of future sales if the investment is to be one which is commercially justified. By and large, the

TABLE 4.4 *Research profile of U.S. pesticide industry (Ernst & Ernst Trade Association Department, May 1971)*

	1967	1970	1985
Total sales	$639m	$722m	$4,406m
R & D on new products	$52.3m	$69.9m	$ 458m
Percentage	8.2	9.7	10.4
No of compounds screened per marketed product	5481	7430	16,000
Cost of development of each marketed product	$ 3.4m	$ 5.5m	$ 43.2m
Time from discovery to marketing	60 months	77 months	88 months

TABLE 4.5 *Minimum requirements for world-wide registration*

	1950	1965	1980
Toxicology	Acute toxicity 30–90 day rat-feeding	Acute toxicity 90 day rat-feeding 90 day dog-feeding 2 year rat-feeding 1 year dog feeding	Acute toxicity 90 day rat-feeding 90 day dog-feeding 2 year rat-feeding 2 year dog-feeding Reproduction 3 rat generations Teratogenesis in rodents Toxicity to fish Toxicity to shellfish Toxicity to birds
Metabolism	None	Rat	Rat and dog Plant
Residues	Food crops 1 ppm	Food crops 0.1 ppm Meat 0.1 ppm Milk 0.1 ppm	Food crops 0.01 ppm Meat 0.1 ppm Milk 0.005 ppm
Ecology	None	None	Environmental stability Environmental movement Environmental accumulation Total effects on all non-target species

Note: the current even more extensive requirements in the U.S.A. are set out in the Federal Register No. 40, Part 158, 24th October, 1984.

costs of searching for new biologically active compounds and of toxicological, residue and environmental studies on candidate products, are both largely independent of the size of the eventual market for the product. The consequence is that discovery and development of new pesticides is becoming more and more an acceptable undertaking for the chemical industry only if there is a reasonable chance of finding a product which has a wide spectrum of activity and which can command a large market in a major crop. As there are a limited number of major crops in the world the markets for new pesticides are becoming increasingly fragmented as more and more products are introduced to the same markets, and the chances of a new product achieving a substantial share of the total market are decreasing steadily. The incidental consequence that minor crop or minor pest problems are not getting sufficient attention and that, often, compounds which are discovered in the laboratory which could be efficacious in dealing with them are not developed commercially because it is not profitable to do so, may be regrettable for agriculture but is not one which the manufacturers can avoid so long as the economics of pesticide development are as they are.

We have already seen that the chance of a new pesticide making large profits is not high, and is getting steadily less. The reason is that, during the past 40 years, a large number of new pesticides have been developed, and many of these have achieved large tonnages and have become patent-free so that they can be made comparatively cheaply because of scale of manufacture and competitive production. More and more pesticides are coming into this category every year. There are, therefore, reasonably satisfactory answers available to the farmer for most crop protection and pest control problems at a reasonable price. The choice for the farmer is not as it was 40 years ago between using a pesticide or suffering substantial crop loss but between using a cheap established pesticide which gives reasonable control or a new and more expensive pesticide which performs marginally better. The available markets for new pesticides are, as we have said, becoming increasingly fragmented and there will be smaller market opportunities and lower tonnage requirements for new products. The chances of achieving sales sufficient to recover development costs and to make an acceptable profit are, therefore, diminishing. The future of discovery and development of new pesticides is doubtful unless the financial prospects for the manufacturer can be made more attractive.

It is an ironic consequence of the increased costs of safety and environmental studies that it has become unprofitable to discover and develop compounds of highly specific activity for restricted and specialized markets. Such compounds are the least likely to give rise to side-effect problems. If all the pesticide needs of the farmer could be covered by a multiplicity and diversity of specialized products, the possibility of cumulative risk to the consumer or the environment would be far less than that for a few very widely used compounds of unspecific activity. Yet a proper concern by the regulating authorities to try to ensure maximum safety to the consumer and the environment is having the effect of making only the least intrinsically safe types of pesticides, namely, those with a wide spectrum of activity intended for extensive use on major crops, economically justifiable as targets for discovery and development.

The Size of the Market for Pesticides

Although there may be doubts about the financial viability of development of new pesticides there is no doubt that world demand for established pesticides will increase. Although alternative methods of crop protection and pest control may be introduced, it is certain that chemicals will be the main weapons in the farmer's armoury against pests and diseases for many years to come. The number of companies engaged in discovery and development of new pesticides is very small, but there are thousands of small companies who are engaged in formulation and marketing of established pesticides which are no longer protected by patents. Thus, in the U.S.A. there are about 3,000 registered active ingredients for pesticides but at least 150,000 different commercial labels.

The most reliable statistics for production and use of pesticides come from the U.S.A. In 1985 U.S.A. manufacturers produced 440,000 tonnes of synthetic organic pesticides having a total value of $4,406m. In Tables 4.6, 4.7, and 4.8 details are given of the amounts of the most important

TABLE 4.6   *Herbicides*

	Amount used by U.S.A. farmers in 1971 tonnes	Amount used by U.S.A. farmers in 1982 tonnes
Inorganic herbicides	820	200
Organic arsenicals	3,600	500
Dalapon	450	200
Chloramben	4,440	1,000
Other benzoic acids	230	340
2,4-D	15,700	11,600
Other phenoxyacetics	2,400	500
Propachlor	10,700	3,800
Alachlor	6,700	42,200
Propanil	3,000	3,000
Naptalam	1,500	2,500
Metolachlor	nil	18,500
Dinitrophenols	3,300	3,000
Fluorodifen	590	800
Trifluralin	5,200	18,000
EPTC	1,700	4,200
Butylate	2,700	27,500
Linuron	820	3,200
Diuron	550	3,000
Fluometuron	1,500	1,500
Noruron	590	500
Other ureas	90	200
Atrazine	26,000	38,000
Other triazines	2,400	4,000
Other organics	9,460	38,760
Total	104,400	225,500
Petroleum oils	66,100	73,400

TABLE 4.7   *Fungicides*

	Amount used by U.S.A. farmers in 1971 tonnes	Amount used by U.S.A. farmers in 1982 tonnes
Copper sulphate	3,500	3,500
Other copper compounds	1,000	1,000
Other inorganics	2,800	2,800
Maneb	1,800	2,000
Zineb	900	900
Ferbam	600	600
Other dithiocarbamates	2,600	400
Captan	3,000	3,200
Other phthalimides	450	300
Other organics	2,600	1,800
Systemics	nil	2,000
Total	19,250	19,500
Sulphur	51,000	72,000

TABLE 4.8   *Insecticides*

	Amount used by U.S.A. farmers in 1971 tonnes	Amount used by U.S.A. farmers in 1982 tonnes
Inorganic insecticides	300	100
TDE	110	nil
DDT	6,500	nil
Methoxychlor	1,400	nil
Toxaphene	17,000	3,200
Aldrin and endrin	4,200	nil
Chlordimeform	nil	600
Disulfoton	1,800	1,000
Methyl parathion	12,500	7,300
Parathion	4,300	2,400
Malathion	1,600	1,600
Dichlorvos	1,100	1,100
Diazinon	1,400	1,000
Phorate	1,900	2,700
Chlorpyrifos	nil	3,500
Terbufos	nil	6,000
Pyrethroids	nil	1,800
Carbaryl	8,100	1,500
Carbofuran	1,300	4,900
Butencarb	1,600	1,600
Methomyl	490	1,200
Other organics (mainly OPs)	9,600	5,000
Total	75,350	45,900
Petroleum oils	34,000	38,000

herbicides, fungicides and insecticides which were used by U.S.A. farmers in 1971 and 1982. It will be seen that production and sales are dominated by a comparatively few products. In herbicides, 17% of the total use of synthetic organics is now accounted for by atrazine, 19% by alachlor, 12% by butylate, 8% by trifluralin, 8% by metolachlor and 5% by 2,4-D. The total usage of petroleum oils for weed control is 33% of the total usage of synthetic organics. In fungicides nearly all the organics are accounted for by the dithiocarbamates and captan but the major fungicide is sulphur, the total usage of which is 3.6 times that of all other fungicides put together. In insecticides, terbufos, chlorpyrifos, methyl parathion and carbofuran together account for 50% of the synthetic organics while the total usage of petroleum oils for insect control is 75% of the total usage of synthetic organics.

The fact that the market for crop protection and pest control chemicals is dominated by a few major products which can be produced comparatively cheaply because of scale of manufacture, should be borne in mind when considering the multiplicity of chemicals described in this book. Many of these have achieved only modest commercial success.

The value of pesticides produced in the U.K. in 1985 is shown in Table 4.9 and of pesticides produced in the U.S.A., Japan, U.K. and in the world as a whole in 1985 in Table 4.10. During the ten years 1964 to 1974 total world production of organic pesticides doubled and production specifically of herbicides trebled. This trend is illustrated by the figures for the U.S.A. in Table 4.11. The overall annual growth rate for sales of organic pesticides was about 8% from 1964 to 1969 and about 5% from 1969 to 1974. In the last decade, the average annual growth rate slowed to about 3% for all organic pesticides. However, some much more optimistic market forecasts have been given, and these are shown in Table 4.12, but take no account of new discoveries.

TABLE 4.9   *U.K. pesticide sales 1985*

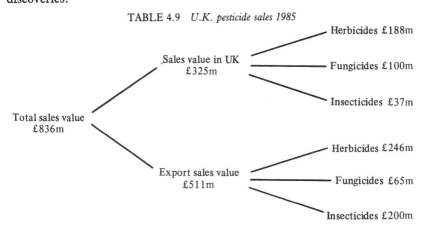

TABLE 4.10   *World pesticide production 1985 millions of dollars*

	U.S.A.	Japan	U.K.	World
Herbicides	2,922	582	650	7,053
Fungicides	283	492	248	2,883
Insecticides	1,000	777	356	5,466
Fumigants	60	—	—	210
Growth regulators	141	—	27	288
Total	4,406	1,851	1,281	15,900

TABLE 4.11   *U.S.A. pesticide production*

	1945 tonnes	1955 tonnes	1964 tonnes	1969 tonnes	1974 tonnes
Herbicides	2,000	20,000	103,000	178,000	274,000
Fungicides	2,000	5,000	51,000	64,000	74,000
Insecticides	24,000	106,000	202,000	259,000	295,000
Total	28,000	131,000	356,000	501,000	643,000

TABLE 4.12   *Projected world demand for pesticides*
Millions of dollars (1975 price levels)

	1975	1980	1985	1990
Herbicides				
Triazines	650	900	1,240	1,710
Carbamates	280	360	460	600
Phenyl ureas	190	315	520	860
Phenoxys	150	260	450	780
Benzoics	140	215	330	500
Arsenicals	30	25	20	20
Others	860	1,275	2,120	3,230
Total	2,300	3,450	5,140	7,700
Fungicides				
Dithiocarbamates	450	580	735	900
Captan	350	500	580	665
Coppers	150	186	215	260
Mercurials	50	40	20	0
Others	35	45	50	55
Total	1,035	1,345	1,600	1,880
Insecticides				
Organophosphates	1,100	1,440	1,870	2,450
Carbamates	470	610	800	1,050
Organochlorines	320	330	400	200
Arsenicals	20	10	0	0
Total	1,910	2,390	3,070	3,700
All pesticides total	5,245	7,185	9,810	13,280

For historical interest and as a comparison to the data in Tables 4.6, 4.7, and 4.8, with which they should be compared, the main pesticides manufactured in the U.S.A. in 1945 and 1955 are shown in Table 4.13.

TABLE 4.13   *U.S.A. pesticide production*
(excluding sulphur and petroleum oils)

	1945 tonnes	1955 tonnes
White arsenic	22,100	11,900
Calcium arsenate	11,600	1,300
Lead arsenate	32,000	6,700
Copper sulphate	113,900	70,900
BHC	1,000	4,600
DDT	15,000	56,800
parathion	1,200	2,300
TEPP	820	90
2,4–D	400	15,400
2,4,5–T	360	1,400
Other organics*	9,000	50,000
Total inorganics	179,600	90,800
Total organic	27,780	130,590

*Mainly allethrin, aramite, aldrin, captan, chlordane, dieldrin, dithiocarbamates, endrin, methoxychlor, malathion and toxaphene.

Economics of Pesticides for Farmers

In 1983 U.S.A. farmers spent $3,000m on crop protection and pest control chemicals. Expenditure by farmers in other developed countries has been comparable, and the total value of world sales of pesticides to farmers was probably around $10,000m in 1986. The amounts spent by farmers in developed countries has been increasing steadily. In the U.S.A. they were $427m in 1964, $1,002m in 1971, $2,200m in 1975, $3,100m in 1980 and $3,500m in 1985, but, in real money terms, this expenditure is constant.

The reason why farmers in developed countries have been willing to spend money on pesticides is that such expenditure has proved to be financially rewarding. It has been estimated that each dollar spent on pesticides in the U.S.A. produces an average of about four dollars additional income for the farmer. In the U.K. the estimate is that each £1 spent on pesticides produces £5 additional income.

It is not easy to calculate precise figures for the financial benefits of pesticides for individual crops grown by individual farmers, as these vary widely from crop to crop, from farm to farm, and from season to season, and depend very much on the skill and economy with which the farmer uses them. Also attacks by pests and diseases are unpredictable. At one extreme pesticide application may prevent total loss of a crop on which a farmer is totally dependent and thus avoid total loss of income to him for that year. In developed countries, the small farmers who grow an assortment of crops and keep various types of animals are tending to disappear and many farmers grow just one type of crop, e.g. wheat, corn, soya, cotton, beet. At the other extreme, money spent on safeguarding against pests and diseases a crop which was eventually ruined for some other reason, such as storm damage, may be money spent needlessly. Money on pesticides is likewise wasted if the farmer cannot sell his crop at a satisfactory price. In the 1968–1969 season in the U.K. about 30% of the brussels sprouts grown were sold at less than the break-even price for the farmer so any money he had spent on crop protection would only have increased his financial loss.

Many farmers use pesticides as an insurance policy, that is, they adopt a regular programme of spraying as a preventive against possible losses. The economics of this procedure are becoming more comprehensible as the tendency towards contract growing and guaranteed prices increases. In such a situation a farmer can calculate accurately how much he can afford to spend on crop protection. From the farmer's point of view a crop which cannot be sold because it is blemished by pests and diseases is as financially disastrous as one which is totally destroyed. The consumer and food processor nowadays demand such high standards of freedom from insect damage or disease blemish that use of pesticides is mandatory and, in the case of contract growing, the programme of crop protection is often precisely specified for the grower in his contract. Nevertheless it is true that money spent on pesticides to safeguard against an attack which does not occur may be regarded as money wasted.

The economics of herbicide usage are clearer than those of insecticides or fungicides, as herbicides are essentially used as a substitute for mechanical or hand weeding and can be assessed on this basis. In 1985 it took 50 man-hours to grow and harvest a hectare of cotton using chemical weeding and defoliation and mechanical picking, compared with 200 man-hours in 1933 using manual hoeing and picking. Similarly in 1985, it took 40 man-hours to grow and harvest one hectare of peanuts compared with 190 man-hours in 1935, and 22 man-hours to grow and harvest 5,000kg of corn compared with 135 man-hours in 1945.

Nevertheless although the financial benefits of pesticide use vary widely from crop to crop, from location to location and from farmer to farmer, it is possible to make some generalization. The most convincing evidence of benefit of pesticides to U.S. farmers is that they did spend $3,500m in 1985 on pesticides, since farmers do not part with their money easily.

One or two specific studies have been made. A series of experiments with potatoes over a period of ten years indicated $6.71 average return for each $1 spent on pesticides, and a similar study on apples showed $5.17 average return for each $1 expended. In Canada, $1 spent in apple orchards on pesticides returned $13 in Nova Scotia, $5 in Quebec and $2.34 in Ontario. A study on tomatoes in the U.S.A. showed that use of pesticides increased farmers' gross incomes by 75%. The increase in value of crops harvested on ten million hectares in Canada treated with herbicides at a cost of $8m was estimated to be $58.8m equivalent to a 7:1 return. Studies on German farms growing cereals and root crops over a period of four years showed a gain in crop value of $47.2 per hectare for an outlay on crop protection chemicals of $20.3 per hectare.

Economics of Pesticides for the Nation

Farmers have used pesticides because it has proved profitable for them to do so, not from any altruistic motives. The consequence, for the nation, has been that pesticides have contributed substantially to the increases in yields per hectare and yields per man-hour for all major crops during the past 40 years. To quote one example, up to 1958 the average yield of wheat in the U.K. had exceeded 2,500 kg/ha on only two occasions in 60 years. Now, in 1986, the average yield is about 4,000 kg/ha. Yields of all other major crops have increased similarly. In the U.K., wheat is produced at 210 kg per man-hour compared with 2 kg per man-hour in subsistence agriculture in the third world. In the U.S.A. rice is produced at 240 kg per man-hour compared with 4 kg per man-hour by peasants in the tropics. Such yield increases are not entirely due to pesticides but also to higher-yielding varieties, irrigation and fertilizers. Nevertheless, it is sometimes possible to unravel the separate contribution of pesticides. Thus, between 1955 and 1970 in Illinois, when the same hybrid corn was grown and the same amounts of fertilizer used, average yields rose from about 3,500 kg/ha to about 5000 kg/ha consequent on an increase in the proportion of the total crop treated with pesticides from about 3% to about 80% during that period. Pesticides have helped to make possible the fact that developed countries have been able to supply steadily increasing populations with adequate food at reasonable prices from a fixed amount of arable land using a decreasing labour force. The result is that, in the U.S.A. and U.K., one agricultural worker produces enough food for himself and 60 other people and the average person in these countries has to spend only about 18% of his disposable income on food. In India, by contrast, one agricultural worker feeds himself and only 4 other people, and the average person has to spend about 66% of his income on food.

It has been estimated that cessation of use of all pesticides in the U.S.A. would reduce total production of all crops and livestock by 30% and would increase the price of farm products to the consumer by 50% to 70%. This would mean that the average person would have to spend a substantially greater proportion of his income on food. As there are 25 million people in the U.S.A. who are on poverty level incomes, this section of the population would suffer privation.

As a specific example of the value of pesticides the United States Department of Agriculture calculated in 1970 that discontinuance of use of the herbicide 2,4-D would add $290m to the production costs of bread and other wheat products and would necessitate 20 million extra man-hours of work by farmers and their families without any increase in income to maintain present levels of wheat production. The use of 2,4-D in wheat cultivation resulted in enough extra wheat in 1975 for 130 billion more loaves than in 1940.

That the adverse effects on the community of lack of crop protection and pest control are not pure conjecture is shown by the experience in the U.S.A. in 1970 when Southern corn leaf blight got out of control and 20 billion kg of corn were lost. Corn prices rose from 5.3 $/kg to 6.6 $/kg and stayed at that level for a year with a total extra cost to the consumer of $2 billion.

Further Reading

British Agrochemicals Association, *Annual Report & Handbook*, London, 1986.

Food and Agricultural Organisation, *Crop Loss Assessment Methods*, United Nations, Rome, 1970.

Green, M. B. Are herbicides too expensive?, *Weed Science*, **21**, 374, 1973.

Green, M. B. *Pesticides: Boon or Bane?*, Elek Books, London and Westview Press Boulder, Colorado, 1976.

Gregory, J. G. (Ed.) *Technological Economics of Crop Protection and Pest Control*, S.C.I. Monograph No. 36, Society of Chemical Industry, London, 1970.

Gunn, D. L. and Stevens, J. G. R. (Eds.) *Pesticides and Human Welfare*, Oxford University Press, 1976.

National Academy of Sciences, *Contemporary Pest Control Practices and Prospects*, Washington, D.C., 1975.

Norton, G. A. and Mumford, J. D. Decision making in pest control. In *Advances in Applied Biology* vol. 8, (ed. T. H. Conker), Academic Press, London and New York, 1983.

United States Department of Agriculture, *Agricultural Research Service Economic Report*, No. 194, Washington, D.C., 1970.

United States Department of Agriculture, *Losses in Agriculture*, Agriculture Handbook, No. 291, Washington, D.C., 1965.

United States Department of Agriculture, *The Pesticide Review*, Washington, D.C., 1975.

United States Department of Agriculture, *Outlook & Situation*, Washington, D.C., 1983.

5

Pesticides and Energy

Agricultural productivity in developed countries is maintained at a level sufficient to feed their populations adequately only by injecting fossil fuel energy into agriculture either directly in mechanical devices such as tractors or, indirectly, as fertilizers and pesticides. Energy is used whenever material is processed or transported so that, at each stage of manufacture, there is an energy input which is carried on to the next stage. The final product has indirect energy inputs from the intrinsic energy of all the hydrocarbon materials used in its manufacture and direct energy inputs from heat and electricity used in processing.

TABLE 5.1

Energy inputs for various crop protection chemicals (GJ/t)

	Naphtha	Fuel oil	Natural gas	Coke	Elec- tricity	Steam	Total
MCPA	53.3	12.6	12.0		27.5	22.3	130
Diuron	92.3	5.2	63.1		85.6	28.3	270
Atrazine	43.2	14.4	68.8		37.2	24.7	190
Trifluralin	56.4	7.9	12.8		57.7	16.1	150
Paraquat	76.1	4.0	68.4		141.6	169.3	460
2,4-D	39	9			23	16	85
2,4,5-T	43	2	23		42	25	135
Chloramben	92	5	29		44	0	170
Dinoseb	49	11	9		3	8	80
Propanil	62	3	40		64	51	220
Propachlor	107	14	29		84	56	290
Dicamba	69	4	73		96	53	295
Glyphosate	33	1	93		227	100	454
Diquat	70	1	65		100	164	400
Ferbam			42	3	13	23	61
Maneb	27	9	23	8	25	7	99
Captan	38		14		52	11	115
Methyl parathion	37	2	24	6	73	18	160
Toxaphene	3	1	19		32	3	58
Carbofuran	137	44	63	1	127	82	454
Carbaryl	11	1	48	26	54	13	153

Computer programs have been developed which sum up all these energy inputs for a given chemical compound. These programs try to take all energy inputs into consideration, including energy which goes into building and maintaining the manufacturing plant, as well as other ancillary energy contributions.

Table 5.1 shows the energy inputs for some widely used herbicides, fungicides and insecticides. These figures are for 100% active ingredient. In fact, formulation adds only about 20 to 50 GJ/t active ingredient unless large quantities of some particular complex formulating agents are used.

TABLE 5.2

Energy Inputs to Crop Production (MGJ)

	U.S. total crops	(1970)	U.K. total crops	(1972)
Direct use of fuel	686	44%	83.7	35%
Fertilizers	370	24%	91.2	38%
Pesticides	24	1.6%	2.1	0.9%
Machinery	303	20%	30.2	13%
Irrigation, transport, etc.	160	10%	29.8	13%

The figures in Table 5.2 show that crop protection, including both the chemicals and their application, accounts for only a very small proportion — less than 2% — of the total fossil fuel energy put into primary agricultural production. The total amounts of energy used in U.S. crop production are 2.2% of the nation's total energy usage for all purposes, and in the U.K. are 2.6%, so pesticides use about 0.04% of the nation's total energy. What do we get out of crop protection in energy terms? The increases in yields and the total or partial losses prevented are very variable quantities, so Price-Jones has suggested a different approach.

Table 5.3 shows that prevention of 10% loss of maize by use of pesticides saves on balance about 19 gallons of oil per hectare.

TABLE 5.3

Energy savings in U.S. maize production from pesticide usage (1970)

Average fossil fuel energy input for pesticide-treated maize	29.98 GJ/ha
Average fossil fuel energy input for non-treated maize	29.57 GJ/ha
Number of hectares of non-treated maize to give yield equal to that of 1 ha of treated maize, assuming non-treatment reduces yield by 10%	1.11
Fossil fuel energy input for 1.11 ha non-treated maize	32.85 GJ
Fossil fuel energy saved by pesticide treatment	2.87 GJ/ha (19 gal oil)

Table 5.4 shows the additional weights of a number of crops which would have to be obtained to provide metabolically utilizable energy equivalent to the fossil fuel energy which is used up in the production and application of a typical pesticide at 1 kg/ha. To compensate in energy terms for a pesticide applied at 1 kg/ha to wheat, for example, it is necessary to obtain 17.6 kg/ha extra crop. A typical wheat yield in the U.K. is 4300 kg/ha, so 17.6 kg/ha represents a yield increase of only 0.4%. Even with a comparatively low energy-yielding crop like peas, which typically yield about 3000 kg/ha, to compensate for the use of the pesticide the yield increase needed is still only 4.3%.

TABLE 5.4
Metabolically utilizable energy of various foodstuffs

Crop	Condition	Metabolically utilizable energy (MJ/kg)	Weight of crop yielding 263 (MJ/kg)
Wheat	Unprocessed	14.95	17.6
Barley	Unprocessed	13.10	18.0
Potatoes	Raw	3.18	83.7
Sugar beet	Unprocessed	2.64	99.6
Peas	Cooked	2.05	128.2
Broad beans	Cooked	2.89	91.0
Apples	Raw	1.92	137.0
Cabbage	Raw	1.17	224.8
Carrots	Raw	0.96	274.0
Celery	Raw	0.33	797.0
Mushrooms	Cooked	0.30	876.7

The crop losses prevented or the yield increases obtained by crop protection are generally very much larger than those that would be needed to compensate for the energy inputs in Table 5.4. Crop protection is consequently a good way to use limited resources of fossil fuel energy because we are using a small amount of such energy to increase greatly the total amount of solar energy which is made available to us via photosynthesis as metabolically utilisable food energy.

Herbicides are essentially used as substitutes for human and mechanical labour, to carry out by chemical means weeding and other cultivation operations. It has been demonstrated by investment appraisal studies that this can result in significant financial savings as a result of the reduced labour requirements. For example, in the U.S.A. it has been estimated that, in 1974, it required 50 man-hours to grow a hectare of cotton compared with 300 man-hours in 1954. The financial gains from increased yields consequent on use of herbicides are well documented. For example, Hurtig estimated $58 million increase in the value of crops harvested on 10 million hectares in Canada treated with herbicides in 1960 at a cost of $8 million.

A typical value for the amount of energy used in carrying out a mechanical weeding operation is 0.56 GJ/ha (1.5 gal/acre of diesel fuel), and for a typical spraying operation is 0.056 GJ/ha (0.15 gal/acre of diesel fuel). A comparison of the total energy input in carrying out a mechanical weeding with the total energy inputs for carrying it out with herbicides, assuming typical rates of application, is shown in Table 5.5. Of course, in practice, for weed control throughout a whole season, the number of herbicide applications needed may differ from the number of mechanical weeding operations, the rates of application of herbicides may differ from crop to crop, and the amount of mechanical energy needed may depend on the nature of the terrain and weather conditions. Also if the herbicide can be applied pre-emergently in conjunction with a sowing operation then the mechanical energy of spraying will be saved. Nevertheless, it should be realized that, in general, at least two mechanical weeding operations are required to achieve the effect of one chemical treatment. However, the data in this table will enable the reader to make a fair approximation for any particular case in which he is interested.

TABLE 5.5
Energy used in mechanical and chemical weeding

Method	Fuel (litres/ha)	Energy (GJ/ha)	Total
Mechanical	16.9	0.56	0.56
Chemical Herbicide (MCPA 0.75 kg/ha=0.67 lb/acre)	1.7	0.06 0.10	0.16
Chemical Herbicide (Diuron 2.3 kg/ha=2.0 lb/acre)	1.7	0.06 0.62	0.68
Chemical Herbicide (Atrazine 1.13 kg/ha=1.0 lb/acre)	1.7	0.06 0.21	0.27
Chemical Herbicide (Trifluralin 1.13 kg/ha=1.0 lb/acre)	1.7	0.06 0.17	0.23

Table 5.6 shows a comparison of energy inputs into mechanical and chemical weeding in forestry. This is based on the use of a Massey Ferguson 165 tractor travelling at 0.56 m/s (1¼ m.p.h.) in a new forestry plantation with a row spacing of 2.1 m. The mechanical weed control achieved 2.6 ha/day and the chemical weed control 13.0 ha/day. The average fuel consumption of the MF165 tractor was 1.27×10^5 J/s (3.0 gal/h). The herbicide used was 2,4,5-T at 3.5 kg/ha active ingredient. The reason why chemical treatment is so much more economical on tractor usage is that the mechanical operation can cope with only one row at a time, i.e. 2.1 m

working width, whereas a mist blower on the tractor gives weed control with the herbicide of a 10 m strip for each pass of the tractor. Furthermore, it is usual to have to carry out two mechanical weed control operations per year, but only one chemical treatment.

An interesting case for comparison is the use of paraquat in minimum tillage and direct drilling operations as an alternative to conventional ploughing and cultivation. An APAS/NIAE Farm Mechanization Study quotes diesel fuel consumption figures for a range of large farm tractors operating on both light and heavy soils. Taking an average figure for a medium soil the amounts of diesel fuel consumed for conventional ploughing and cultivation and direct drilling respectively are shown in Table 5.7. To the direct drilling figure has been added the energy content of the paraquat used to give a total energy input.

TABLE 5.6
Comparison of mechanical and chemical weeding in forestry

	Mechanical	Chemical
Area treated per day	2.6 ha	13.0 ha
Energy used per 8 h day by tractor	3.48 GJ	3.48 GJ
Energy used per ha	1.34 GJ	0.27 GJ
Energy in 2,4,5-T used (3.5 kg-ha=3.1 lb/acre)		0.47 GJ
Total energy for two mechanical weedings	2.68 GJ/ha	–
Total energy for one chemical weeding	–	0.74 GJ/ha
Annual energy saving for chemical weeding	–	1.94 GJ/ha (= 13 gal/ha of diesel fuel)

Energy content of 2,4,5-T=135 GJ/t.
Other data supplied by U.K. Forestry Commission.

TABLE 5.7
Energy used in conventional cultivation and direct drilling

Ploughing and cultivating		
Operation	Fuel (litres/ha)	Energy (GJ/ha)
Ploughing	22.5	0.75
Heavy cultivating (1 × 2)	22.5	0.75
Light harrowing	5.6	0.19
Drilling	11.2	0.38
Light harrowing	5.6	0.19
Total		2.26

TABLE 5.7 (Continued)

Direct Drilling		
Operation	Fuel (litres/ha)	Energy (GJ/ha)
Spraying	1.7	0.06
Drilling	11.2	0.38
Harrowing	5.6	0.19
Paraquat (0.84 kg/ha=0.75 lb/acre)		0.39
Total		1.02

The results suggest that direct drilling and minimum tillage techniques can save about 1.0 GJ/ha of total energy (equivalent to 2.7 gals/acre of diesel fuel).

Further Reading

Baird, C. D. and Fluck, R. C. *Agricultural Energetics*, AVI Publishing Company, Westport Connecticut, 1980.
Green, M. B. *Eating Oil*, Westview Press, Boulder, Colorado, 1977.
Green, M. B. Energy in agriculture, *Chem. & Ind.*, 641, 1976.
Green, M. B. and McCulloch, A. Energy considerations in the use of herbicides, *J. Sci. Fd. Agric.* 27, 95, 1976.
Leach, G. *Energy and Food Production*, IPC Press, Guildford, 1976.

6

Types of Pesticides

Classification

What is included under the word "pest" in our usage, is explained in the preface. The term is not descriptive of any intrinsic characteristics of a particular organism but merely of the way in which it behaves in certain circumstances. In broadest terms, any living organism which is somewhere that you do not wish it to be, doing something that you do not wish it to do, is a "pest". "Weed" is not a description of a particular type of plant, but of behaviour, and a weed has been defined as "any plant growing in a place where you do not wish it to grow".

The main pests of economic importance are weeds, fungi and insects but there are also mammals, birds, molluscs, mites, nematodes, bacteria and viruses. The main groups of pesticides are therefore herbicides (weeds), fungicides and insecticides with minor groups rodenticides, avicides (birds), molluscicides, acaricides (mites), nematicides, bactericides and antivirals.

Pesticides are often sub-classified according to their "mode of action". However, this phrase means different things in different scientific disciplines, and misunderstanding often results. The field biologist may distinguish some herbicides as "pre-sowing" or "pre-emergent", being those best suited to apply to the soil to kill seedlings in the absence of a crop, and some as "contact", being those applied, with good coverage, to foliage to kill all leaves (of susceptible species) contacted but which probably allow regrowth from perennial rootstock. There are several equivalent classes of this kind and subdivisions dependent on, e.g. persistence. If a pre-sowing herbicide is a persistent one no crop could be sown shortly afterwards unless of a biochemically resistant species. Thus atrazine can be applied to soil before or after sowing maize because the crop is resistant to it, but paraquat can be used to clear ground before any sowing because it is inactivated by soil.

The biologist may describe an insecticide as "contact", usually adding the adjective "residual", if it stays on the surface of walls and kills insects which walk thereon; as a "stomach poison" if it kills caterpillars which eat treated leaves; or as "systemic" if it enters the tissue fluids of the host plant and kills sucking insects on parts of the plant not directly treated.

The biochemist, on the other hand, will, under "mode of action", distinguish different disturbances of essential biochemistry which lead to the final observed symptoms. Some compounds arrest photosynthesis, others inhibit oxidative phosphorylation, others the enzymic hydrolysis of acetylcholine, etc.

In this predominantly chemical book it might seem natural to adopt the biochemical classification, but this is not a book about biochemistry but more a book for chemists about pesticide practice and for the pesticide practitioner about the chemistry he is called upon to use. Our interest is therefore mainly in the field biologists' classification, but we must try to sort out some inconsistencies which have arisen during the development of the subject — of the kind which tries to distinguish between green things and square things. For example "systemic" and "contact" insecticides are often contrasted, but "systemic" refers to behaviour of the compound in the tissues of the plant or animal host while "contact" refers to the mode of entry into the pest insect. We can quote no example of an insecticide arriving in a leaf only via the systemic route (from application to root or to another leaf) and killing an insect by contact, but such behaviour might be found. Certainly some insecticides have a useful direct contact effect (e.g. dimethoate on flies) but also have a useful systemic behaviour, killing sucking insects after systemic transfer.

Confusion arises mainly because the differences are not in the action of the compounds within the final target but in the means of transfer from the site of application to the target. To describe an insecticide as having "vapour action" is misleading. No "action" goes on in the gas phase, only transfer. What is meant is that the compound can reach the target from the site of application via the vapour. We know of no insecticide which has, exclusively, "stomach" or "contact" action. The insecticide can get into the vital tissues from the body integument, from the tarsi, by ingestion or (as vapour) through the trachea. Which route is most important depends on the situation, i.e. the habitat and behaviour of the pest, the habit of the host and the means of application. It is not a property descriptive of the insecticide as such. One insecticide may best be used, and be the best to use, in a situation where direct contact is the main means of transfer, another where systemic transfer is called for, but change the situation and the choice may change.

"Volatile", "Superficial", "Systemic" might be the best main classifications of insecticide and fungicide, "Contact" and "Systemic" parallel classification of herbicides but the distinctions are not clear. We will consider the first of these at some length to illustrate the dependence on situation.

Volatile Pesticides

Some pesticides, in some applications, redistribute themselves in the environment by purely physical processes. These are compounds used as fumigants. They do not form a biological class since they are used against many widely different organisms. They do not form a chemical class. More logically they can be regarded as a physical class but this defines the compound and method of use together, rather than the compounds themselves. Obviously a fumigant must be sufficiently volatile to be effective in any particular situation but there is no absolute limit of volatility. The words "volatile", "involatile", "of negligible vapour pressure", are used very carelessly in a good deal of pesticide literature, and the last phrase particularly can be very misleading. The laboratory chemist naturally regards a substance as involatile if it can be handled by ordinary laboratory procedures and in at least milligram quantities without special precautions against loss. It may nevertheless be quite sufficiently volatile for a lethal dose to be transmitted through the vapour phase under favourable conditions. Thus, if flies are caged and the cage suspended in a closed vessel containing lindane they will be dead in a few hours although no direct contact has been made. When triallate is incorporated in the surface layer of soil to control wild oat, there is good reason to believe that the main route of access of the compound to the seedling is through the air spaces in the soil and the cuticle of the shoot rather than through the water phase and the root. Neither compound would be classed as volatile on ordinary laboratory standards.

Calculation, as well as example, may serve to emphasize this point. The vapour pressure of lindane at 20°C is 9×10^{-6} mm Hg, corresponding to a saturation concentration in air of 0.15 mg/m^3. If a man, breathing at an average rate of 15 l/min, were to absorb into his lungs all the lindane from a saturated atmosphere, he would take in only 3 mg in 24 hr. Several years would be necessary to take in an amount which would be lethal if ingested as a single dose, and the rapid excretion of most of the compound would make this prediction unrealistic. If a pellet of this substance 2 mm in diameter were suspended freely in air it would lose by evaporation at ordinary temperature only about 0.8 μg in 24 hr.

In both of these examples, lindane could apparently justifiably be said to have "negligible volatility". Suppose, however, that the 2mm object in air is the body of a small insect and that it can take up the substance from saturated air just as efficiently as a pellet of the substance can lose weight into pure air. It gains 0.8 μg in 24 hr, but its body weight is only 4 mg. Its content of toxicant at the end of 24 hr is 200 mg/kg body weight, well into the lethal range for insects. In this context the volatility is far from negligible.

It may seem unrealistic to consider insects having free access to the saturated vapour in simple laboratory vessels, because, in nature, there will be many other substances present — soil particles, crop leaves, etc., all have adsorbing surfaces. The significance of these depends on whether the environment permits only reversible adsorption or whether chemical decomposition of the adsorbed substance occurs. It depends also on the distance through which the toxicant must diffuse and on the effect of speed of intake on toxicity. Lindane would be quite ineffective in killing insects distributed in a store of grain if it were itself only applied to the top of the heap. An intrinsically less toxic but much less adsorbed toxicant, such as methyl bromide, is far more effective. On the other hand, applied to the curling leaves in the centre of a young *Brassica* plant, lindane is effective even against aphids and the necessary transfer of toxicant occurs mainly in the vapour phase. An equal dose of methyl bromide would evaporate during spraying before the target was reached.

An insecticide having more rapid vapour action than lindane but not normally considered a fumigant is dichlorvos. It has a vapour pressure of 0.01 mm mercury at 20°C. The saturated vapour is rapidly lethal to insects but eventually lethal also to mammals. By using a slow-release source, the vapour concentration in ordinary rooms can be held in a range lethal to insects but harmless to mammals. A special formulation of this compound consisting of thick plastic pads containing the insecticide in slowly diffusible form can be hung up on walls, in number depending on room size, and effectively keep the rooms free of flying insects.

Volatility not only provides in some situations an effective means of transfer, it also provides a means of loss from the gross target. This is not wholly disadvantageous since toxic residues can in this way be reduced more quickly. Compromise must be made between conflicting requirements. Some compounds are so volatile that they are useful only in closed environments, from rabbit burrows to warehouses.

Transport Systems in Plants

There are two long-distance transporting systems in higher plants. The xylem system consists of continuous tubes formed of dead cells which carry water and mineral nutrients from root to leaf in response to some pumping mechanism in the root and suction due to evaporation from the leaf. The phloem system is more complex, less well understood, has a flow rate of at most a few centimetres per hour and is concerned in the transport of products of photosynthesis from mature leaves to growing tissues. The content of the phloem vessels is a fairly concentrated (8–16%) solution of sucrose — the universal fuel of plant metabolism — together with much smaller concentrations of amino acids and proteins. It is only in these systems that long-distance transport can take place and, as the moving fluid is essentially aqueous, only water-soluble materials can be transported.

The xylem vessels can transport any water-soluble substance. This is particularly easily demonstrated by the schoolboy device of putting the cut stalk of a white flower in a bottle of red ink. Within a half hour or so the main veins of the white petals have turned bright pink. This demonstration cannot be repeated if an intact root system is immersed, or if a damaged root system is placed in soil moistened with red ink. In these more realistic experiments water enters the xylem vessels by diffusion through cellular outer tissues which form an effective barrier to large molecules. Entry into the xylem rather than transport by it is the limiting factor. If compounds are to be effective systemically after application to foliage, they must enter the more elaborate phloem vessels after first diffusing through the cuticle or through fine protoplasmic strands which penetrate it and then through or around the epidermal and mesophyll cells.

The blood stream of mammals is a very much more rapid means of distribution than the xylem and phloem streams of plants. It has to be in order to fulfil its primary function of oxygen transport, whereas plants rely on a thin and wide extension of their actively growing tissues to secure adequate oxygen (and carbon dioxide) exchange with the air by diffusion. The blood is, moreover, adapted to the transport of liquid fats in emulsified form. Compounds can therefore be effective systemically in mammals even when they partition favourably to oil from water.

Insecticides Systemic in Plants

The first example of systemic behaviour in plants might be considered to be demonstrated by the natural toxicity (to mammals as well as insects) of crops growing on certain soils with a high selenium content. The first commercial exploitation of systemic behaviour of a deliberately applied compound was made with schradan. It was outstandingly successful in the protracted control of the cabbage aphis, *Brevicoryne brassicae*, without damage to the natural enemies of this pest.

All compounds effectively systemic in plants are much more soluble in water than oils, or are converted in the plant to water-favourable substances. Thus dimefox and schradan partition very strongly in favour of water from mineral and glyceride oils, dimethoate strongly so. Demeton and its relatives are rapidly oxidized at the thioether position to form the strongly water-favourable sulphoxides. The oxidation products are the systemic compounds. The applied demeton itself is effectively a transient superficial insecticide and much less selective than schradan. Amiton, in which the C_2H_5S of demeton is replaced by $(C_2H_5)_2N$ is water-favourable by virtue of the basic character of the tertiary amino group which is cationic at plant sap pH. This compound is a very effective and persistent systemic aphicide but too toxic to mammals for its use to be permitted.

For translocation within the plant, it is water:oil partition ratio rather than absolute solubility which must be high. The majority of good systemic insecticides are effective at a concentration of at most a few parts per million in plant sap. If, however, they were strongly oil-favourable, they would be held up in the lipid membranes, organelles and deposits in the plant tissues. The slow-moving water in the conducting vessels would not be able to translocate them effectively. The behaviour is similar to that in a chromatographic column where only compounds partitioning favourably to the moving phase can progress nearly as rapidly as the moving phase itself.

There is no really sharp distinction between "systemic" and "superficial" insecticides. Only exceptionally water-favourable and stable compounds like dimefox can be effective at remote sites, for example killing aphids on mature trees after application to the soil. Oil solubility, however, does not arrest transport, but only retards it, and unstable compounds can diffuse through short distances before decomposition. Thus even the oil-favourable lindane and the very rapidly hydrolyzed TEPP can exert useful "translaminar" action, as it is called, i.e. they can kill insects feeding on the surface of a leaf after application only to the reverse surface. They cannot, however, exert useful control on leaves other than those actually sprayed.

Systemic insecticides, to be of value for control of insects in agriculture, must not damage the crop. Ideally, therefore, they should be completely without physiological effect on plants, although this ideal is never fully attained. Being almost without effect on the plant, they diffuse passively within the cells or through the apoplast between them. Their penetration and translocation is governed mainly by solubility, partition properties and molecular size and shape. Since diffusion through cellular tissue into the conducting tissue must occur, it is not surprising to find that diffusion from one set of conducting vessels to the other also occurs. Distribution becomes rather general. In all rapidly growing crop plants, which must have adequate water supply, the net water movement is upward and outward. This produces a tendency for the systemic insecticide to accumulate in rapidly transpiring young, not fully developed, leaves. There is no net movement down into the root. Even a soil-applied systemic insecticide is not accumulated in the root, but in the leaves a much higher concentration can build up than that present in the soil water.

Systemic insecticides are therefore effective against leaf- and stem-sucking insects but have not achieved any success against root-feeding insects. Even the aphids, which are in general most vulnerable to systemic insecticides, are safe from this method of attack when they inhabit roots only. The systemic insecticide has as yet made no contribution to the control of the root-sucking aphids responsible for the phylloxera disease of vines.

The water-soluble insecticides which behave systemically are more effective against the sucking insects, aphids and mealybugs, than against grossly phytophagous insects. It seems that the more generally effective insecticides are dominantly oil- rather than water-soluble, even when judged by direct spraying tests under laboratory conditions. When used by the systemic route only — for example by application to the soil to kill leaf-sucking aphids — an additional factor comes into play.

The sucking insects take in a very large supply of sap from the phloem vessels. Indeed they do not, strictly speaking, suck. They probe with their hollow stylets selectively in the phloem vessels where the strong sugar solution is under high osmotic pressure. The host then in fact pumps food solution into the passive insect. This device of the aphis is used by the plant physiologist to obtain samples of pure phloem contents. He lets the aphis establish its feeding posture and then cuts the head and body off the inserted stylets, from the cut ends of which the solution can be collected.

The phloem solution is over-rich in sugar for a complete animal diet and deficient in protein. The aphid metabolism rejects most of the sugar from a very massive intake, filtering out the more valuable nitrogen compounds. The rejected sugar, which is squirted out as fine droplets, forms the "honeydew" associated with a heavy aphid infestation. This is responsible for the dirty appearance of aphid-infested trees, since it collects mineral dust and cultures dark-coloured superficial fungi. A successful systemic insecticide is retained along with the food compounds and the aphis thus accumulates a disproportionate dose as compared with a grossly phytophagous insect taking a more balanced diet.

If attack on root-feeding insects or the very important nematodes is ever to result from spraying the aerial parts of a plant, it seems necessary either that the compound applied must be in some way fixed in the root tissue or that it should exert its effect indirectly via the chemical processes of the host itself. The phloem system can transport sucrose very effectively from leaves to roots and other necessary chemicals in much lower concentration, but none of these can accumulate in the roots unless they are fixed there or converted chemically to fixed substances — as occurs, of course, when new root tissue is formed from substances mainly supplied from the leaves. One should not dismiss the possibility of the discovery of a compound that will be so fixed and also be insecticidal, but the solution to the problem will depend on biochemical, not plant-physical, processes. One evident danger is that a compound so fixed, being involved in the chemical processes of the host, may well have phytotoxic properties.

Systemic Fungicides

Until recent years all commercially used fungicides were protective and unless sprayed in advance to stop the initial infection were of very little curative value. During the past two decades a large number of compounds have been discovered which act systemically on the fungal disease. These are described in detail in the chapter on systemic fungicides (Chapter 17). Many of them have only very limited movement in the host plant and merit the adjective only by contrast. Some, however, would be classed as systemic even were they insecticides.

Contact Herbicides

It is doubtful if any herbicide has a truly local action. If it did, it could not be lethal to plants except following a coverage so uniform that it could not be realized in field practice. The incidental damage sometimes arising from insecticide or fungicide application, often referred to as "phytotoxicity" which should, of course, include all herbicide action, is more strictly local, often resulting in necrotic spots under the spray residues.

The dinitrophenols, cyanophenols and pentachlorphenol are usually called contact herbicides because they usually kill off top growth only and need reasonably good spray coverage to do so, but some translocation obviously occurs. Even paraquat has been called a contact herbicide despite clear evidence of upward translocation with lethal effect. The reason for this misnomer is that spray drops on many species do produce local scorch spots before the general systemic kill.

Systemic Properties of Herbicides

The translocation of herbicides is considerably more complex than that of the present plant-indifferent insecticides. A herbicide necessarily interferes with the plant's physiology and many, particularly both "hormone" and "scorching" herbicides, interfere drastically with their own translocation.

Despite the low solubility, due to high melting point, of the substituted phenylurea and aminotriazine compounds, they are water-, rather than oil-, favourable and are truly systemic. The low solubility restricts their effectiveness by foliage application, but they are taken up from dilute solution in the very extensive volume of the soil water and translocated to the photosynthetic cells of the shoot. There, non-interference with function, except that of chloroplasts, enables them to move in the xylem stream as inert compounds.

MCPA and 2,4-D are usually looked upon as translocated herbicides but, although they can enter leaves and produce bending of stems both above and below the leaves treated, they have a strong affinity for root tissue and are held there. They are not easily translocated from root to shoot and hardly at all from one part of the root system to another. They can effectively kill plants after foliage application, but they do so by concentrating in the upper part of the root system, to which they do irreparable damage, rather than by migrating throughout the whole plant. Death of a plant is very unsatisfactory evidence for systemic distribution of the herbicide. Death of aphids feeding on every part of a plant is very clear evidence of systemic behaviour of an insecticide. Not only is systemic movement of herbicides more complicated than that of insecticides but it produces results less easy to interpret without ambiguity.

Not all "hormone" herbicides are strongly fixed in particular tissues. Mecoprop and 2,4,5-T appear to be generally more mobile that MCPA and 2,4-D. 2,3,6-TBA is extremely mobile and always moves into, and deforms, newly developed shoots while having very little direct effect on root development.

The systemic effect of a herbicide is often markedly dependent on seasons and on stage of growth of the weed. The effectiveness of MCPA, for example, on perennial weeds such as nettle is greatest when the herbicide is applied to young leaves early in the season or to mature, but not senescent, leaves late in the season. This herbicide is much more effective on bracken (*Pteridium aquilinum*) in early autumn than at any other time. Amitrole is more effective against perennial weeds when sprayed in autumn. This compound is, under favourable conditions, very effective in killing underground tissue after being applied to the leaves. It is probably fixed in roots by conjugation with sugars. Glyphosate also shows outstanding power to kill underground tissues when applied to leaves.

Nomenclature of Pesticides

Manufacturers market pesticides under trade names, which refer to the particular formulation, not specifically to the active ingredient. Thus, one active ingredient may be marketed in several different formulations under several different trade names, and often, with different trade names in different countries. When a pesticide comes out of patent protection and can be manufactured and sold by anybody who wishes to do so, this situation is multiplied. The result is that, in the U.S.A. for example, there are about 3,200 registered active ingredients and 150,000 different trade names. This causes confusion to the farmer who wants to know exactly what he is buying so that he can compare costs accurately. Rapid and precise identification in case of accidental spillage or ingestion is also necessary. It is desirable, therefore, that there shall be some internationally agreed common name for every active ingredient and that the common name shall uniquely specify a definite chemical compound. This aim has not been entirely achieved.

The International Standards Organization Technical Committee 81 is supported by most countries except the U.S.A. and U.S.S.R. It tries to get agreement on common names for pesticides between the standards organisations of the various participating countries. In the U.K., the British Standards Institute is responsible through its committee PCC/1. It is often a long and tedious procedure to get agreement between member countries.

The U.S.A., through the American National Standards Institute Committee K62, decides its own common names for use in the U.S.A. In the past there have been considerable differences between A.N.S.I. and I.S.O. but they now work much more closely together and most common names are now the same in the U.S.A. and the rest of the world. The U.S.S.R. follow their own course without reference to anybody and there are considerable variations from I.S.O., although many I.S.O. names are used in the U.S.S.R.

The problem of coining a short common name becomes progressively more difficult as it must (a) be easily pronounceable in any language; (b) not resemble any word in any language too closely; (c) not conflict too closely with any trade mark in any country; (d) desirably have some relationship to the chemical name.

Nearly all registration authorities now require that labels shall bear, in addition to the trade name, the percentage composition of active ingredient in terms of its common name.

Throughout this book all pesticides are referred to only by their common names. There are a number of publications which catalogue pesticides in current use. Probably the most useful is "Farm Chemicals Handbook" (Meister Publishing Co., Willoughby, Ohio 44094, U.S.A.) which contains common names, trade names, chemical structures, physical properties, toxicities, uses, formulations and manufacturers, formulators and distributors. This book is brought completely up to date each year. In England, the "Pesticide Manual" (British Crop Protection Council, London, England) gives similar information and is revised from time to time.

Further Reading

BSI Standard 1831 and Supplements, *Recommended Common Names for Pesticides*, British Standards Institution, London, 1969 onwards.

Büchel, K. W. (Ed.) *Pflanzenschutz und Schädlingsbekämpfung*, Georg Theme Verlag, Stuttgart, 1977.

Cremlyn, R. *Pesticides*, John Wiley and Sons, Chichester, 1978.

Ennis, W. B. (Ed.) *Introduction to Crop Protection*, American Society of Agronomy, Madison, Wisconsin, 1979.

Farm Chemicals Handbook, Meister Publishing Co., Willoughby, Ohio.

Frear, J. *Pesticide Index*, Entomological Society of America, Washington, D.C., 1977.

Kilgore, W. W. and Doutt, R. L. *Pest Control*, Academic Press, London and New York, 1967.

Worthing, C. R. and Walker, S. B., *Pesticide Manual*, 8th edition British Crop Protection Council, London, 1987.

Martin, H. *Scientific Principles of Crop Protection*, Arnold, London, 1928; Successive editions to 6th 1973, 7th revised by D. Woodcock 1983.

National Academy of Sciences, *Scientific Aspects of Pest Control*, Washington, D.C., 1961.

Rose, G. J. *Crop Protection*, Hill, London, 1963.

Thomson, W. T. *Agricultural Chemical Books* I to IV, Thomson Publications, Fresno, California, 1976.

Woods, A. *Pest Control*, McGraw-Hill, London and New York, 1974.

7

Oils as Pesticides

Except within the narrow context of some particular technology, where, for example, the motor mechanic has a particular conception of "gear oil" or the perfume manufacturer of "oil of lemon", the word "oil" has a wide and not very precise meaning. When one "pours oil on troubled waters" or speaks of the "oil phase" of an emulsion one is thinking quite generally of any liquid of very low water solubility and usually of low volatility. The chemist restricts the word to liquids which are predominantly hydrocarbon in composition but which may have a small proportion of oxygen in ester groups, as in the liquid glycerides, or even in keto or hydroxyl groups, as in many essential oils and castor oil.

Most vegetable and animal fats, the triglycerides, are at least partly liquid in their natural situation, where they are mainly stored in fairly massive layers as reserve energy foods or for thermal insulation. More complex oily substances are more widely distributed in living tissue, in the very thin membranes which keep appropriately separated the important biochemically active substances in the aqueous phases of cells. Oils are therefore by no means foreign to living organisms. Like many vital substances, they can, out of place, have lethal disorganizing effects.

If kerosine is spilt on almost any green leaf, the latter, if held up to the light, will be seen to become more transparent in patches. The oil displaces air from the spaces between the mesophyll cells, reducing the differences of refractive index. The process continues, not through further direct spread of oil but because the disorganized cells now release water, a further consequence of which is that the leaf wilts more rapidly than an untreated one, due to increased rate of evaporation of water.

Insects, particularly small ones, are even more vulnerable to applied oils, because they must rely on an even more efficient organization of native fatty molecules to prevent disastrous water loss. Oil can also flood the spiracles (breathing pores) of insects, as they do the stomata of leaves, and produce, in this case, rapid asphyxiation. A further effect is mechanical. In small-scale structures, surface tension of liquids becomes a very important force. Most insect cuticle is not wetted by water, a property necessary to prevent legs and other protruding organs becoming entangled by surface tension forces much greater than the muscle forces available. Oils do wet the cuticle.

The suffocating and entangling effects of oils are used together in the practice of spreading of oils on water surfaces in which mosquitoes breed. The larvae of these insects are free swimming but must take their oxygen directly from the air. The spiracles are united to an extended breathing tube at the posterior end which has a sharp and unwettable tip. When this is forced into the surface of clean water it connects with the atmosphere and anchors the insect in the surface so that it can remain for long periods at rest. Oil spread on the water surface blocks up the breathing tube and at the same time prevents the insect from anchoring itself in the surface. Other insects, such as Gerris spp, which skate upon water of normal high surface tension, are also incapacitated by an oil film. This method of destroying mosquito larvae in small water volumes (rain-butts, puddles, etc.) is still widely used. The oil must spread spontaneously on water. Refined mineral oils therefore require the addition of a small percentage of fatty acid or other oil-favourable surface-active compound. Waste engine oil from automobile maintenance is effective without adjuvants, being contaminated with oxidation products, and is widely used. Proprietary oils for mosquito larva control contain a chemically active insecticide to improve their action.

In control measures which rely on the gross "physical" toxicity of oils, it is the "oiliness" — the antithesis to water — which is important. Various oils differ, however, in their effectiveness and not solely because of differences in viscosity, volatility and surface behaviour. Associated chemical effects, not understood mechanistically, play an important part. Thus many plant leaves are undamaged by light applications of refined, saturated mineral oils, particularly when these are applied as emulsions. Unsaturated oils, aromatic oils and particularly those containing phenolic substances are much more damaging. Some essential oils, e.g. oil of citronella, have use as insect repellents. In this case, subtle and specific sensory responses to the vapour are called upon and the classification "oil" is almost accidental. Oils are, of course, widely used as solvents for more active pesticides, a subject dealt with in the chapter on formulation.

Vegetable oils had at one time a minor use in the control of powdery mildews. Soaps formed by their hydrolysis were moderately effective against some *Botrytis* fungi, the spores of which become lethally engorged with microscopically visible oil globules. Nearly all oils of pesticidal interest are, however, now derived from "mineral" sources, i.e. from distillation of the fossil fuels, coal and petroleum. The requirements of essentially paraffinic oils have come mainly from petroleum and of aromatic oils from coal tar. These distinctions, however, become increasingly less clear as both industries develop improved means of separation of valuable chemical intermediates from the complex mixtures of hydrocarbons present in the raw material and produced by pyrolysis or "cracking".

The largest tonnage of oils applied to the land is contributed by low-value, low-volatility by-products of petroleum refining which are used to bind soil to form primitive roadways in dry areas. The toxicity to vegetation of these heavy applications of crude oil provides a herbicidal bonus in this practice which is mainly confined, for economic reasons, to regions not far from oil-fields or refineries. More refined heavy petroleum oils are applied to the lanes between orchard trees in arid areas, and therefore mainly to citrus orchards, to reduce water loss directly from the soil, again with a herbicidal bonus. Low-grade oil fractions high in content of phenolic substances have been used for total weed suppression on gravel and earth roads on both domestic and industrial sites but this function is now taken over by much smaller dosages of less messy and objectionable but highly phytotoxic substances. One should perhaps include among herbicidal applications the use of oils as fuels in the flame gun to destroy top growth by heat. Research is actively carried out by the oil companies to make this process usefully selective by careful choice of flame temperature and time of exposure.

The next most massive use of oils as pesticides is that of coal-tar creosote for preservation of wood against fungal rots and insect attack. This application is confined to outside timber structures, farm buildings, telegraph poles, railway sleepers, etc., because staining and smell make it unsuitable for domestic timber. Its use is decreasing as mineral and synthetic materials take over some of these outside timber functions and as it becomes more worthwhile to work up crude coal-tar fractions for more valuable purified intermediates. The usage, however, is still enormous. Approximately 800 million litres of creosote, a substantial fraction imported, are used each year in the U.S.A. for timber preservation. The amount so treated is about 1% of the total weight of domestic production of sawn timber.

Creosote (a crude mixture of aromatic hydrocarbons with a minor proportion of phenol and naphthol homologues) is not very active in comparison with most synthetic pesticides, but it is cheap and can therefore be used in high dosage. The best results are obtained by pressure impregnation or heating and cooling in the liquid. Well-impregnated timber may contain several percent of the oil. There is, incidentally, a good technical reason why timber preservation should be carried out with cheap, although not very active, chemicals in massive dose rather than with very active chemicals in much smaller dose. Adsorption on to the large internal surface of porous wood is high so that low doses have no possibility of deep penetration.

More active chemicals are mainly used in the impregnation of timber for domestic building, but are usually provided in oil solution since oils, because they do not swell the wood fibres themselves nor quickly penetrate their microstructure, spread throughout the gross porosity of the wood more quickly than aqueous solutions. Aqueous treatments, if heavy enough to be useful, also produce undesirable warping. Pentachlorophenol is widely used as a good fungicide very effective also against termites which are a major factor in wood deterioration in the subtropics. Organochlorine insecticides are added to kill wood-boring beetles.

The good fungicidal properties of copper are used in oil treatments by forming the oil-soluble copper naphthenates (naphthenic acids are mixtures of cyclic carboxylic acids derived from certain petroleum fractions by oxidation and alkali extraction). The green colour of such treatments is for some purposes objectionable. Zinc naphthenates provide a less active but colourless substitute, but they are now being displaced by triphenyltin derivatives. Proprietary oil formulations for treatment of timber may contain mixtures of these compounds.

Oil washes have been used for a long time to control some insect and spider-mite pests in orchards. Only light applications of emulsified paraffinic oils can safely be made to trees in leaf but these so-called "summer oil" treatments are effective against red spider. After a period of displacement by more active chemical acaricides, oils are now coming back into use because of the ability of this rapidly breeding pest to evolve strains resistant to chemical attack. Summer oil is now the most widely used acaricide in the U.S.A. In the citrus growing areas of the U.S.A. in 1977 5.7 million gallons were applied. It may be added that its rate of application may be reduced, with greater safety to the foliage, by dissolving polyisobutene in the oil. This solution leaves a permanent sticky deposit (the "active ingredient" of self-adhesive tapes and bandages) which immobilizes the pest.

While refined oils of limited activity must be used in summer, cruder and more aggressive oils are tolerated by the dormant trees of deciduous orchards in winter. Several important pests overwinter on the bark in the egg stage and "winter washes" are effective against these. Although tar oils with a high phenolic content are more effective against *aphid* eggs, the more paraffinic petroleum oils have a greater action on *acarid* (spider mite) and *capsid* eggs. Mixtures are preferred and addition of dinitrocresol extends the range of and certainty of control. The action is certainly partly physical and best results are obtained when the emulsion used for spraying is rendered unstable by exposure so that a thin, continuous oil layer, able to penetrate into crevices, is left on the bark. Winter oil washes have tended to be displaced by systemic insecticides applied in the spring, but some orchardists, particularly on the European continent, are tending to return to the winter oils because of the development of resistance of insects to the alternative chemicals. In the U.S.A. in 1977 about 5 million gallons of oils were used on apples and pears.

Another use where the physical property of "oiliness" is partly responsible for the toxic action is that of petroleum for selective weed control. A special fraction, less volatile than kerosine and containing a moderate proportion of unsaturated compounds, derived from a particular oil-field, gives good weed control in carrots. It is also used to a small extent, in other crops of the family Umbelliferae. Many farmers have been successful with a home-made emulsion of tractor vaporizer oil. It is not known why seedlings of the family Umbelliferae should be so much less vulnerable to oil damage than most other seedlings, but it may be associated with the fact that these plants are naturally rich in oils and their seeds particularly so. This use is declining as other, chemically active, herbicides have been discovered which are more reliable.

Liquid fatty acids in the C_6-C_{12} range are used as emulsions in the tobacco crop to inhibit the development of lateral shoots. Their action is not highly specific and they are sprayed at rates allowing accumulation in the leaf axils. The action may be essentially a physical one. Other oils have been used for this purpose although with more risk of damage to the leaf. The practice is known as chemical "anti-suckering". The methyl esters of acids in the C_8-C_{12} range are likewise used as a chemical "pinching" agent on ornamental plants such as azaleas.

An interesting recent hypothesis is that the sensitivity of various plants to certain soil-applied herbicides may depend on the amount of internal lipids in the plants and that this sensitivity, and therefore the selectivity of the herbicide, might be altered by adding suitable lipids around the roots of the crop seedlings, or by treating the seeds with lipids before sowing. This effect has been demonstrated with the herbicide trifluralin on barley, wheat and cotton seedlings.

Further Reading

American Chemical Society, *Agricultural Application of Petroleum Products*, Washington, D. C., 1952.

Findlay, W. P. K. *Timber Pests and Diseases*, Pergamon Press, Oxford, 1967.

Guthrie, V. B. (Ed.) *Petroleum Products Handbook*, McGraw-Hill, London and New York, 1960.

8

Synthetic Insecticides: Miscellaneous and Organochlorines

Inorganic Compounds

The first synthetic insecticides were inorganic. In 1867 the pigment Paris green, a crystal compound of acetate and arsenite of copper, having approximate composition $Cu_4(CH_3CO_2)_2(AsO_2)_2$, was used successfully in the U.S.A. against the increasing population of Colorado beetle in the potato fields. It was later used against a wide variety of leaf-eating insects and against codling moth larvae on apples.

Paris green can make little claim to be specifically insecticidal. Rather is it a generally toxic compound which kills leaf-eating insects shortly after application but is relatively harmless to the eventual human consumer of the mature product. Selectivity depends upon timing and placement of the poison and on the feeding habits of different species. The insect is much more voracious than man, consuming a much greater weight of fresh vegetable matter in relation to its body weight and its diet is restricted to a particular crop. The insect moreover eats the crop when it is freshly contaminated. Man eats only a portion of the crop, after the lapse of a safety interval. Tubers, roots and fruit have increased in size and were either not touched by the spray or have been subject to weathering since spraying.

Various other arsenites and arsenates were tested but many produced troublesome and unpredictable damage to the crop with symptoms of arsenic poisoning. Atmospheric carbon dioxide and exudates from the leaf cells are probably responsible for liberation of soluble arsenate from combination with the heavy metal. Lead arsenate, $PbHAsO_4$, first used against the gypsy moth in 1892, established itself as the compound safest to the crop but the addition of lead to the consumer hazard has never been popular among safety authorities. The use of lead arsenate, still the most effective product against codling moth, is nowhere prohibited, but a maximum level of residual contamination of the marketed produce is set in most countries. Washing of apples before marketing is widely practised to ensure conformity.

Sodium fluoride has been known, at least since 1842, to be highly toxic to insects. It has been used mainly in situations where a concentrated bait or barrier is effective, e.g. against cockroaches, earwigs, ants and other gregarious crawling species. It has limited value out of doors because it is too soluble (about 2%) in water to persist except in arid districts. The almost insoluble silicofluoride Na_2SiF_6, and native cryolite, Na_3AlF_6, are much more persistent and still sufficiently rapid in action to be useful. Silico-fluoride is a by-product of the fertilizer (superphosphate) industry, the fluorine of the mineral apatite, $Ca_4F_2(PO_4)_2$, a component of all phosphate deposits, being released as fluosilicic acid during treatment of the phosphate rock with sulphuric acid.

Small terrestrial insects are very dependent on an organized fatty cuticle to prevent evaporation of body water. Many mineral dusts exert some insecticidal action by damaging this protective layer. The damaged cuticle is usually more permeable to insecticides, particularly if they are highly polar compounds. The formulation of fluorides with abrasive or adsorptive mineral dusts increases their effectiveness in dry situations and such dusts are used for protection of roof timbers against termite attack. A mixture of silica aerogel and ammonium fluosilicate is used as a dust or aerosol in agricultural premises and on farm animals.

Borax or boric acid is still widely used against cockroaches by dusting into their hiding places. It is much less active than many modern insecticides, judged on a milligram/kilogram basis, but the cockroach appears to be a very suspicious insect and is effectively repelled by most insecticides and even formulating substances. Boric acid is almost unique in not showing this repellent action.

Several other inorganic substances have been used for killing insects, including lead chromate and ammonium reineckate, $NH_4^+(Cr(NH_3)_2(SCN)_4)2H_2O^-$, but only those noted above still have any commercial importance.

Thiocyanates

The modern era of synthetic insecticides begins with the thiocyanates in the early 1930s. All the alkyl thiocyanates, $R - S - CN$, prepared by reaction of an alkyl halide with sodium thiocyanate, are insecticidal. In tests where the compound enters mainly from body contact, the activity is at its highest with R = dodecyl, but where fumigant effect is important, lower alkyl compounds are more effective. Lethane, introduced in the U.S.A. in 1936, consisted mainly of a compound with ether links in the alkyl chain, $C_4H_9OC_2H_4OC_2H_4SCN$. Such compounds, products of ethylene oxide technology, have advantage in production because the chlorine atom in $R - O - C_2H_4Cl$ is more reactive than that in $R - Cl$. They also provide a cheap route to compounds of 6–10 atom chain length, which are scarce among the natural fats. They have also a much higher water solubility than compounds having only CH_2 groups in the chain.

Lethane and similar compounds had some minor use in agriculture and were being considered for public health problems early in World War II when DDT arrived on the scene. Their development was, perhaps prematurely, arrested by the dramatic success of DDT. Their interesting properties as insecticides have remained largely unexploited. They are extremely rapid in action, in marked contrast to DDT, having "knock-down" properties almost as good as those of pyrethrum. They have, however, considerable irritant effect on human skin which would probably have stopped their use for impregnation of clothing against the body louse and for space-sprays against flying mosquitoes and flies. They tended also to damage the leaves of many crops.

The only compound of this series of present commercial importance is a more complex one, thanite, a thiocyanoacetic ester of the terpene alcohol, isoborneol. Thanite is used to a limited extent in sprays to control flies, mosquitoes and bed-bugs in non-food situations. Its use on milk and meat animals and poultry is prohibited in the U.S.A. but it may be used against fleas and lice on pets. Now that the use of organochlorines has been discontinued, further research in this field, particularly active in the U.S.S.R. may produce more useful compounds.

$$CH_3$$
$$|$$
$$C$$
$$CH_2 \diagup \diagdown CH - OCOCH_2SCN$$
$$| \; C(CH_3)_2$$
$$CH_2 \diagdown \diagup CH_2$$
$$CH$$

Thanite

Thanite is prepared by esterification of the alcohol with chloroacetyl-chloride, followed by reaction of the product with sodium thiocyanate.

DDT

The insecticidal properties of the compound 1,1-bis (4-chlorophenyl)-2,2,2-trichloroethane were discovered in 1939. DDT, and compounds of similar action which followed it, had a profound effect on the whole subsequent history of pest control. DDT was produced in enormous quantities during the war and its use, under the direction of the U.S. Army, arrested a potential epidemic of typhus (Naples, 1943) for the first time in medical history. Its continued use in the next decade greatly reduced the enormous death-toll in many countries from another insect-borne disease, malaria, and it was, for many years, the mainstay of the W.H.O. malaria control programme.

DDT was first prepared in 1874, by condensation of chloral and monochlorobenzene, agitated with some three times their combined weight of strong sulphuric acid (monohydrate), but its insecticidal properties remained undiscovered for 65 years.

This reaction is the basis of the very economical commercial

DDT

production of the compound. The mixture must be well agitated but needs no external heating, the temperature rising by heat of reaction to about 60°C when it is complete. After partial cooling, the mixture is poured, with further agitation, into excess water and the solid DDT, after washing on the filter, is sufficiently pure for most purposes.

As would be expected, chloral does not condense exclusively in the 4-positions of the benzene ring. In addition to the desired 4,4' compound, some 20–30% (according to conditions) of 2,4' compound is produced and a trace of the 2,2'. The isomers are also crystalline compounds, not of great insecticidal significance, but their formation involves some wastage of raw materials. Traces of more oily by-products, probably arising from reactions involving self-condensation of chloral and condensation with only one molecule of chlorobenzene, are more troublesome in the efficient production of wettable powder formulations. Improvement of the crude product can be achieved by a further hot-water washing or by washing with cold alcohol. Recrystallization from hot alcohol yields a substantially pure product but the increased cost of a very cheap commodity prohibits the use of purified material except for special purposes, e.g. in aerosol packs where the presence of traces of sticky impurities insoluble in the solvents used may completely block the fine orifice through which the liquid is discharged.

One of the advantages of DDT was that its manufacture could be carried out if necessary in easily constructed, or even improvised, plant. It has been manufactured on various scales in many countries throughout the world. Records of production are not available for most countries. In the U.S.A. which probably made nearly half the world total, about 15,000 tonnes was produced in 1945, rising to nearly 100,000 tonnes/year in the late 1950s, since then there was a decline to 20,000 tonnes in 1971 under the impact of pressure to withdraw permission for most uses of this very persistent compound. It is now manufactured in the United States only for export.

The great stability of DDT seemed, at the time of its introduction, an advantage almost as important as its cheap and easy production. The only facile reaction it undergoes is loss of hydrogen chloride in the aliphatic centre of the molecule to give 1,1-bis(4-chlorophenyl)-2,2-dichloroethylene (DDE), a compound with no insecticidal action. This reaction, carried out under reflux in a solution of caustic soda in 95% alcohol, is used in control analysis. The same dehydrochlorination reaction can also take place in anhydrous systems in the presence of ferric chloride and some other catalysts. Loss of hydrogen chloride is the only reaction of significance in the storage of DDT formulations as pressure heating with an anhydrous solution of sodium alcoholate is necessary to remove the remaining chlorine atoms. Since hydrogen chloride is produced in the reaction the catalyst can form by reaction with the iron of a container, if exposed. Under normal conditions of storage, the risk is sufficiently reduced by ensuring that the DDT and other ingredients have negligible initial content of free acid.

A third advantage of DDT, which encouraged its rapid war-time and post-war development, was its very low toxicity to mammals and absence of skin irritancy. It seemed to have all the virtues and no vices at a time when there were pressing problems in the control of insect-borne diseases. It is now generally appreciated, in retrospect, that the low acute toxicity of DDT to mammals was accepted too easily as a guarantee of safety, but it must be remembered that DDT was developed when there was urgent need of it and most of the world was preoccupied with products far more dangerous. The atmosphere of struggle for immediate survival was not conducive to quiet thought about the possible long-term effects of synthetic insecticides.

DDT has a very wide spectrum of activity among the different families of insects and related organisms. Its properties gave it outstanding success as a residual deposit. It was active not only when ingested, but also against insects which only crawled on the deposit. Later compounds of the organochlorine class have equalled or even surpassed it in this respect and it is easy to forget how novel and important this property was when arsenicals requiring ingestion and the transient pyrethrum and nicotine dominated the scene.

DDT is not, of course, uniformly effective against all species. In general, aphids and spider mites are less susceptible than most. In the case of aphids the poor control is mainly due to the inability of the water-insoluble insecticide to reach colonies of stationary wingless aphids under, or within the folds of, leaves. A high proportion escape contact with the spray, but their predators, intrinsically more susceptible and making contact with residual deposits during their hunting activity, succumb. Use of a DDT spray against immobile aphids such as *Brevicoryne* on *Brassica* crops often therefore results in a drastic resurgence. *Acyrthosiphon pisi* on the pea crop, an unusually easily disturbed aphis, is effectively controlled.

The weakness of DDT against spider mites is more intrinsic, but the defect is again exaggerated in the field by the susceptibility of the predators, which are a very important factor in natural control. Extensive use of DDT in orchards, in the early years of its spectacular success, resulted in a very greatly increased red spider populations which required other compounds for control.

Compounds Related to DDT

The 4,4' chlorine substituents in the DDT molecule can be replaced by several other groups yielding compounds of comparable activity. The unsubstituted compounds is, however, of very low activity and the 4,4'-dihydroxy compound is quite inactive. The 4,4'-dibromo and dimethyl compounds have no advantages to justify their higher cost, but the even more expensive difluro compound was fairly extensively used in Germany during World War II in preference to DDT for reasons which were obscure and presumably not valid, since it is no longer available. Its much lower melting point (19°C) makes it much more soluble than DDT so that the spray drops can leave a liquid residue. On a non-porous surface, this is quickly active but it disappears more rapidly into the capillaries of a porous surface.

The only 4,4' analogue to have achieved an important commercial position is the dimethoxy compound (methoxychlor). It is made by the very facile condensation of anisole and chloral. It is not in general quite so active as DDT but is more vulnerable to biochemical attack so that it has much less tendency to accumulate in fat depots. The use of DDT to keep cow houses free of flies is now prohibited in most countries because of the significant transfer of DDT to the milk fat. Methoxychlor is permitted for this purpose as it is decomposed in the body before it reaches the milk.

In other compounds the aliphatic centre of the molecule is altered. The dichloroethylene derivative is, as noted above, inactive, but the dichloroethyl compound, TDE

TDE

has found limited use in the U.S.A. on food crops, being significantly less toxic than DDT. DDT has acute oral LD50 (rat) 375 mg/kg whereas TDE has acute oral LD 50 (rat) 3,400 mg/kg. It is prepared similarly to DDT, but requires dichloroacetaldehyde in place of chloral. This is obtained by controlled action of chlorine on ethyl alcohol at a temperature under 30°C and the product is condensed with monochlorobenzene immediately after preparation. Its manufacture and use have now been discontinued and registration in the U.S.A. has been cancelled.

Lindane

This insecticide, with broadly similar biological potential to DDT, followed it very closely in development. By the action of elementary chlorine on benzene in the dark and with suitable catalysts, true chlorination (replacement of H by Cl) occurs in stages. By the action of elementary chlorine in the cold, without catalysts and in the presence of mercury arc light, an addition reaction occurs yielding benzene hexachloride or 1,2,3,4,5,6-hexachloro-cyclohexane. It is formed without significant concentration of compounds intermediate between C_6H_6 and $C_6H_6Cl_6$, because, as soon as the aromatic ring becomes partly saturated, further addition of chlorine is almost instantaneous. The crude crystalline insecticidal product, with a strong and persistent musty smell, has been known at various times and places as BHC or HCH.

Each C atom in the compound is attached to two different other atoms and the linkage into a chain prevents free rotation. Several structural isomers are therefore possible as in inositol, $C_6H_6(OH)_6$, or in ring sugars. Only the γ-isomer, which has three adjacent axial chlorine atoms and three adjacent equatorial, has insecticidal activity.

The purified γ-isomer is now in most countries called lindane. The preparation of lindane will be seen to necessitate the wasteful production of some seven times its weight of unwanted isomers. The potential economic loss is partly offset by splitting the by-products by strong heating into hydrogen chloride and trichlorobenzene, $C_6H_6Cl_6 \rightarrow C_6H_3Cl_3 + 3HCl$. The same dehydrochlorination occurs in alcoholic alkali, except in the case of the β isomer. The trichlorobenzene is mainly the 1,2,4 compound which can readily be further chlorinated and led into the production of higher chlorobenzenes.

Lindane has broadly similar action to DDT. Even the melting point (112°C) is close and both compounds leave a residue active via body contact. Lindane is in general rather more potent, the crude HCH being more nearly equivalent to DDT, but the response to both is variable with species and therefore some are more responsive to one than the other. Both can induce resistance but resistance developed to lindane is more likely to be coupled with resistance to the cyclodienes than to DDT. The biochemistry of its action is therefore probably basically different from that of DDT.

Lindane is considerably more volatile than DDT (9×10^{-6} mm at 20°C compared with 2×10^{-7} mm) but only slightly more volatile than aldrin ($6 \times$

10^{-6} mm). It is significantly more soluble in water than either and a saturated solution will quickly provide a lethal dose to insects in contact with it. While its volatility gives it significant fumigant effect in a dry environment, its water solubility restricts its vapour phase movement in moist soil, but facilitates diffusion under the cuticle, and there is evidence of short-range systemic effect in plants. These properties make lindane a very effective seed dressing against soil insect attack.

Cyclodiene Insecticides

From 1945 onwards a number of very active contact insecticides were produced by the Diels-Alder reaction on hexachlorocyclopentadiene. The latter compound, unlike most dienes, will not easily react with itself and so it can be condensed with a wide range of adducts to give specific products in high yield. Development of a satisfactory manufacturing process for hexachlorocyclopentadiene presented some problems as the intermediate chlorination products self-polymerize explosively, but the problem was solved either by using a very large excess of chlorine in the gas phase or by using chlorine and alkali in an organic solvent.

Reaction of hexachlorocyclopentadiene with cyclopentadiene gave chlordene, which, on chlorination with chlorine in carbon tetrachloride, gave the first commercial insecticide of this type, chlordane.

Chlordene   Chlordane

Structures of this type exist in two forms, the "endo", which has the three five-membered rings in a "boat" form, and the "exo", which has the three rings in a "chair" form. Isomers also arise from different spatial arrangements of the chlorine atoms.

Chlorination of chlordene with sulphuryl chloride in carbon tetrachloride in the presence of catalytic amounts of benzoyl peroxide gave heptachlor, a more effective insecticide than chlordane. A related insecticide is chlorbicyclen.

Heptachlor   Chlorbicyclen

The most important insecticides in this group contain four fused five-membered rings. Cyclopentadiene is reacted with acetylene to give dicyclo-heptadiene which is then condensed with hexachlorocyclopentadiene

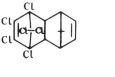

Aldrin (exo - endo)
Isodrin (exo - exo)

Endrin (endo - endo)
Dieldrin (endo - exo)

The exo-endo compound is aldrin and the exo-exo compound is isodrin. These can be readily oxidized with hydrogen peroxide to the epoxy compounds, endrin, the endo-endo form, and dieldrin, the endo-exo form.

Hexachloropentadiene can be dimerised by heating in the presence of aluminium chloride, yielding mirex, a stomach insecticide with little contact activity, used mainly against ants, which carry it in baits back to their nests.

Mirex

Aldrin, dieldrin and endrin were the most powerful general insecticides known until the modern synthetic pyrethroids appeared. They are particularly effective where contact action and long persistence are required, but their lack of systemic action makes them of little use against sap-sucking species unless these are exposed to direct spray. The significant volatility of aldrin makes it the least persistent as an exposed deposit, but gives it an advantage for application in the soil against soil-dwelling insects. Dieldrin has been the most effective compound to date against ectoparasites (lice, ticks, blowflies, etc.) of sheep and cattle and was until recently used very widely in dips and sprays for this purpose. It gave a longer period of protection than any other compound. Its affinity for, and effectiveness on, animal hair extended this use to protection of woollen cloth and carpets from the ravages of moth and beetle, but in competition with other more specific protectants.

These compounds are significantly more toxic to mammals than DDT and lindane (approximate acute oral LD50 to rats in milligrams per kilogram body weight are DDT, 115; lindane, 125; aldrin, dieldrin, 50; endrin, 12). It is indeed remarkable that such a stable compound as dieldrin can be highly toxic to any species. It must undergo reactions in living tissues which have no parallel *in vitro*.

In the past 20 years the cyclodiene insecticides have come into disfavour because of their high mammalian toxicities and very ready absorption through skin, their extreme persistence in the environment which has resulted in their widespread accumulation in the body fats of animals and humans and their indiscriminate activity against beneficial insects as well as pests, and against birds and fish. Gross misuse of these products in the early days resulted in those incidents of widespread damage to domestic animals and wildlife which were dramatized by Rachel Carson in "Silent Spring" and which initiated a strong public reaction against these pesticides, a reaction which, unfortunately, has been indiscriminately extended by many groups to all pesticides. In most developed countries the cyclodiene insecticides have been withdrawn from many uses and greatly restricted for many others. It is now generally accepted by all who are concerned with pesticides that compounds of very high persistence are undesirable.

Most polychlorinated cyclodienes are chemically very stable and do not lose chlorine even when refluxed with alcoholic potassium hydroxide or treated with liquid ammonia. This stability has created problems because of their persistence in the environment and attempts have been made to find insecticidally effective compounds which are less stable. Some commercially successful products of this type are endosulfan and isobenzan which are oil-soluble compounds similar in activity to aldrin. However, although the spray residues are protected from reaction with water by their low solubilities, when the compounds penetrate living tissue, they are broken down by hydrolysis.

Isobenzan   Endosulfan

Endosulfan is manufactured by reaction of hexachlorocyclopentadiene with 4,4-diacetoxybut-2-ene to give an adduct which is hydrolyzed to give thiodandiol which is treated with thionyl chloride to give a high yield of endosulfan. Endosulfan consists of two isomers which differ in the orientation of the sulphite group.

Endosulfan is not only a broad spectrum insecticide but also an acaricide. Used at the correct application rate it does not harm bees and other beneficial insects so can be used in orchards and vegetables. Its low dermal toxicity makes it a safe compound to handle and its rapid breakdown in the body and the fact that it does not accumulate in body fats make it free from chronic toxic effects. It is the only chlorinated insecticide which has not had its use cancelled or restricted in the U.S.A. In the U.S.A. it is now mainly used on cotton but it is very widely used throughout Africa on all types of crops. It has the interesting property, which has been substantiated both in the laboratory and in the field, that it potentiates the activity of organo-phosphorus insecticides. This appears to be a synergistic, not just an additive, effect.

Chlorocamphene (toxaphene)

This product results from direct chlorination of camphene to a chlorine content of 67%. It is a mixture of several compounds and stereoisomers which are always formulated without separation. It has similar biological properties to lindane but is more soluble in petroleum hydrocarbons. It was first introduced in 1948 but was overshadowed by DDT and the cyclodiene insecticides. However, when the latter products came into disfavour and were withdrawn from the market in the 1970s chlorocamphene emerged for a time as the most acceptable compound. In 1976 it topped the sales of all insecticides in the U.S.A. when farmers used 17,000 tonnes, almost one quarter of the total synthetic organic insecticides used in the U.S.A. that year. It seemed to have the advantage that it has a reasonably low mammalian toxicity (oral LD50 90 mg/kg, dermal LD50 1,075 mg/kg) and it does not accumulate in body fats persistently but is eliminated rapidly when intake is stopped. It is non-phytotoxic except to cucurbits. However, it has come under the same cloud as the other organochlorine insecticides, and in 1982 the EPA decided to cancel its registration in the U.S.A. for most uses except for certain uses under specific terms and conditions in corn, cotton and small grains and for certain treatments of cattle and sheep.

Modes of Action

Although the organochlorine insecticides have been used for 30 years comparatively little is known about their precise biochemical modes of action. They clearly act on the nervous system as they produce violent tremors of the body and appendages followed by loss of movement, convulsions and death. Evidence has accumulated that DDT acts on the peripheral nerve as distinct from the central nerve. DDT appears to act on the nerve axon rather than on the neuromuscular junctions and to be bound to the nerve membranes, thus interfering with movement of ions across them and transmission of nervous impulses. A single nerve impulse arriving at an area treated with DDT triggers numbers of subsidiary impulses. An interesting phenomenon is that insects showing marked signs of poisoning at 15° become normal at 30° and the effect is reversible. This is thought to be due to dissociation of the complex between DDT and the nerve as the temperature is raised.

Lindane and the cyclodiene insecticides produce effects which are essentially similar to those of DDT but there are differences which suggest that the sites of action may not be the same as for DDT. This is supported by the observation that flies which are resistant to DDT are generally still sensitive to lindane and the cyclodienes.

There is now a substantial body of evidence that the sub-lethal effects of the organochlorine insecticides especially on the reproductive capacities of birds, which have been responsible for so much public opposition to their use, are due to action on the thyroid glands. The effects which can be produced by altering the activity of the thyroid are exactly the same as those produced in birds and mammals by prolonged ingestion of small amounts of organochlorine insecticides.

Toxicological and Environmental Hazards of Organochlorine Insecticides

Commencing with the United States in 1972 very severe restrictions have been put on the use of DDT in all developed countries. It is not appropriate in this book to attempt to review all the controversy that has raged about the possible toxicological and environmental effects of DDT. There is evidence that accumulation of this compound in food chains has impaired the reproductive capacities of some species of birds and that discharge of it into estuaries has harmed sensitive marine organisms such as oysters. Also, because it is a very stable compound and is not metabolized, it accumulates in the fatty tissues of men and animals and, with modern highly sensitive analytical methods, it is possible to demonstrate its presence in humans and animals throughout the world. There is no evidence that this has done any harm to any species except some birds and shellfish but there was public unease about its ubiquitous presence which led to public pressure for its withdrawal which was exacerbated by reports that ingestion of large amounts by laboratory animals increased tumour formation. In most developed countries it is now restricted to emergency public health uses.

TABLE 8.1

Country	Year	Number of malaria cases
Mauritius	1948	46,395
	1969	17
Cuba	1962	3,519
	1969	3
Dominica	1950	1,825
	1969	Nil
Dominican Republic	1950	17,310
	1968	21
Grenada	1951	3,223
	1969	Nil
Jamaica	1954	4,417
	1969	Nil
Trinidad	1950	5,098
	1969	5
Venezuela	1943	817,115
	1958	800
India	1935	100,000,000
	1969	286,962
Sri Lanka	1946	2,800,000
	1961	110
Bulgaria	1946	144,631
	1969	10
Italy	1945	411,602
	1968	37
Romania	1948	338,198
	1969	4
Spain	1950	19,644
	1969	28
Taiwan	1945	1,000,000
	1969	9
Turkey	1950	1,118,969
	1969	2,173
Yugoslavia	1937	169,545
	1969	15

Despite the widespread world-wide use of DDT during 30 years there have been few poisonings because its acute toxicity is so low, and there is no epidemiological evidence of any kind that it has promoted development of cancer. The tremendous contribution that DDT has made to human welfare and to the prevention of human suffering should never be forgotten. Its use in the late 1940s in war-ravaged Europe prevented those major outbreaks of insect-borne disease which have, in the past, always been part of the aftermath of war and in many instances have claimed as many victims as the war itself.

In the 1950s the World Health Organization started a malaria eradication programme in 124 countries with a total population of 1,724 millions. It is believed that 1,000 million people in the world are at risk from malaria. The results of the programme shown in Table 8.1 speak for themselves. DDT has been and still is the mainstay of this programme even though problems have arisen as a result of evolution of resistant mosquitoes. The reason is that W.H.O. need an insecticide which is very cheap, long-lasting and with low acute toxicity. Thousands of possible alternatives have been tested by W.H.O. but not one has emerged which is as cost effective or as safe as DDT. The use of DDT in the antimalarial programme does not present any environmental hazards to wildlife as the compound is applied to the interior walls of buildings and W.H.O. have discontinued all outdoor uses.

The main effect of the restrictions on DDT in the developed countries has been to transfer its production to the developing countries. The total amount of DDT used world-wide has not been significantly reduced. The reason is that the developing countries desperately need crop protection and pest control but DDT is, with the exception of aldrin, dieldrin, endrin and a few cheap organophosphorus insecticides, the only insecticide which they can afford. The Ministries of Agriculture of the various countries decide which pesticides should be used in their agriculture and, while it is reasonable for the developed countries to give advice, they have no right to try to impose their standards on these countries. The circumstances and needs are different. A risk: benefit analysis gives a different answer if carried out in the context of a poor, starving population than in the context of a well-fed, affluent society and the balance between risks to wildlife and risks to humans assumes a different perspective.

The real reason why it is desirable that the use of DDT should be restricted is not environmental or health risks but because its continuous use can promote resistance and thus render it ineffective. This is happening in many developing countries where the number of applications annually and the application rates have been continually increased. Eventually these countries will no longer be able to control insects and will face starvation because their populations are increasing rapidly and because they cannot afford the alternative methods of insect management available to the developed countries. Another reason why use of DDT should be restricted is because it is a broad spectrum insecticide which kills not only the pests but also their predators and parasites, sometimes to an even greater extent. This happened in the cotton-growing areas of the Sudan where the whitefly, *Bemisia tabaci*, has, during the past 20 years, emerged as a major intractable pest because it is largely unaffected by organochlorine insecticides.

The way out of this impasse is to make money available to the developing countries to buy safe and selective pesticides and to provide expert technical assistance to teach them to use these pesticides wisely in conjunction with cultural practices. The International Development Association, the World Bank and many international aid organizations are making massive loans available to these countries as are organizations such as the U.S. AIDS programme and the British Commonwealth Bureau. Also the Food and Agricultural Organization of the United Nations is providing technical aid though on a comparatively small scale. Extensive technical advice and assistance are given by the scientists and technicians of the major international agrochemical companies. But the difficulties are formidable. By and large the obstacles are not scientific and technical, since most of the scientific and technical solutions are known: they are human, social, political and economic.

Most other organochlorine insecticides besides DDT have now been severely restricted in developed countries. Registrations in the United States of aldrin, dieldrin, endrin, chlordane and heptachlor were cancelled in 1974 and of chlordecone in 1976, mirex in 1977, and endrin in 1980. Registration for most uses of chlorocamphene have been cancelled except for certain uses under specific terms and conditions in corn, cotton and small grains and for certain treatments of cattle and sheep. In all these cases, apart from possible effects on wildlife there was evidence from animal experiments of carcinogenicity and teratogenicity. Lindane has been under review since 1977 because of suspected oncogenicity and teratogenicity but the final decision on it has not yet been published. The only organochlorine insecticide which has survived is endosulfan. A similar picture of gradual withdrawal or restriction of organochlorine insecticides has evolved in other developed countries.

There is no longer any justification for use of organochlorine insecticides in developed countries as they have been superceded by less persistent, less toxic and more selective (but more expensive) insecticides. However, as has been discussed already, the developing countries cannot afford these luxuries. As an interim measure continued careful use of DDT supplemented by whatever alternatives can be provided by foreign aid, and in conjunction with sound cultivational practices would appear to be justified. The cyclodiene insecticides are, however, in a different class from DDT with respect to acute and chronic toxicities, especially acute dermal toxicities. The acute oral toxicities of aldrin, dieldrin and endrin are respectively 67 mg/kg,

46 mg/kg and 10 mg/kg compared with DDT acute oral toxicity of 375 mg/kg, and the acute dermal toxicities of aldrin, dieldrin and endrin are 98 mg/kg, 50 mg/kg and 15 mg/kg compared with DDT acute dermal toxicity of over 2000 mg/kg. It is the low dermal toxicity of DDT that makes it a very safe compound to handle in practice whereas the high dermal toxicities of the cyclodiene insecticides and their very ready absorption through skin make them extremely hazardous to human health especially in the developing countries where they are generally handled by unskilled workers with no protective clothing. As a result, the cyclodiene insecticides, together with some very toxic organophosphorus insecticides which are very cheap, account for most of the 500,000 poisonings and 5000 deaths which occur annually from pesticides in the developing countries according to F.A.O. and W.H.O. This is a problem which the developed countries should address.

Further Reading

Brooks, G. T. *Chlorinated Insecticides*, vols I and II, CRC Press, Cleveland, Ohio, 1974.

Moriarty, F. (Ed). *Organochlorine Insecticides*, Academic Press, London and New York, 1975.

O'Brien, R. D. *Insecticides, Action and Metabolism*, Academic Press, London, 1967.

Tahori, A. J. (Ed). *Insecticides*, Proc. 2nd Int. IUPAC Cong. Pest. Chem., 2 volumes, Gordon & Breach, London and New York, 1972.

West, T. F. and Campbell, G. A. *DDT and Newer Persistent Insecticides*, Chapman-Hall, London, 1950.

World Health Organisation, *The Place of DDT in Operations against Malaria*, WHO Record No. 190, Geneva, 1971.

9

Synthetic Insecticides: Organophosphates, Carbamates and Formamidines

Research into toxic organophosphorus compounds was begun during World War II and was followed up in military research establishments in Germany, the U.K. and the U.S.A. The activities of competing investigation teams, as they followed the terminal advance of the allied armies, ensured greater publicity for the German work, while that in the U.K. and U.S.A. remained largely in secret files, but it is certainly true that the Germans had gone further towards practical development. Small stocks of two potential war gases had been charged into weapons and two other compounds were coming into use as insecticides.

The vapours of the war "gases", sarin and tabun, are much more lethal to insects than to man, but the public would not have tolerated the agricultural use of military weapons. Safer insecticidal compounds had to be developed, particularly since DDT and lindane had just become available and were, at the time, considered to be quite harmless to mammals. It was natural that in the immediate post-war years official and public attitudes overemphasized the significance of acute toxicity and the dangers of inhalation and skin-contamination because of the analogy with war gases. Now that the very long persistence of the organochlorine insecticides such as DDT, aldrin and dieldrin has been established, there is perhaps a tendency towards the opposite overemphasis.

The organophosphorus poisons are very numerous but form a well-recognized class. More is known about their mode of action, and the features of chemical structure and reactivity necessary for this action, than is the case with almost any other class of poison. The field is therefore one in which a great deal of chemical research towards new insecticides has been concentrated. Many thousand compounds must have been synthesized, mainly in industrial laboratories. It is probably true to say that most of these have proved to be insecticidal, a much higher proportion than when chemical synthesis explores wholly new fields. The objective of synthesis of organophosphorus compounds is not, however, to produce just another insecticide but to find some substantially improved selectivity, safety to mammals or desirable level of persistence.

In all the toxic compounds the three acidic functions of orthophosphoric acid are neutralized as esters or amides, or occasionally by direct P-C linkages. The co-ordinate linkage completing the four valencies of phosphorus is with S or O. In some compounds, too expensive for commercial interest, a higher group VI element, Se or Te, can serve this function. These compounds have a well-defined primary toxic action which is best illustrated by a few examples.

Mode of Action

All of these compounds inhibit the action of several ester-splitting enzymes in living organisms. They are particularly effective against cholinesterase, which hydrolyses the acetylcholine generated in myoneural junctions during the transmission of motor-commands. In the absence of effective cholinesterase, the acetylcholine accumulates and interferes with the co-ordination of muscular response. Such interference in the muscles of the vital organs produces serious symptoms and eventually death.

Paraoxon has been the most studied simple example. Its formula is:

$$C_2H_5O \diagdown \diagup O$$
$$P$$
$$C_2H_5O \diagup O—\langle\rangle—NO_2$$

Paraoxon

When paraoxon is presented to the enzyme in dilute solution, the phosphorus of one molecule of the inhibitor becomes locked up in every molecule of enzyme inhibited. At the same time one free nitrophenate ion appears. The active site of the enzyme evidently splits the molecule of the inhibitor, but is then unable to release the phosphoryl moiety. This blocks further action whereas the unchanged enzyme can attack, split and release some thousands of its normal substrate molecules per second.

This is the general reaction of all organophosphorus poisons. One substituent, generally the most acidic one, is released on contact with the enzyme and the disubstituted phosphate becomes firmly attached. Actual behaviour in the living organism, or even on enzymes *in vitro*, is, of course, more complex than this. The blockage of the enzyme by the substituted phosphate group is not necessarily quite permanent and the phosphate ester may be hydrolyzed *in situ*. Thus there may be reactivation of the attacked enzyme, although most recovery from partial intoxication must await replacement of the enzyme. The compound itself is in some cases not directly active and requires chemical alteration before it becomes so. The compound, or its derivatives, may be subject to other reactions which compete with the toxic one. The disposition of groups other than those directly concerned in the inhibition reaction may assist adsorption of the toxic molecule on to the enzyme in a suitable posture for reaction to occur.

Paraoxon is a direct inhibitor of cholinesterase, i.e. it reacts rapidly in this respect in sterile solution. It is also very generally highly toxic to animals and is not now used as such. Parathion, in which $P \rightarrow O$ is replaced by $P \rightarrow S$ is not a direct inhibitor and is much more slowly hydrolyzed by alkali. In general there is strong positive co-relation between *in vitro* inhibition and alkaline hydrolysis rate. Parathion however can be oxidized to paraoxon. Its toxicity is dependent both on the occurrence and limitation of oxidation.

Dimefox is inactive against cholinesterase *in vitro* and hydrolysis is very

$$(CH_3)_2N \diagdown \underset{(CH_3)_2N \diagup}{P} \diagup{\diagup{O}} \diagdown F$$

Dimefox

slow. It is oxidized *in vitro* by hydrogen peroxide and *in vivo* in the liver and some other tissues. Oxidation starts by addition of O to N, proceeding via N-O-CH$_3$ to demethylation: all three oxidation stages, especially the first, greatly increase the rate of P-F fission in alkaline solution and the rate of *in vitro* inhibition of the enzyme.

$$C_2H_5O \diagdown \underset{C_2H_5O \diagup}{P} \diagup{\diagup{S}} \diagdown OCH_2CH_2SC_2H_5$$

Demeton

Oxidation occurs at another site in the case of demeton. The thioether is oxidized to sulphoxide and then sulphone. The original compound is, however, in this case an inhibitor and the oxidation causes less increase than that at N in the case of dimefox, but it has an important effect on the solubility balance of the compound, which becomes much more hydrophilic. The compound is a very effective systemic aphicide. The lipophilic nature of the applied compound is probably useful in helping penetration of the leaf cuticle and the hydrophilic oxidation product formed in the leaf cells is then transported in the vascular system.

$$CH_3O \diagdown \diagup S$$
$$P$$
$$CH_3O \diagup \diagdown SCH_2.CO.NH.CH_3$$

Dimethoate

In dimethoate, as in parathion, there is need for oxidation of $P \rightarrow S$ to $P \rightarrow O$ before inhibition of cholinesterase is effective, but in this case another type of reaction is important. The P-S link is the one subject to fission during reaction with the enzyme and is also subject to hydrolysis, but the amide, -CO-NH-, link can also be hydrolyzed and this reaction appears to be much more favoured by enzyme systems of some species than of others. Amide hydrolysis can occur to a significant extent in mammals before activating oxidation of $P \rightarrow S$ takes place and the resulting thiophosphoryl acetate ion is rapidly excreted in the urine.

Mechanisms of Selectivity

The enzymic hydrolysis of liberated acetylcholine seems to be essential to nerve-muscle relations in all animals. The organophosphorus poisons may therefore seem at first to be wholly unsuitable for selective action. Selectivity, however, arises from the important complex of other reactions outlined in the last paragraph. A compound may be intrinsically toxic to all animals but, of similar doses externally administered, the fraction which can reach the active site sufficiently quickly can vary widely between species. The examples we have just given illustrate how differences can arise. In more complex compounds more possibilities of alternative reactions are opened up, leading to more competition between toxicant-producing and toxicant-destroying reactions.

Most insecticides act, finally, on some very general biochemical mechanism and rely for their selectivity on quantitative rather than qualitative differences. Most biochemical mechanisms are remarkably universal. Essentially quantitative differences in basically the same biochemical processes account for the difference in shape, life history and behaviour between man and his louse. They can fairly be relied on to make a compound safe for one but lethal to the other.

The significant competition is also not confined to that between parallel or consecutive reactions. Physical transport processes are always involved — diffusion through cuticle, cells and cell membranes; flow in blood, lymph, sap or phloem. If decomposition goes on during transport, the fraction of applied compound which can reach its destination unchanged depends on the relative speeds of transport and reaction. The transport processes are not all favourable. An externally applied compound can be lost by evaporation or by rain-washing. These rates are in competition with rate of entry.

If all the applied substance were to reach the vital site it might seem not to matter how long it would take to do so. All toxic reactions, however, destroy or inactivate some chemical which is so essential that it must be continually replaced. The rate of arrival of the toxicant is therefore in competition with the rate of replacement of the vital chemical attacked. Wide differences in the balance between rates of destruction and replacement are responsible for some poisons — e.g. lead — having a long-term chronic or cumulative effect, while, at the other extreme, oxalate and cyanide have acute significance only.

Rates of diffusion through tissues and of transport by flow of liquid in conducting vessels are determined by the size and shape of molecules and by partition between water and oily phases. In these respects, the organophosphorus insecticides cover a wide range — much wider than most pesticides. At one extreme, schradan is so strongly water-favourable that only the exceptionally good solvent, chloroform, is useful for extracting it from water. At the other, parathion and many similar compounds partition favourably into vegetable oils from water.

With so wide a range of physical properties in compounds of considerable reactivity, it is not surprising that a wide range of toxicity is found among different species and different modes of application. It is generally found that the more direct means of administration to a living organism — such as injection into the blood stream of higher animals or presentation of volatile compounds in the ambient air — show less difference between species than less direct means. The latter, of course, include most of the practical ways of using insecticides, such as leaving on vegetation a deposit which will be ingested or picked up in walking or applying a spray which directly contaminates the body cuticle.

This brief account of the reactivity of the organophosphorus insecticides and the part it can play in their selective action is, of course, very incomplete. It is not the purpose of this book to go at all deeply into the biochemistry of toxicity. Longer and more specialist books must be consulted for full accounts of the present knowledge of biochemical mechanisms. Although much is known, and this knowledge can be applied to alter structures in ways that will probably affect selectivity in a desirable direction, much more is still unknown. Synthetic work cannot make useful progress without the guidance at every stage of biological experiment. The study of toxicants discovered fortuitously contributes much more to knowledge of normal biochemistry than can the latter, as yet, contribute to the design of new toxicants.

The organophosphorus compounds have been used here to outline some general principles because their toxic mechanism is much better known than that of many pesticides.

Inter- and Intra-Molecular Reactions

Most organophosphorus insecticides are rather reactive compounds and the methods of preparation generally have associated side-reactions. Most of the compounds moreover are liquid at ordinary temperatures and their reactivity makes purification by distillation impossible on an industrial scale. Knowledge of the impurities, particularly of their toxicities, and good control of reaction conditions, is essential. It is desirable therefore to deal with some internal reactions, before classifying the numerous compounds available.

A common preparative reaction is that of a phosphorus acid chloride with an alcohol, phenol, amine or mercaptan which we will represent by HX

$$\underset{R'}{\overset{R}{\diagdown}}\hspace{-0.3em}\underset{Cl}{\overset{O}{P}} + HX \longrightarrow \underset{R'}{\overset{R}{\diagdown}}\hspace{-0.3em}\underset{X}{\overset{O}{P}} + HCl \qquad (1)$$

If water is present during this reaction this does not necessarily lead to complete hydrolysis of the acid chloride, but, initially to a substituted pyrophosphate. If R is C_2H_5O, the resulting pyrophosphate, called TEPP, is a powerful insecticide, one of the earliest. It is very rapidly hydrolyzed by alkali and a direct inhibitor. Its half life in neutral water is only about 8 hours and its toxicity to mammals very high. For these reasons it has now little use as such and is an undesirable impurity in less toxic products. In the reaction with cholinesterase, one half of the molecule acts as the acid "leaving" group. If R is CH_3O the compound is too easily hydrolyzed to have any use. If R is $(CH_3)_2N$, the pyrocompound, schradan, is very stable, is not an inhibitor *in vitro*, is a very good systemic aphicide (requiring N oxidation *in vivo*) but too toxic to mammals to be now used. The general reactions above must be carried out in presence of an unreactive base to prevent acid accumulation, but the pyrophosphate formation can result from reaction of the acid chloride with anhydrous alkali carbonate. Where R is C_2H_5O and the initial acid chloride has S rather than O attached to P, the pyro product is sulfotep, more stable than TEPP but still of low persistence in the field and generally too toxic, although it is still used as a fumigant in glasshouses.

$$\underset{C_2H_5O}{\overset{C_2H_5O}{\diagdown}}\hspace{-0.3em}\underset{O}{\overset{S}{P}}\diagdown\underset{OC_2H_5}{\overset{S}{\underset{OC_2H_5}{\diagup}}\hspace{-0.3em}P}$$

Sulfotep

This type of linkage exchange is responsible for the complex behaviour of phosphoric acid itself and the universal biochemical importance of the ATP:ADP conversion. Important intramolecular conversions can also occur in the compounds of insecticidal interest. One is the spontaneous change where S in the coordinate position interchanges with S in the ester position, exemplified in the case of parathion.

(2)

This reaction is very slow at ordinary temperatures but proceeds cleanly to near 80% completion in 10 hours at 170°. An apparently similar reaction in demeton takes place much more quickly but a transient dissociation into a sulphonium salt is responsible and a change of partners occurs as can be shown using a mixture of compounds with different alkoxy groups. The S atom transfers to the labile group.

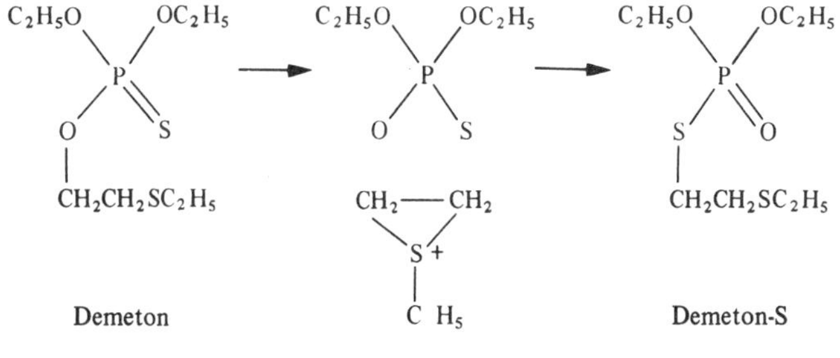

(3)

In some compounds phosphorus is directly linked to carbon. They are called phosphonates. The most important commercially are fonofos and EPN. In 1982, U.S.A. farmers used 2500 tonnes and 1000 tonnes respectively Trichloromate is fonofos with 2,4,5-trichlorophenoxy instead of phenylthio.

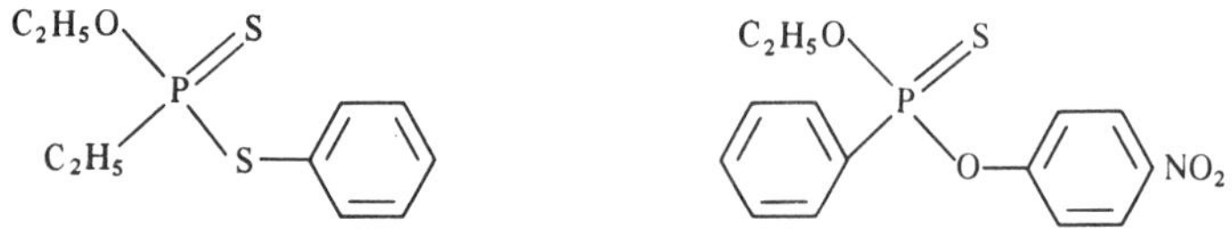

(4)

Usually the group linked to phosphorus is stable and remains attached in the blocked enzyme, but in one case it is the leaving group and first it undergoes an intramolecular change slowly *in vivo* or quickly on introduction of one mol of a strong base.

$$\underset{\substack{\text{Dimethyl}\\\text{phosphite}}}{\overset{\text{CH}_3\text{O}}{\underset{\text{CH}_3\text{O}}{>}}\text{P—OH}} + \underset{\text{Chloral}}{\overset{\text{CCl}_3}{\underset{\text{CHO}}{|}}} \longrightarrow \underset{\text{Trichlorphon}}{\overset{\text{CH}_3\text{O}}{\underset{\text{CH}_3\text{O}}{>}}\overset{\text{O}}{\underset{\underset{\text{OH}}{|}}{\overset{||}{\text{P}}}-\underset{}{\text{CH—CCl}_3}} \xrightarrow{\text{HCl}} \underset{\text{Dichlorvos}}{\overset{\text{CH}_3\text{O}}{\underset{\text{CH}_3\text{O}}{>}}\overset{\text{O}}{\overset{||}{\text{P}}}-\text{OCH=CCl}_2} \qquad (5)$$

With reservations about the biochemical significance in view of the reactions exemplified above we can now group the presently available organophosphorus insecticides according to their simple starting structures. Some, and they necessarily include the most recent developments, do not fit into well-defined groups. In the majority of the compounds the groups attached to the P atom, which remain attached when reaction with the enzyme takes place, are lower alkoxy groups. Nearly always the two groups, for convenience of manufacture, are the same and either methoxy or ethoxy. Propoxy occasionally occurs but higher esters have not been usefully insecticidal. A few are of herbicidal interest (see Chapter 19). Methyl esters are always the most active.

Phosphates

Generally, the simple phosphates, like paraoxon, have too high an acute toxicity to mammals to be acceptable. In nearly all those approved for use, the group which becomes the mobile one after activation is a substituted vinyl. Much the most widely used is dichlorvos, which is sufficiently volatile and of sufficiently low toxicity to mammals to be used as a vapour active fly killer in domestic premises.

Dimethyl phosphates $(CH_3O)_2.PO.OX$

X	common name
2,2-dichlorovinyl	dichlorvos
1,2-dibromo-2,2-dichloroethyl	naled
2-methoxycarbonyl-1-methylvinyl	mevinphos
1-methyl-2-methylcarbamoylvinyl	monocrotophos
1-methyl-2-dimethylcarbamoylvinyl	dicrotophos
2-chloro-2-diethylcarbamoyl-1-methylvinyl	phosphamidon
1-methyl-2-(1-phenylethoxycarbonyl)vinyl	crotoxyphos
2-chloro-1-(2,4,5,-trichlorophenyl)vinyl	tetrachlorvinphos
3,5,6-trichloro-2-pyridyl	fospirate
7-chlorobicyclo(3,2,0)hepta-2,6-dien-6-yl	heptenophos

CIPM-D*

Diethyl phosphates $(C_2H_5O)_2.PO.OX$

X	common name
4-nitrophenyl	paraoxon
2-chloro-1-(2,4-dichlorophenyl)vinyl	chlorfenvinphos
2-bromo-1-(2,4-dichlorophenyl)vinyl	bromfenvinphos

Phosphates can be manufactured by reaction of a dialkyl phosphorochloridate with an hydroxy compound, generally in an organic solvent in presence of sodium carbonate or an organic base. Thus mevinphos is prepared by heating dimethyl phosphorochloridate with the sodium enolate of methyl acetoacetate (Eq. 6).

$$(CH_3O)_2.PO.Cl + \underset{NaO}{\overset{CH_3}{\diagup}}C{=}CHCOOCH_3 \longrightarrow (CH_3O)_2.PO.O\underset{}{\overset{CH_3}{\diagup}}C{=}CHCOOCH_3 \qquad (6)$$

Mevinphos (95% *trans*)

The dialkyl phosphorochloridates can be easily manufactured from phosphorus oxychloride and an alcohol (Eq. 7) or by reaction of dialkyl phosphites either with chlorine (Eq. 8) or with carbon tetrachloride in presence of a tertiary amine (Eq. 9). Dialkyl phosphites are made from phosphorus trichloride and an alcohol; in the absence of added base the reaction stops at the dialkyl phosphite stage (Eq. 10). More economically, a mixture of alcohol and water may be used (Eq. 11).

$$POCl_3 + 2ROH \longrightarrow (RO)_2.PO.Cl + 2HCl \qquad (7)$$

$$(RO)_2.P.OH + Cl_2 \longrightarrow (RO)_2.PO.Cl + RCl \qquad (8)$$

$$(RO)_2.P.OH + CCl_4 \longrightarrow (RO)_2.PO.Cl + CHCl_3 \qquad (9)$$

$$PCl_3 + 3ROH \longrightarrow (RO)_2.P.OH + RCl + 2HCl \qquad (10)$$

$$PCl_3 + 2ROH + H_2O \longrightarrow (RO)_2.P.OH + 3HCl \qquad (11)$$

Phosphates can also be manufactured by the Perkow reaction of a trialkyl phosphite with an α-halogenated carbonyl compound and this is the process used for all the vinyl phosphates — mevinphos, monocrotophos, dicrotophos phosphamidon, crotoxyphos, tetrachlorvinphos, chlorfenvinphos and bromfenvinphos. For example, trimethyl phosphite and methyl α-chloroacetoacetate give mevinphos (Eq. 12). The product from this route is 2:1 cis:trans whereas the alternative route from dimethyl phosphorochloridate (Eq. 6) gives 95% trans. Dichlorvos is similarly manufactured by heating trimethyl phosphite and chloral in benzene at 60–70° (Eq. 13).

$$(CH_3O)_3P + CH_3COCHClCOOCH_3 \longrightarrow (CH_3O \quad PO.O \overset{\displaystyle CH_3 \diagdown}{\diagup} C{=}CHCOOCH_3 \qquad (12)$$

Mevinphos (2:1 *cis:trans*)

$$(CH_3O)_3P + CCl_3CHO \longrightarrow (CH_3O)_2.PO.O.CH{=}CCl_2 + CH_3Cl \qquad (13)$$

Trialkyl phosphites are manufactured from phosphorus trichloride and an alcohol in presence of base (Eq. 14).

$$PCl_3 + 3ROH \longrightarrow (RO)_3.P + 3HCl \qquad (14)$$

O-Phosphorothioates

This is the general name given to all phosphates where one O attached to P is replaced by S and where this is in the co-ordinate position. The compounds are not direct inhibitors, requiring activation, usually by oxidation, to become so. The most important commercially are parathion-methyl and chlorpyrifos-ethyl. In 1982, U.S.A. farmers used 6900 tonnes and 3500 tonnes respectively.

Dimethyl O-phosphorothioates $(CH_3O)_2.PS.OX$

X	common name
2-(ethylthio)ethyl	demeton-0-methyl
2-(ethylsulfinyl)-1-methylethyl	oxydeprophos
2-methoxycarbonyl-1-methylvinyl	methacrifos
4-nitrophenyl	parathion-methyl
3-methyl-4-nitrophenyl	fenitrothion
4-cyanophenyl	cyanophos
2,5-dichloro-4-iodo-phenyl	iodofenphos
2,6-dichloro-4-methylphenyl	tolclofos-methyl
4-bromo-2,5-dichlorophenyl	bromophos
3-methyl-4-methylthiophenyl	fenthion
2-diethylamino-6-methylpyrimidin-4-yl	pirimiphos-methyl

Diethyl 0-phosphorothioates $(C_2H_5O)_2.PS.OX$

X	common name
2-(ethylthio)ethyl	demeton-0
4-nitrophenyl	parathion
4-methylsulphinylphenyl	fensulfothion
4-bromo-2,5-dichlorophenyl	bromophos-ethyl
α-cyanobenzylideneamino	phoxim
2-chloro-α-cyanobenzylidene amine	chlorphoxim
3,5,6-trichloro-2-pyridyl	chlorpyrifos-ethyl
5-phenyl-3-isoxazolyl	isoxathion
2-diethylamino-6-methylpyrimidin-4-yl	pirimiphos-ethyl
2-isopropyl-6-methylpyrimidin-4-yl	diazinon
6-ethoxy-2-ethylpyrimidin-4-yl	etrimfos
1-isopropyl-5-chloro-1,2,4-triazol-3-yl	isazophos
2,4-dichloro-5-methylthiophenyl	chlorthiophos
1-phenyl-1,2,4-triazol-3-yl	triazophos

The compounds are manufactured by reaction of an hydroxy compound with a dialkyl phosphorochloridothionate in the presence of bases and often, also, of copper powder. Careful control of temperature is essential, especially with 0-methyl esters, to prevent isomerization into S-methyl esters and to restrict decomposition. For example, fenitrothion is manufactured by heating 3-methyl-4-nitrophenol with dimethyl phosphorochloridothionate at 60–80° in methyl isobutyl ketone in presence of potassium carbonate (Eq. 15).

$$(CH_3O)_2.PS.Cl + HO\!\!\!\bigcirc\!\!\!NO_2 \longrightarrow (CH_3O)_2.PS.O\!\!\!\bigcirc\!\!\!NO_2 \qquad (15)$$
$$\qquad\qquad\qquad\quad CH_3 \qquad\qquad\qquad\qquad\qquad\qquad CH_3$$

Dialkyl phosphorochloridothionates can be prepared by reaction of phosphorus thiochloride with an alcohol in presence of a base (Eq. 16) but a more economical manufacturing process is to chlorinate the dialkyl phosphorodithioic acids made by reaction of phosphorus pentasulphide with an alcohol (Eq. 17 and 18).

$$PSCl_3 + 2ROH \longrightarrow (RO)_2.PS.Cl + 2HCl \qquad (16)$$

$$P_2S_5 + 4ROH \longrightarrow 2(RO)_2.PS.SH + H_2S \qquad (17)$$

$$2(RO)_2.PS.SH + 3Cl_2 \longrightarrow 2(RO)_2.PS.Cl + 2HCl + S_2Cl_2 \qquad (18)$$

S-Phosphorothioates

Dimethyl S-phosphorothioates $(CH_3O)_2.PO.SX$

X	common name
2-(ethylthio)ethyl	demeton-S-methyl
2-(ethylsulphinyl)ethyl	oxydemeton-methyl
methylcarbamoyl methyl	omethoate
2-(1-methylcarbamoylethylthio)ethyl	vamidothion
2,3-dihydro-2oxo-oxazolo (4,5-bipyridin)-ylmethyl	azamethiphos

Diethyl S-phosphorothioates $(C_2H_5O)_2.PO.SX$

X	common name
2-(ethylthio)ethyl	demeton-S
ethoxycarbonylmethyl	acetofos

Reaction of dialkyl phosphorochloridate with a mercaptan is not a suitable manufacturing process for S-phosphorothioates because attack takes place on the O-alkyl group as well as on the chlorine atom (Eq. 19).

$$(RO)_2.PO.Cl + NaSX \longrightarrow R.S.X + \begin{array}{c} RO \\ \diagdown \\ \diagup \\ NaO \end{array}PO.Cl \qquad (19)$$

However, demeton-S is manufactured from diethyl phosphorochloridate and the sodium salt of 2-ethylthioethylthiol (Eq. 20).

$$(C_2H_5O)_2.PO.Cl + NaSCH_2CH_2SC_2H_5 \longrightarrow (C_2H_5O)_2.PO.SCH_2CH_2SC_2H_5 + NaCl \qquad (20)$$

Demeton-S

Generally, S-phosphorothioates are manufactured by reaction of a dialkyl phosphorothioate with a halo compound. Thus, acetofos is made from ammonium diethyl phosphorothioate and ethyl chloroacetate (Eq. 21).

$$(C_2H_5O)_2.PO.SNH_4 + ClCH_2COOC_2H_5 \longrightarrow (C_2H_5O)_2.PO.SCH_2COOC_2H_5 \qquad (21)$$

Acetofos

The dialkylphosphorothioates are manufactured by treatment of dialkyl phosphorochloridothionates with alkali (Eq. 22), by reaction of dialkyl phosphorochloridates with sulphides (Eq. 23), or by reaction of dialkyl phosphites with sulphur and ammonia at room temperature (Eq. 24).

$$(RO)_2.PS.Cl + KOH \longrightarrow (RO)_2.PO.SK + KCl \qquad (22)$$

$$(RO)_2.PO.Cl + K_2S \longrightarrow (RO)_2.PO.SK + KCl \qquad (23)$$

$$(RO)_2.P.OK + S + NH_3 \longrightarrow (RO)_2.PO.SNH_4 \qquad (24)$$

Phosphorodithioates

This is the most commercially important class of phosphorus insecticides. In contrast to the phosphates and phosphorothioates, aryl esters are unimportant. Nearly all useful compounds have a methyl group attached to the -S, and this methyl group carries an ester, amide, carbamoyl, sulphide or heterocyclic grouping. The most widely used compounds of this class are disulfoton, malathion, phorate, terbufos and dimethoate.

Dimethyl phosphorodithioates $(CH_3O)_2.PS.SX$

X	common name
2-(ethylthio)-ethyl	thiometon
methylcarbamoylmethyl	dimethoate
1,2-di (ethoxycarbonyl)ethyl	malathion
ethoxycarbonylbenzyl	phenthoate
3,4-dihydro-4-oxobenzo [d]-1,2,3,-triazin-3-ylmethyl	azinphos-methyl
formylmethylcarbamoylmethyl	formothion
mercaptomethylphthalimide	phosmet

Diethyl phosphorodithioates $(C_2H_5O)_2.PS.SX$

X	common name
ethylthiomethyl	phorate
ethylsulphinylmethyl	oxyphorate
tert butylthiomethyl	terbufos
2-(ethylthio)ethyl	disulfoton
2-(ethylsulphinyl)ethyl	oxydisulfoton
ethoxycarbonylmethyl	acethion

Diethyl phosphorodithioates $(C_2H_5O)_2.PS.SX$

X	common name
isopropylcarbamoylmethyl	prothoate
ethoxycarbonylmethylcarbamoylmethyl	mecarbam
methylene-bis-	ethion
4-chlorophenylthiomethyl	carbophenothion
1,4-dioxan-2,3-ylidene-bis-	dioxathion
3,4-dihydro-4-oxobenzo [d]-1,2,3-triazin-3-ylmethyl	azinphos-ethyl
2-chloro-1-phthalimidoethyl	dialifos
6-chloro-2-oxybenzoxazolin-3-ylmethyl	phosalone
chloromethyl	chlormephos

They are manufactured from dialkyl phosphorodithioic acids by reaction with a halo-compound (Eq. 25), by addition to an aldehyde (Eq. 26), or by addition to an olefin (Eq. 27).

$$(CH_3O)_2.PS.SNa + Cl.CH_2CH_2.S.C_2H_5 \longrightarrow (CH_3O)_2.PS.SCH_2CH_2SC_2H_5 + NaCl \qquad (25)$$

Thiometon

$$(C_2H_5O)_2.PS.SH + CH_2O + C_2H_5SH \longrightarrow (C_2H_5O)_2.PS.SCH_2SC_2H_5 \qquad (26)$$

Phorate

$$(CH_3O)_2.PS.SH + \underset{\overset{\displaystyle |}{\displaystyle CH.COOC_2H_5}}{\overset{\displaystyle ||}{CH.COOC_2H_5}} \longrightarrow (CH_3O)_2.PS.S.\underset{\overset{\displaystyle |}{\displaystyle CH_2.COOC_2H_5}}{CH.COOC_2H_5} \qquad (27)$$

Malathion

Direct formation of a P-S bond by reaction of dialkyl phosphorochloridothioates with sodium derivatives of thiols is not a suitable manufacturing process because of a side-reaction (Eq. 28).

$$(RO)_2.PS.Cl + Na \longrightarrow R.S.X + \underset{NaO}{\overset{RO}{>}}PS.Cl \qquad (28)$$

The required dialkyl phosphorodithioic acids can, as described previously (Eq. 17), be easily manufactured by reaction of phosphorus pentasulphide with an alcohol.

Other Organophosphorus Insecticides

Several compounds of importance, mostly recent, do not fit into the above classes. Although bis-dimethylamino substitutions are not now used, except for limited application of dimefox, three compounds have a mono alkylamino in place of one ester group. These are phosphoramidothioates

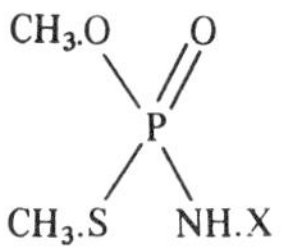

X = H Methamidophos   Propetamphos   Fenamiphos
X = COCH₃ Acephate

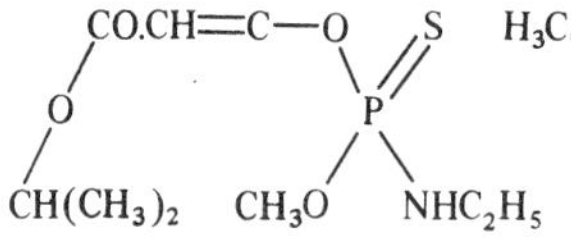

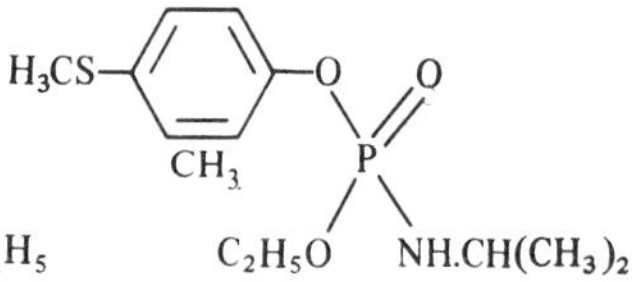

In three other compounds a more complex substituent is attached to P through N and functions as the leaving group. All are diethyl phosphates with the leaving groups shown below:

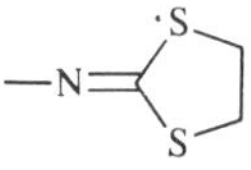

Phosfolan 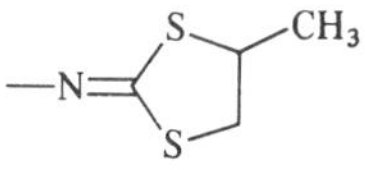   Mephosfolan 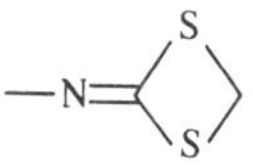   Fosthietan

Three other compounds have an active phenol expected to function as the leaving group. All are phosphorodithioates being O-phenyl-O-ethyl-S-n.propyl esters. The substitutions in the phenyl group are 2,4-dichloro in prothiofos, 2-chloro-4-bromo is profenofos and 4-methylmercapto in sulprofos. Ethoprop is O-ethyl-S,S-dipropylphosphorodithioate and is active in soil against insects and nematodes. Presumably oxidation of S in P-S-C activates a thioester to function as the leaving group.

Carbamate Insecticides

The carbamates are closely related in biological action and in resistance development to the organophosphorus insecticides and, like them, inhibit cholinesterase. The activity of different members of the class is rather more dependent on substituent positions and on stereoisomerism than is the case with organophosphorus compounds. The three classes which have yielded commercially useful products are (1) the N-methylcarbamates of phenols and hydroxyheterocyclic compounds, the most widely used of which are carbaryl, carbofuran and bufencarb (2) the N-methylcarbamates of oximes, the most widely used of which is methomyl (3) the N,N-dimethylcarbamates of hydroxyheterocyclic compounds, the most widely used of which is pirimicarb.

Methylcarbamates of phenols RO.CONHCH₃

R	common name
1-naphthyl	carbaryl
3-methylphenyl	MTMC
3,4-dimethyl	xylylcarb
2-isopropylphenyl	isoprocarb
3-(1-methylbutyl) + 3-(1-ethylpropyl)	bufencarb
3-methyl-5-isopropylphenyl	promecarb
2-isopropoxyphenyl	propoxur
3,5-dimethyl-4-methylthiophenyl	methiocarb
2-ethylthiomethylphenyl	ethiophencarb
4-dimethylamino-3-methylphenyl	aminocarb
2-(1-methoxy-2-chloro)-ethoxyphenyl	cloethocarb
2,3-dihydro-2,2-dimethylbenzofuran-7-yl	carbofuran
2,3-(dimethylmethylene)dioxyphenyl	bendiocarb
2-(1,3-dioxolane-2-yl)phenyl	dioxacarb

Dimethylcarbamates of heterocycles RO.CO.N(CH₃)₂

R	common name
5,6-dimethyl-2-dimethylaminopyrimidin-4-yl	pirimicarb
1-isopropyl-3-methylpyrazol-5-yl	—
1-dimethylcarbamoyl-5-methylpyrazol-3-yl	dimetilan

Methylcarbamates of oximes R=NO.CONHCH₃

parent aldehyde or ketone	common name
2-methyl-2(methylthio)propionaldehyde	aldicarb
1-(methylthio)acetaldehyde	methomyl
Dimethylcarbamoyl-methylthioformaldehyde	thioxamyl
1-(2-cyanoethylthio)acetaldehyde	thiocarboxime
1-methylthio-3,3-dimethyl-but-2-one	thiophanox
3-methylthio-but-2-one	butocarboxim

$$\text{naphthyl} + COCl_2 \longrightarrow \text{naphthyl-OCOCl} + HCl \qquad (29)$$

$$\text{naphthyl-OCOCl} + 2NH_2CH_3 \longrightarrow \text{naphthyl-OCONHCH}_3 + CH_3NH_2.HCl \qquad (30)$$

Phenyl methylcarbamates can be manufactured by reaction of the appropriate sodium phenoxide with phosgene at 10–50°, generally by adding a toluene solution of phosgene to an alkaline aqueous solution of the phenoxide (Eq.

29), and then reacting the intermediate chloroformate thus formed with an aqueous solution of methylamine (Eq. 30). The products are usually crystalline solids which can be filtered off. The reactions producing carbaryl are exemplified.

Alternatively, and preferable with more reactive hydroxy compounds, phosgene is first reacted with methylamine to give methyl isocyanate which then forms the carbamate by an addition reaction, as in equations (33) and (37). The disastrous explosion of a methylisocyanate storage tank in Bhopal must not be taken as indicating exceptional hazard in insecticides derived from this intermediate (see Chapter 25). The dimethylcarbamates must be made by the chloroformate reaction.

Aldicarb is manufactured by reaction of isobutene with nitrosyl chloride to give the dimer of 2-chloro-2-methyl-1-nitrosopropane (Eq. 31) which is then treated with methanethiol in aqueous sodium hydroxide to form 2-methyl-2-methylthiopropionaldehyde oxime (Eq. 32) which is converted to aldicarb by reaction with methyl isocyanate in methylene chloride. (Eq. 33.)

$$(CH_3)_2C{=}CH_2 + NOCl \longrightarrow (CH_3)_2.CCl.CH_2.NO \tag{31}$$

$$(CH_3)_2.CCl.CH_2.NO + CH_3SH \longrightarrow (CH_3)_2.C(SCH_3).CH{=}NOH \tag{32}$$

$$(CH_3)_2.C(SCH_3).CH{=}NOH + CH_3NCO \longrightarrow (CH_3)_2.C(SCH_3).CH{=}NOCONHCH_3 \tag{33}$$

Methomyl is manufactured by preparing acetaldoxime from acetaldehyde and hydroxylamine (Eq. 34) and chlorinating this in water at $-10°$ to give 1-chloroacetaldoxime (Eq. 35). This is then reacted with methanethiol in aqueous sodium hydroxide and the 1-(methylthio)acetaldoxime (Eq. 36) thus formed is refluxed with methyl isocyanate in methylene chloride (Eq. 37).

$$CH_3CHO + NH_2OH \longrightarrow CH_3CH{=}NOH \tag{34}$$

$$CH_3CH{=}NOH + Cl_2 \longrightarrow CH_3CCl{=}NOH \tag{35}$$

$$CH_3CCl{=}NOH + CH_3SH \longrightarrow CH_3C(SCH_3){=}NOH \tag{36}$$

$$CH_3C(SCH_3){=}NOH + CH_3NCO \longrightarrow CH_3C(SCH_3){=}NOCONHCH_3 \tag{37}$$

The other thioimidates, thioxamyl and thiocarboxime are manufactured similarly.

Formamidine Derivatives

Several compounds containing the formamidine, $HN{=}CH{-}NH_2$, linkage with three or all H atoms substituted have been found to have interesting insecticidal behaviour and may become an important group. They are only slightly related to carbamates but some a little more closely to thiocarbamates. Their biochemical mode of action is probably quite different although some of the symptoms of poisoning are similar. They are included in this chapter only for convenience. It is possible that compounds will be discovered in this group having activity approaching that of the pyrethroids, i.e. application rates of 10–20 g/ha. During the last ten years the main focus of attention for research in the major agrochemical companies has been on the pyrethroids but more attention may now be given to the formamidines.

CH$_3$—⟨⟩—$\overset{CH_3}{}$—N=CH—N—CH=N—⟨⟩$\overset{CH_3}{}$CH$_3$
                          |
                         CH$_3$

Amitraz

Amitraz, N-methyl-bis-(2,4-dimethylphenyliminomethyl)amine, is effective against the eggs and larvae of cotton bollworm, tobacco budworm and cotton whitefly, and also against pear psylla and various tetranychid and eriophyid mites on citrus, fruit and ornamentals. It is also used to control animal parasites such as ticks, lice and mange. About 25 tonnes of amitraz were used in the United States in 1980 on pears and about 175 tonnes on cotton in the Sudan.

Cl—⟨⟩$\overset{CH_3}{}$—N=CHN(CH$_3$)$_2$ CH$_3$NHCOO—⟨⟩—N=CHN(CH$_3$)$_2$

Chlordimeform   Formetanate hydrochloride

Chlordimeform, N'-(4-chloro-2-methylphenyl)-N,N-dimethylformamidine has both ovicidal and insecticidal activity. It is used mainly to control bollworm and budworm on cotton, and 500 tonnes were used for this purpose in the United States in 1982. It is also active against many lepidopterous species and against mites, particularly those that have become resistant to organophosphorus acaricides.

Formetanate hydrochloride, N'-(3-methylcarbamoylphenyl)-N, N-dimethyl formamidine, is a related compound which is used to control mites, thrips, leafhoppers and leaf miners on deciduous fruit and citrus.

Amitraz is manufactured by reaction of 2,4-xylidene with ethyl orthoformate and methylamine, and chlordimeform by reaction of 2-methyl-4-chloroaniline with dimethylformamide in the presence of phosphorus oxychloride.

$$CH_3 - \text{(ring, } CH_3\text{)} - NH_2 \ + \ 2\ CH(OC_2H_5)_3 \ + \ CH_3NH_2 \longrightarrow$$

$$CH_3 - \text{(ring, } CH_3\text{)} - N = CH - \underset{CH_3}{N} - CH = N - \text{(ring, } CH_3, CH_3\text{)}$$

$$Cl - \text{(ring, } CH_3\text{)} - NH_2 \ + \ OHCN(CH_3)_2 \longrightarrow \ Cl - \text{(ring, } CH_3\text{)} - N = CHN(CH_3)_2$$

That high activity can be retained even when the formamidine grouping $-N=CH-N=$ is part of a complex molecule is shown by the insecticidal effect of 2-phenylimidazoline and by the development of clenpyrin.

2 - phenylimidazoline   Clenpyrin

In chlordimeform type molecules it is essential for high activity that there is 2,4 substitution in the phenyl ring and a hydrogen atom on the carbon atom linked to the two nitrogen atoms. However, an exception appears to be when this carbon atom is attached to sulphur as in chloromethiuron, a compound that is mainly used against cattle ticks. Research along these lines has led to buprofezin, 2-tert.butylimino-3-isopropyl-5-phenyl-3,4,5,6-tetrahydro-2H-1,3,5-thiadiazin-4-one, which is a highly selective compound active almost exclusively against Hemiptera such as planthoppers, leafhoppers, whiteflies

Chloromethiuron   Buprofenzin

and scales in the nymphal stage from instar to moulting. Its biochemical effects appear to be essentially similar to those of amitraz and chlordimeform. It appears, therefore, that selectivity as well as activity can be discovered in formamidine type molecules.

Buprofezin and its analogues are very easily manufactured by reaction of N-chloromethylcarbamoyl chlorides with thioureas.

$$RN{\overset{\displaystyle CH_2Cl}{\underset{\displaystyle COCl}{}}} + R'NHCSNHR'' \longrightarrow \quad {\overset{\displaystyle R'-N-\!\!\!=\!\!\!NR''}{\underset{\displaystyle R-N-\!\!\!/}{O=\!\!\!<\quad S}}}$$

Mode of Action

The effects of the formamidines on the behaviour of insects and mites is of greater significance for control in the field than direct lethal action. The amidines appear not to have any direct ovicidal effects as embryonic development continues normally after exposure. Direct lethal effects occur only as the larvae emerge from the egg and consume chemical absorbed on the chorion. As the larvae grow they become increasingly insensitive to direct lethal action and the adult stages are generally not affected.

However, complex effects on behaviour occur at every stage of development and can cause the insect or mite to die. These effects result from increased excitability and locomotor activity. They include deterrence of feeding in larvae, probably as a result of production of tremors in the mouthparts, and dispersal from the feeding sites. In adults they include disruption of mating and oviposition and often continuous attempts to fly which result in shredding of wings and death from exhaustion. The number of eggs laid is greatly diminished, they are deposited at random and most are not viable. These behavioural effects are induced at very much lower doses than are direct lethal effects. For example, the dose needed to produce effects on behaviour in the adult cockroach is 0.5 mg/kg, whereas the lethal dose is 700 mg/kg.

Biochemically there appear to be two modes of action. One is to affect the membrane ion channels and cause repetitive discharges of nervous activity followed, at higher doses, by an anaesthetic-like action. The second mode of action, which appears to be of much greater importance, involves agonistic activity at octopamine-sensitive nerve junctions as a result of blocking of the octopamine receptors. In invertebrates, the function which the catechol amines perform as neurotransmitters in the adrenergic systems of vertebrates, is carried out by octopamine.

$$\text{HO}\underset{\text{HO}}{\bigcirc}\text{CHOHCH}_2\text{NHCH}_3 \qquad \text{HO}\bigcirc\text{CHOHCH}_2\text{NH}_2$$

Epinephrine   Octopamine

In vertebrates and invertebrates these amines have a very wide range of effects on the central nervous system. The binding of formamidines to octopamine receptors has been demonstrated *in vitro*. The structural requirements for *in vivo* activity correlate closely with those for octopamine agonists in isolated octopamine-sensitive adenylate cyclase systems. The evidence suggests that the active metabolites at the site of action are those produced by removal of one methyl group from the dimethylamino group.

Investigation of octopamine agonists may prove as fruitful a source of new insecticides as anticholinesterases have been. The development of the amidines suggests that there may be other chemically mediated systems in insects which might be targets for chemical inhibition, for example, those mediated by γ-aminobutyric acid (GABA).

Further Reading

Corbett, J. R. *The Biochemical Mode of Action of Pesticides*, Academic Press, London and New York, 1974.

Eto, M. *Organophosphorus Pesticides: Organic and Biological Chemistry*, CRC Press, Cleveland, Ohio, 1974.

Heath, D. F. *Organophosphorus Poisons*. Pergamon Press, Oxford, 1961.

O'Brien, R. D. *Insecticides, Action and Metabolism*, Academic Press, London and New York, 1967.

O'Brien, R. D. *Toxic Phosphorus Esters*, Academic Press, London and New York, 1960.

Street, J. C. (Ed.) *Pesticide Selectivity*, Marcel Dekker, New York, 1975.

10
Synthetic Insecticides: Pyrethroids

Pyrethrum

In 1851 Koch stated, for what appears to be the first time, that a peasant-produced insecticide, well-known in Persia and the Caucasus, consisted of a mixture of the powdered, dried flowers of *Chrysanthemum roseum* and *C. carneum*. The discovery and early commercial development of powders based on *C. cinerariaefolium* from which a later "Dalmatian powder" was prepared is equally obscure. The term "pyrethrum" is now applied to *cinerariaefolium* since the other pyrethrin-containing plants are not of commercial interest. Serious cultivation of *C. cinerariaefolium* began in 1886 and extended until World War I, when the supply from Europe was cut off and Japan became the principal world source. In about 1927 the growing of pyrethrum was taken up in the highlands of Kenya and later in other parts of Africa. For many years African production has provided the main source of the world's supply.

World production of dried flowers totalled 23,000 tonnes in 1974–5. During the 1970–1974 period Kenya produced about 60% of total world output of pyrethrum, Tanzania 20%, Rwanda 8% and Ecuador 9%. A number of other countries produce pyrethrum in smaller quantities, including Bolivia, Brazil, Hungary, Indonesia, India, Japan, Papua New Guinea, Peru, Zimbabwe, Taiwan, U.S.S.R. and Zaire.

Processing of Flowers

The flowers are harvested and dried in the country of origin and ground in various types of mill depending upon the use for which the product is intended. Nowadays the bulk of the flowers is subjected to an extractive process with an organic solvent of low boiling point in factories located close to the flower-growing areas. The active insecticides — the pyrethrins — are soluble in a wide range of organic solvents such as ethylene dichloride and petroleum fractions. After removing the solvent these extracts are dark green in colour and are used in the preparation of synergized mixtures and other formulated products. Considerable quantities are subjected to further treatment with selective solvents or to molecular distillation to give pale-coloured extracts. In some cases a solution of the extract in the synergist piperonyl butoxide is subjected to vacuum distillation.

Extraction and refining plants for pyrethrum now exist in Kenya, Tanzania, Ecuador and Rwanda. Some 80% (in value terms) of pyrethrum exported by the principal world producers is in extract form. Most of this output is exported to industrialized countries; the main markets are the U.S.A., U.K., Italy and Australia (taking some 60% of world output).

Uses

The pyrethrins rapidly lose activity in the presence of oxygen and light but despite this weakness, the use of pyrethrum, unlike that of derris and nicotine, has grown with the increase in the use of synthetic chemicals. The pyrethrins owe their importance to their outstandingly rapid knock-down action and to their very low mammalian toxicity, which is largely due to the ease with which they are metabolized into non-toxic products. Today the main use of natural pyrethrins is as constituents of the increasingly popular convenience canisters liberating aerosol sprays for indoor use against flies and mosquitoes where these advantages are most important. Exploitation in the field had to await the development of synthetic analogues described below.

The majority of the formulators are located outside the countries producing pyrethrum. In only a few cases have developing countries themselves begun producing insecticide formulations. Kenya is the principal example in producing both coil and aerosol insecticides based on pyrethrum and also exporting some ready-made formulations to a number of countries.

Structure of the active principles

The structures of the active esters of pyrethrum flowers are shown below

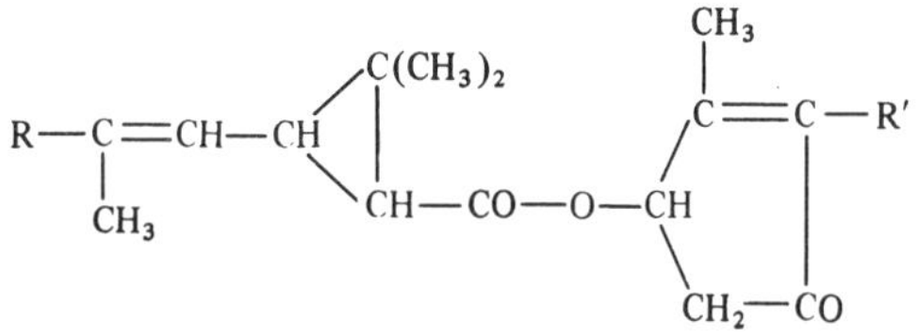

$$R-C=CH-CH \underset{\displaystyle CH-CO-O-CH}{\overset{\displaystyle C(CH_3)_2}{\big|}} \qquad \overset{\displaystyle CH_3}{\underset{\displaystyle CH_2-CO}{\big|}} C=C-R'$$

For pyrethrin I	$R = CH_3$; $R' = CH_2.CH:CH.CH:CH_2$
For pyrethrin II	$R = COOCH_3$; $R' = CH_2.CH:CH.CH:CH_2$
For cinerin I	$R = CH_3$; $R' = CH_2.CH:CH.CH_3$
For cinerin II	$R = COOCH_3$; $R' = CH_2.CH:CH.CH_3$
For jasmolin I	$R = CH_3$; $R' = CH_2.CH=CH.CH_2.CH_3$
For jasmolin II	$R = COOCH_3$; $R' = CH_2.CH=CH.CH_2.CH_3$

and the composition of the active principles of a typical extract of pyrethrum is pyrethrin I 35%, pyrethrin II 32%, cinerin I 10%, cinerin II 14%, jasmolin I 5% and jasmolin II 4%.

The pyrethrum extracts of commerce contain 25% of the active principles.

Pyrethrum synergists

An examination of the constituents of sesame oil, which had been shown to increase the activity of pyrethrum, led to the development of a number of compounds containing the methylene-dioxyphenyl group as synergists. The most widely used synergist for the pyrethrins is an ether of propylpiperonyl alcohol always known by the pseudo systematic name of piperonyl butoxide.

Synthetic pyrethroids

Pyrethrin I is the most important natural constituent lethal to insects while pyrethrin II provides much of the rapid knock-down effect. The jasmolins are lower in activity than the four main insecticidal constituents. The insecticidal activity of pyrethrin I is thought to depend upon the overall structure of the ester; in particular on methyl groups at C-2 on the cyclopropane ring maintained in a definite stereochemical disposition with respect to an unsaturated side chain at C-3 and the ester link at C-1. Without steric constraint, the ester probably takes an S-trans conformation and, supported by the near planar cyclopentenolone ring, the *cis*-pentadienyl side chain can adopt only certain orientations with respect to the features of the acid structure mentioned above. High insecticidal potency is probably related to the ability of the molecule to adopt at the site of action an appropriate shape or conformation which will be influenced by the absolute configurations of the asymmetric centres at C-1 of the cyclopropane ring and at C-4 of the cyclopentenone ring. In pyrethrin I, these configurations are respectively [R] and [S] and inverting either diminishes or eliminates insecticidal activity.

The definition of a pyrethroid is less straightforward than with other chemical classes of insecticides, but the term can be applied to the group of synthetic compounds and naturally occurring pyrethroids which display similar stereochemical configurations with different chemical groupings on a common molecular framework. Almost all active pyrethroids are esters. The constituent acids and alcohols and simple derivatives of them are practically inactive insecticidally and it can reasonably be concluded that the potency is related to the overall shape of the molecule. For high insecticidal activity at least two centres in the molecule must possess appropriate chirality, viz in chrysanthemates the configuration at C-1 must be [R], in the 3-methyl-butyrates it must be the sterically equivalent [S], while in alcohols the configuration must be [S] at C-4 in cyclopentenolones and [S] at C-α in α-cyano-3-phenoxybenzyl alcohol.

A substantial extension of the class of synthetic pyrethroids came when it was found that the dimethyl cyclopropane ring, long thought to be essential for insecticidal activity, could be replaced by 3-methylbutyrate in which a dimethyl group and a carboxylic acid group are held in more or less the same spatial and steric relationship. These matters are discussed in greater detail in the review papers by Elliott and others and the volume on synthetic pyrethroids by Naumann which are listed at the end of this chapter.

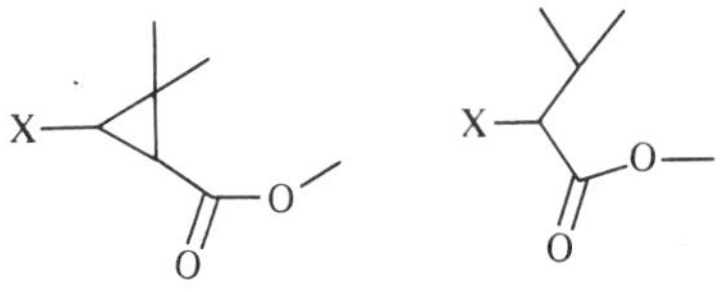

X - substituted
dimethylcyclopropane
carboxylic acid ester

X - substituted
3 - methylbutyric
acid ester

In 1949 LaForge and Schechter announced the synthesis of allethrin which has R=CH$_3$ and R^1=CH$_2$−CH=CH$_2$, that is, cinerin I with the 2-butenyl group replaced by allyl. The structure of allethrin permits geometrical isomerism about the cyclopropane ring and each geometrical isomer has optical isomers. In allethrin all the isomers were present but allethrolone, the alcoholic component, is now resolved on a commercial scale. The (+)-form esterified with synthetic (±)-*trans* chrysanthemic acid gives bioallethrin and esterified with the (+)-*trans* acid, S-bioallethrin. The latter corresponds to pyrethrin I in stereochemical form and displays an outstandingly rapid knock-down action against some species of insects. Allethrin is less effective than the pyrethrins against a variety of insects and when synergized the disparity in toxicity between allethrin and the pyrethrins becomes even more marked. Because of its volatility and thermal stability much allethrin is used in mosquito coils.

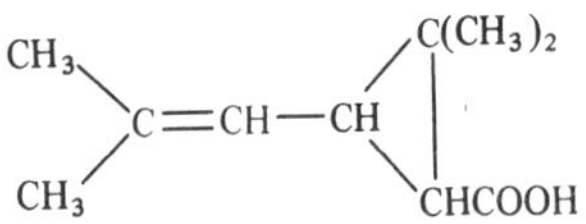

Chrysanthemic acid

Tetramethrin, reported in 1964, was the next synthetic pyrethroid to be produced commercially. The alcoholic component differs from that in other synthetic pyrethroids and, although tetramethrin knocks down insects rapidly, it is not generally a good lethal agent.

In 1966 esters of 5-benzylfuryl-3-methanol were shown by Elliott and co-workers to possess properties superior to those of the natural esters containing pyrethrolone as the alcoholic component. The furylmethyl esters were low in mammalian toxicity and warranted commercial production of resmethrin and bioresmethrin. The latter prepared from (+)-*trans* chrysanthemic acid had especially high insecticidal activity and very low mammalian toxicity. Other pyrethroids derived from furan alcohols include K-othrin, kadethrin, proparthrin and prothrin.

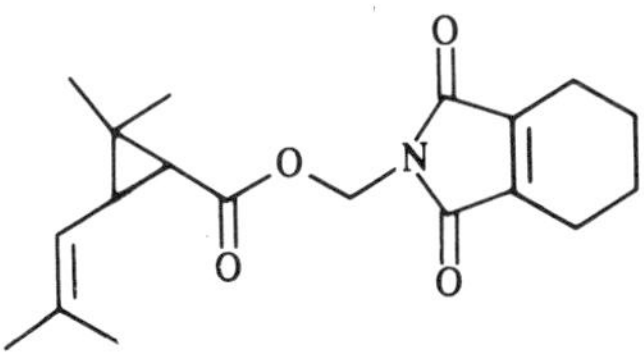

Tetramethrin

The pyrethroid K-othrin has an even greater toxicity against some insect species than bioresmethrin but the mammalian toxicity is also higher. Kadethrin knocks down houseflies more rapidly than any other compound yet reported. Proparthrin and prothrin have found a use in Japan as

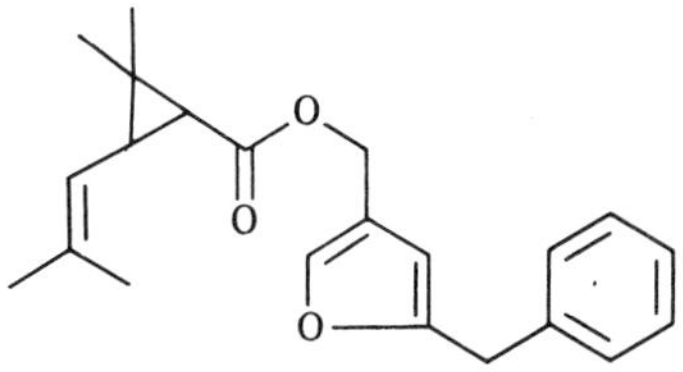

Bioresmethrin

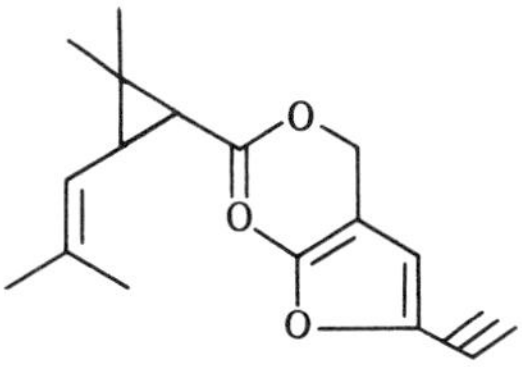

Proparthrin

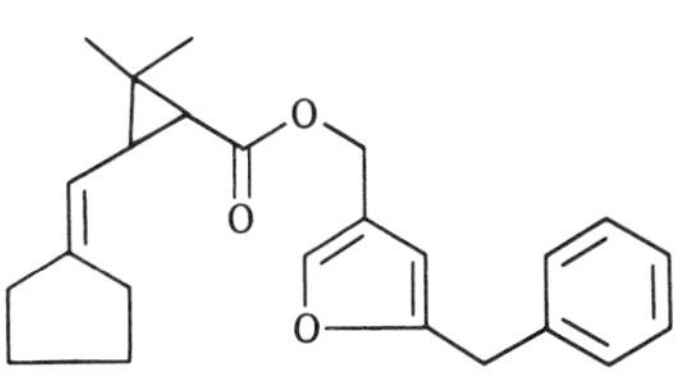

K - othrin

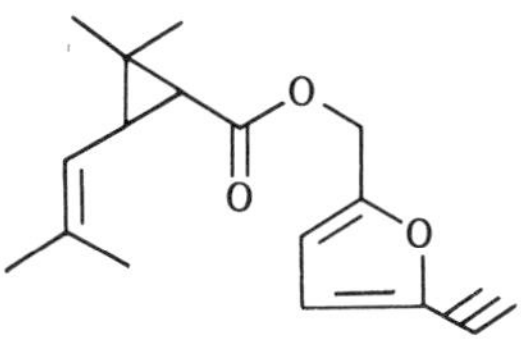

Prothrin

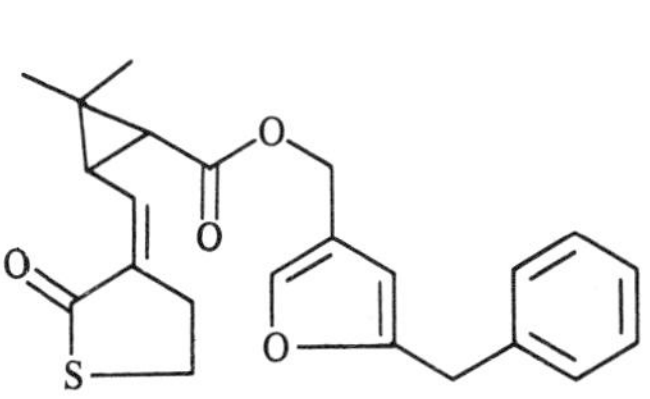

Kadethrin

constituents of aerosol sprays.

Workers in Japan and Great Britain next discovered, independently, that the 5-benzylfuryl-3-methanol could be replaced by 3-phenoxybenzyl alcohol, thus providing more accessible and less expensive esters such as phenothrin.

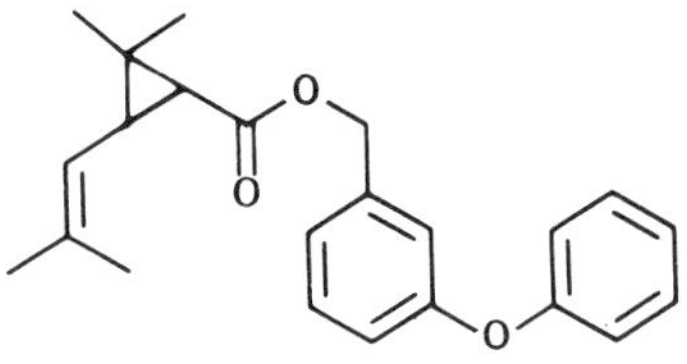

Phenothrin

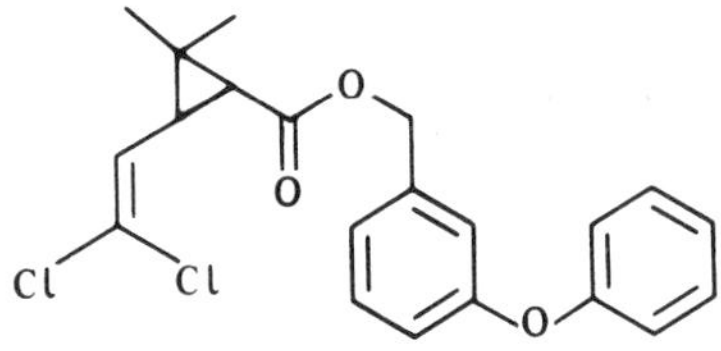

Permethrin

The synthetic pyrethroids mentioned so far failed to extend the range of

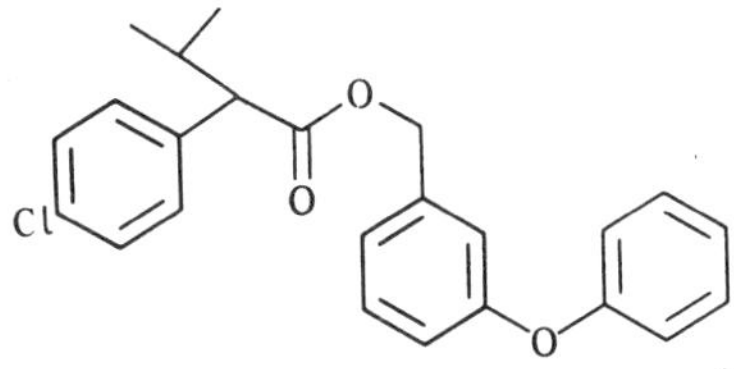

S - 5439

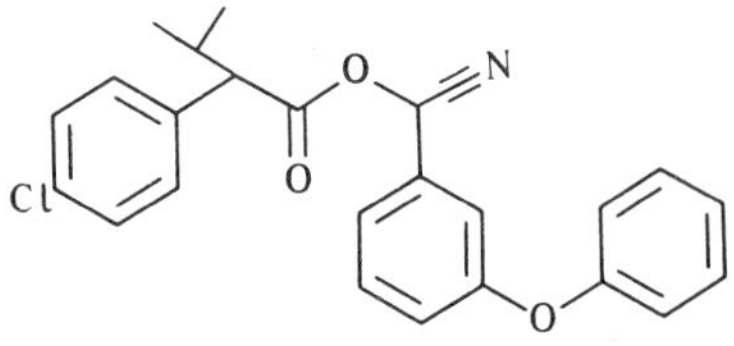

Fenvalerate

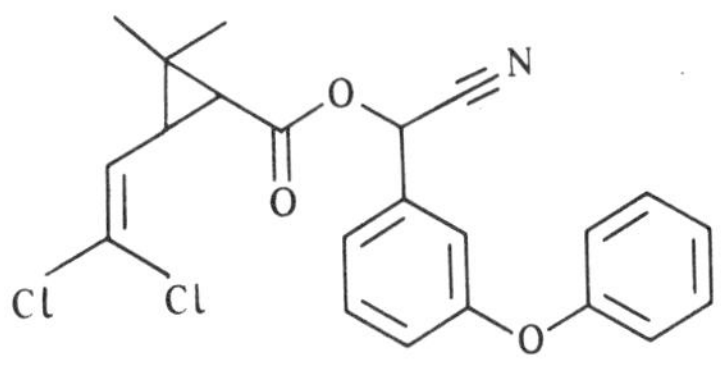

Cypermethrin

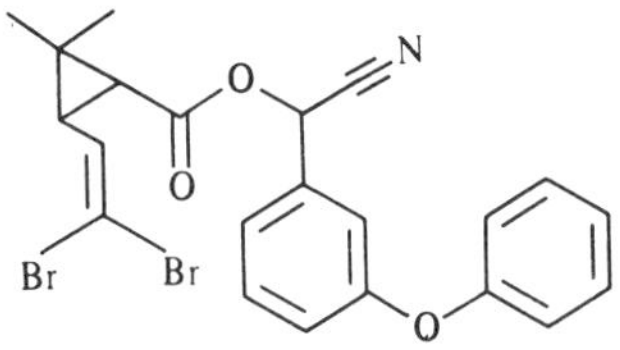

Deltamethrin

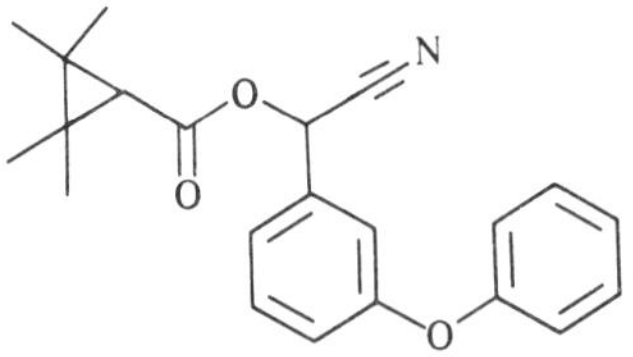

Fenpropathrin

application established over many years for natural pyrethrum, because they were all unstable to light and air. At Rothamsted Experimental Station in 1972 an exceptionally valuable combination of properties was found in the esters (of which permethrin is an example) of 3-phenoxybenzyl alcohol with *cis*- and *trans*-dichlorovinyl analogues of chrysanthemic acid having chlorine atoms in place of the methyl groups in the isobutenyl side chain. Not only was permethrin active against a number of insect species but it was very much more stable in oxygen and light than the other pyrethroids and exerted a prolonged residual action. This opened up for the first time the possibility of using synthetic pyrethroids for control of pests of plants and animals in the field. As the speed of knockdown of insects is less than that of the natural pyrethrins, permethrin exerts both contact and stomach action.

The further important discovery that the cyclopropane ring could be replaced by an open chain came from Japan in 1974 when Ohno and co-workers showed that highly active esters (e.g. S-5439) could be obtained when various 2-aryl-3-methylbutyric acids replaced chrysanthemic acid. Further increase of insecticidal potency was generally obtained by substituting an α-cyano group into 3-phenoxybenzyl esters (e.g. fenvalerate). In the chrysanthemic series, esters, such as fenpropathrin, derived from α-cyano-3-phenoxybenzyl alcohol, were two to three times more active than those from 3-phenoxybenzyl alcohol. The dichlorovinylcyclopropane ester (cypermethrin) is of particular interest.

The ester formed between (±)-α-cyano-3-phenoxybenzyl alcohol and (IR, *cis*)-3-(2,2-dibromovinyl)-2,2-dimethylcyclopropane carboxylic acid gave an active compound from which a single isomer deltamethrin was separated. This crystalline compound reported by Elliott in 1974 has an insecticidal activity (on a molar basis) approximately 1700 times that of pyrethrin I to houseflies. It is (S)-α-cyano-3-phenoxylbenzyl (IR,3R)-3-(2,2-dibromo-vinyl)-2,2-dimethylcyclopropane carboxylate.

Related compounds such as the dichloro- and trifluoro-methyl analogues (cypermethrin and cyhalothrin respectively) share the unprecedented insecticidal potency of deltamethrin for which field application rates of 7 to 10 g/ha are feasible. Vivithrin is a similar compound with one of the phenyl rings in the phenoxybenzyl alcohol replaced by a pyridine ring. Cyfluthrin has a fluorine atom in one phenyl ring of the phenoxybenzyl alcohol. Fenfluthrin has pentafluorobenzyl alcohol instead of phenoxybenzyl. Compounds of high activity can also be obtained by replacing one of the fluorine atoms with a number of substituents. Another new compound, phencyclate, has two chlorine atoms in place of the two methyl groups in the cyclopropane ring. This is an interesting compound because, unlike other pyrethroids, its toxicity to fish is very low. It is claimed that the compound has repellent and anti-feeding activity as well as contact toxicity. NCI 85193 has a substituted phenyl group in place of the dichloroethenyl group in cypermethrin and is

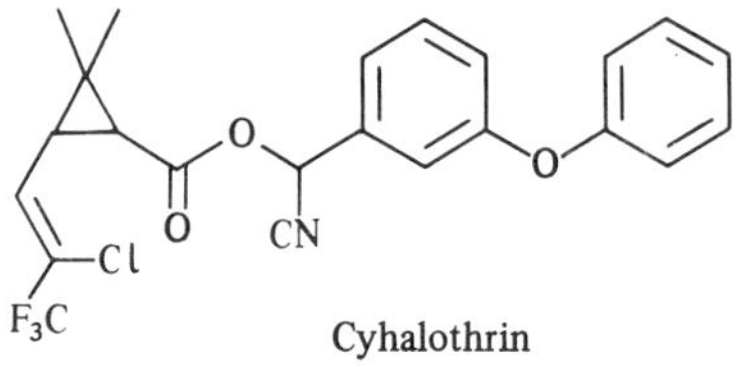

Cyhalothrin

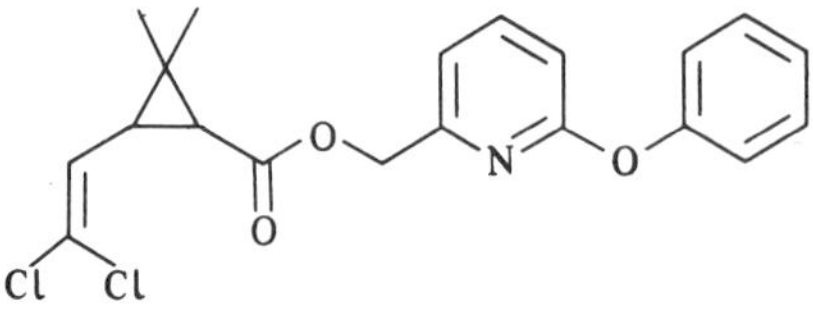

Vivithrin

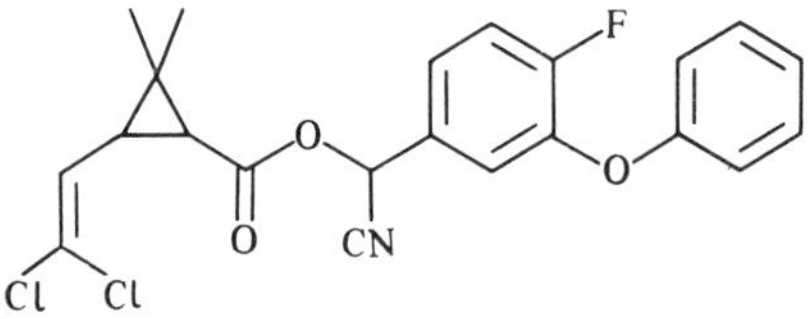

Cyfluthrin

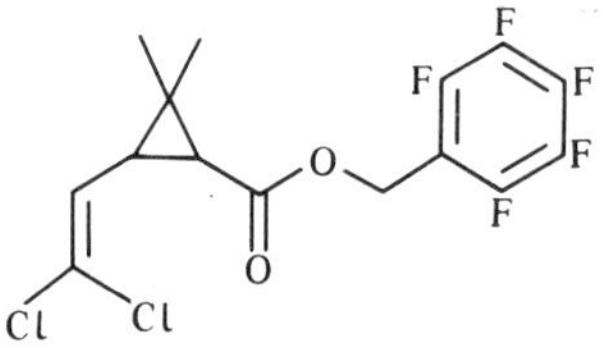

Fenfluthrin

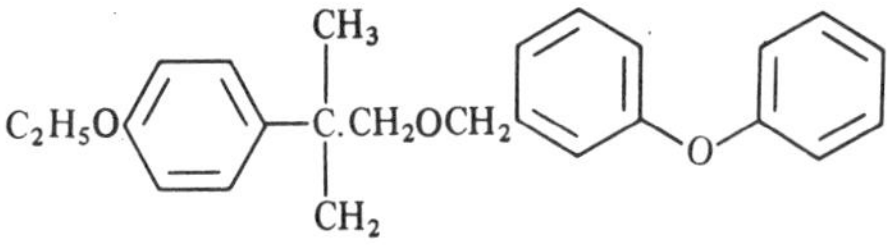

Ethofenprox

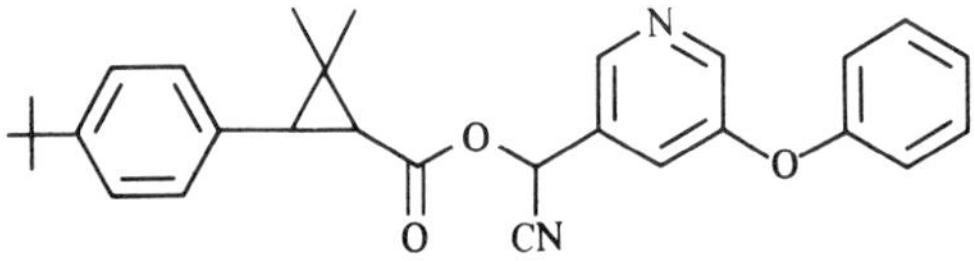

NCI 85193

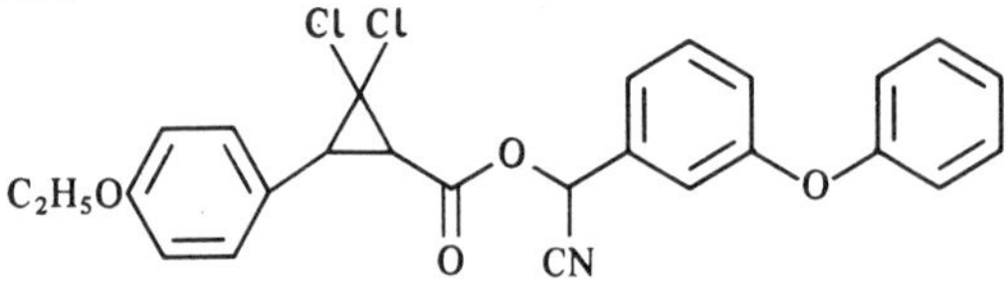

Phencyclate

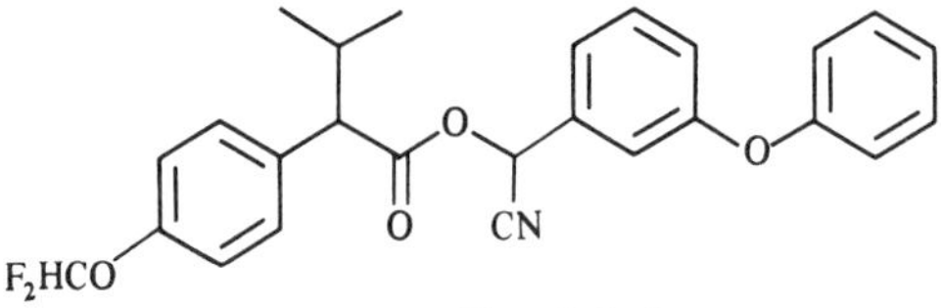

Flucythrinate

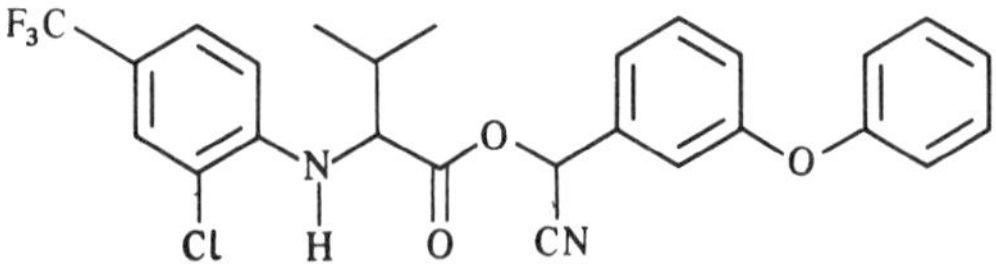

Fluvalinate

interesting because, unlike other pyrethroids it has high activity against mites such as tetranychus and panonychus. The 4-*tert.*-butylphenyl compound is the most active in the series. It has been reported that analogues of fenpropathrin in which two of the methyl groups are replaced by other alkyl groups are more active than the parent compound.

Developments in the 3-methylbutyrate series include flucythrinate and fluvalinate. The 4-chlorophenyl group in fenvalerate can be replaced by phenylethenyl, 2-indenyl, 2-naphthyl, 2-benzothienyl or 2-benzofuranyl groups and still retain insecticidal activity.

An interesting new development in the synthetic pyrethroids is discovery of high insecticidal activity in ethofenprox. It controls a wide range of insect larva and has low toxicity to fish. Although the structure is reminiscent of the methylbutyrates it is quite significantly different which suggests that there may be many related structures with pyrethroid-like activity.

The compounds at present in commercial use are cypermethrin, delta-methrin, cyfluthrin, fenvalerate and flucythrinate, shortly to be joined by cyhalothrin, vivithrin, and fluvalinate.

Pyrethroids are not easy compounds to synthesize as there are not many efficient methods of building up the dimethylcyclopropane carboxylic acid that forms half the molecule. The most commonly used route is condensation of a diene with ethyl diazoacetate.

The dienes are most conveniently prepared on a manufacturing scale by reaction of isobutene with a halogenated alkene in the vapour phase over a catalyst or, under milder conditions, in presence of a copper catalyst. By varying the substituents on the halogenated alkene a wide range of dienes can be produced. Ethyldiazoacetate is not nearly as toxic or volatile as diazomethane and it is not explosive so it does not present insuperable manufacturing problems.

The dimethylcyclopropane carboxylic acids thus prepared can be esterified with a wide range of hydroxy compounds, most usually in the more recent commercial pyrethroids, 3-phenoxybenzyl alcohol or its α-cyano derivative. The 3-phenoxybenzyl alcohol is manufactured by oxidation of the methyldiphenylether obtained by catalytic dehydrogenative coupling of 3-methylphenol with benzene in the vapour phase.

The "open chain" pyrethroids which do not contain a cyclopropane ring, such as fenvalerate, are manufactured by building up the required carboxylic acid by standard synthetic procedures and condensing this with the benzyl alcohol.

The synthetic pyrethroids are very expensive to prepare on a tonnage basis compared with, for example, DDT. But, as they are used at only 50 g/ha, the cost of treatment per hectare is low. They represent a tendency, which will become even more evident in the future, for the search for new pesticides to be directed towards complex molecules which, although expensive to manufacture, are cheap to use because of their very high activities. The new generation of synthetic pyrethroids, now in development in the major agrochemical companies, will have application rates as low as 5 g/hectare.

Insecticidal properties and applications of synthetic pyrethroids

The high insecticidal activity and low mammalian toxicity of pyrethroids are especially significant now that compounds stable to light and oxygen are potentially available. Lepidoptera, especially the larval stages, are serious economic pests of crops such as cotton, maize, tobacco, rice, sugar beet and cane sugar. The natural pyrethrins are effective against lepidopterous larvae but, in the past, instability has precluded their use in the field. The recently synthesized pyrethroids are also very potent and the stability of some of them has opened up large scale use in crop protection. This illustrates how just one particular property, in this case stability to air and light, can make the difference between a very limited commercial utility and a major world-wide use in horticulture and agriculture.

The synthetic pyrethroids have very low toxicities to mammals and to birds but their toxicity to fish is rather high and creates a need for caution in application near watercourses, rivers and lakes. They are rapidly degraded in soil and have no detectable ill-effects on soil microflora and microfauna. As their insecticidal activity is not specific they are likely to prove hazardous to bees and to other beneficial insects so care has to be taken in the way they are used. They are also not active against mites so the problems of resurgence of mites which arises with DDT has to be guarded against. There is some evidence that resistant species of insects may develop when they are used on a large scale under field conditions.

The major symptoms of pyrethroid poisoning in insects can be accounted for by effects on the kinetics of nerve membrane sodium channels. The mean open times of these channels are prolonged with consequent hyperactivity of nerves. The differences between various compounds in knockdown and killing effects may result from differences in penetration and transport to the sites of action or in the transmission of information from the peripheral to the central nervous system. Although the molecular mode of action is known there is much to be discovered about the total effects.

The synthetic pyrethroids have been found to be exceptionally useful as early season sprays to control the variety of insects that occur on cotton including bollworms, leafworms, jassids, thrips, stainers and whitefly. They are generally used in combination with an organophosphorus insecticide as an ultra-low volume spray. The products currently used commercially in the Sudan, for example, include cypermethrin, deltamethrin, cyfluthrin, flucy-thrinate and fenvalerate. Their great virtue is that they are non-toxic to humans and animals (the average oral LD50 to rats is around 8,000 mg/kg) and they do not significantly upset the ecological balance of pests, predators and parasites. The widespread use of DDT and organochlorine insecticides on cotton in the 1950s and 1960s has led to the eruption of secondary pests, which were resistant to this class of insecticides, into major problems because their predators were killed off. Examples of such "man-made" problems in cotton are the current prevalence of mites in California and of whitefly in the Sudan. The pyrethroids also have the advantage of being cheap in terms of cost per hectare because they are so active and are applied at rates of around 50 grams/hectare. Over 2,000 tonnes were used in the U.S.A. in 1982, mainly on cotton.

An unexpected advantage is that they appear to produce higher yields of cotton than when organophosphorus insecticides are used. There is also some evidence that pyrethroids may suppress plant diseases caused by viruses transmitted by aphids.

There is some danger that resistance to synthetic pyrethroids may occur. This can be avoided by "rotating" the various pyrethroids from year to year and, if necessary, every fourth or fifth year suspending use of pyrethroids and using only organophosphates for control, possibly together with endosulfan.

Where important pests are not resistant to any group of insecticides, maintenance of this state is of vital importance. Most insect populations are at present susceptible to the synthetic pyrethroids, which should therefore in general not be used prophylatically but only in response to developing infestations. This is particularly important with the newer, more stable pyrethroids, unnecessary applications of which could select resistant strains of insects from populations that develop immunity readily (houseflies), emulating the damaging induction of kdr (nerve insensitivity) resistance mechanisms to pyrethroids.

Synthetic pyrethroids are also being used commercially on grape vines, soft fruits and stone fruits, citrus, coffee, tea, cocoa, hops, bananas, root and leaf vegetables of all kinds, tobacco, and ornamental plants.

Total end-user sales for the photostable pyrethroids have been estimated to be $350 millions for 1980 — an increase of 42% over the 1979 value. Pyrethroids captured 9% of the insecticide market in 1980, with the United States accounting for 20% of this amount. Pyrethroids had increased their share of the total insecticide market to 20% by 1986.

This extremely versatile class of compounds — the most potent insecticides yet discovered — is only in its infancy and the discovery of many more active compounds with various ranges of uses can be expected. The development of the agriculturally useful synthetic pyrethroids is an instructive example of the value of research over a long period. The work was started at Rothamsted in 1941 in response to a request from the British Government for a synthetic alternative to natural pyrethrum, supplies of which had been cut off by the war. At that time DDT was not known and there was need to control lice amongst the troops. Although active compounds were discovered it was not until 1972 that a pyrethroid suitable for use in agriculture was discovered. For 30 years Michael Elliott had worked in this field. This was only possible in an independent research station since no industrial firm would have allowed a research programme to go on for this length of time. It is also instructive that introduction of one single property into the molecule — photostability — turned the synthetic pyrethroids from a small-scale indoor use to a \$350 million market which is still growing. On such small factors does commercial success or failure depend.

Further Reading

Casida, J. E. (Ed) *Pyrethrum: The Natural Insecticide*, Academic Press, London, 1973.

Crosby, Guy A. Recent developments in pyrethroid insecticides, *Chemical Times and Trends*, October 1981.

Elliott, M. Properties and applications of pyrethroids. In *Environmental Health Perspectives*, March 1976.

Elliott, M. Future use of natural and synthetic pyrethroids. In *The Future for Insecticides: Needs and Prospects*, eds. R. L. Metcalf and J. J. McKelvey Jr., John Wiley & Sons Inc., 1976.

Elliott, M. (Ed.) *Synthetic Pyrethroids*, ACS Symposium Series No. 42, Washington D.C., 1977.

Elliott, M. Established pyrethroid insecticides, *Pesticide Science*, **11**, 119, 1980.

Elliott, M. The future for insecticides. In *Insect Biology in the Future*. Academic Press, London, 1980.

Elliott, M. and Janes, N. F. Synthetic pyrethroids — a new class of insecticide, *Chemical Society Review*, 7, 473, 1978.

Elliott, M. and Janes, N. F. Recent structure-activity correlations in synthetic pyrethroids. In *Advances in Pesticide Science*, Part II, ed. H. Geissbühler, Pergamon Press, Oxford, 1979.

Elliott, M. Janes, N. F. and Potte., C. The future of pyrethroids in insect control, *Ann. Rev. Entomol.* **23**, 443, 1978.

Fowden, L. and Graham-Bryce, I. J. (Eds.) *Crop Protection Chemicals: Directions of Future Development*, Royal Society, London, 1981.

Naumann, K. Chemie der Pflanzenschulz-und Schädlings-bekämpfungsmittel, Band 7. *Chemie der Synthetischen Pyrethroid-Insektizide*, Springer-Verlag, Berlin, 1981.

Pesticide Science, June 1976.

Pyrethrum Post, **14** (4), 103, 1978.

United States Department of Agriculture, *Insecticides from Plants*, USDA Handbook, No. 154, Washington D.C., 1954.

11

Other Insecticides

During the past 20 years the search for new insecticides has been concentrated on the objectives of reduced toxicity to mammals and development of analogues of naturally occurring defensive chemicals. These objectives are not necessarily related, but are usually assumed to be by opponents of synthetic pesticide usage. The first important success we describe came in fact from chemical studies of a natural poison which blocks nervous transmission yet, surprisingly, is much more toxic to insects than to mammals.

It had long been known in Japan that insects which fed on the bodies of a species of annelid much used as a fish bait were rapidly killed. The active principle, nereisotoxin, was isolated and identified in 1960. Synthetic compounds having common features in the molecule, bensultap and cartap were developed as commercial insecticides for use particularly against Colorado beetle but active against many insects at less than 500 g/ha. A dithiane compound, formed by reaction of bensultap with malonic ester, is also insecticidal as is the trithiane, thiocyclam.

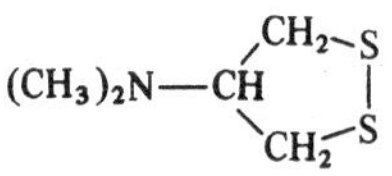

Nereisotoxin

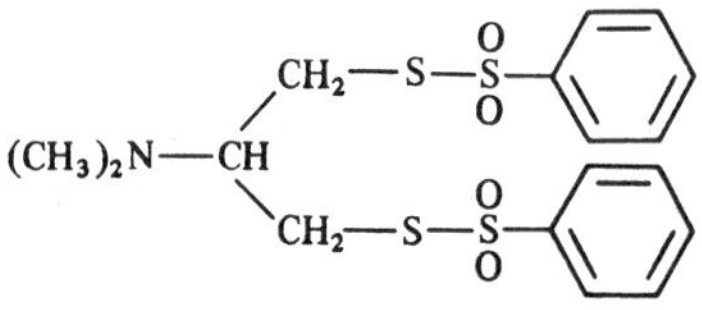

Bensultap

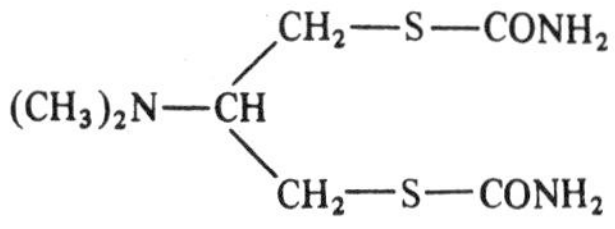

Cartap

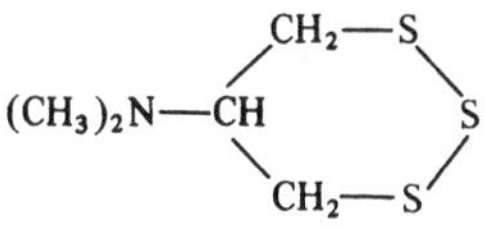

Thiocyclam

The physiological action of synthetic compounds is similar to that of the natural toxin. The molecules all have 1,3-disubstitution of 2-dimethylamino propane. It is probable that closure to a 5 or 6 membered ring may occur *in vivo* when bensultap or cartap is applied. The dimethylamino group confers ionic solubility in acid solution in which the compounds are stable, but hydrolyzed under alkaline conditions. Cartap is available as the solid hydrochloride and thiocyclam as the hydrogenoxalate. These insecticides have significant systemic action and are effective against stem borers.

Another natural insecticide, azidirachtin, contained in the Neem tree and chinaberry in India, has been isolated and its structure elucidated. Its empirical formula $C_{37}H_{48}O_{13}$ is built up of 1 7-membered, 3 6-membered and 2 5-membered rings which can be represented in planar form but with two rings bridged. Four of the O atoms are ring members but there is only one double bond. Three carboxyl groups are attached, two esterified with methyl and one with the enol form of butanone. Two hydroxy and one acetyloxy groups are attached. Simpler synthetic compounds related to this complex structure are being sought. The natural extract is strongly repellent and larvae which do consume the compound despite this repellency have both moulting and growth delayed and eventually die.

Another remarkable compound has been isolated and characterized by Japanese workers from another Indian plant species. Called treviasine, it is a macrocycle having a main ring of 18 C atoms and 1 N. It was known for exceptional tumour-inhibiting action and is associated with related compounds, tenudine and N-methyltenudone having the eight-membered side chain of treviasine bridged across four atoms of the main ring to form a second macro ring of 12 atoms. The compounds are very strongly toxic and antifeedant. They have no commercial use at present but exemplify the sort of molecular complexity which may be developed now the research on pyrethroids has shown that compounds effective at a few g/ha can justify high production costs.

Moulting Hormones

Organophosphates, as has been said, act on an enzyme system common to both animals and insects. Much thought has been given to the differences in physiology and biochemistry between animals and insects and to ways in which these differences might be exploited for selective control of insect pests.

Arthropods have no internal skeleton. Their shape is maintained by a horny outer casing incapable of continued growth. Characteristically, at regular intervals, they produce a new soft integument inside the old one, which is then split and discarded. The new integument hardens after expansion. These moulting operations separate each stage of development (instar) from the next. Although successive instars may differ mainly in size, sometimes a considerable change of structure is involved. Such change of structure (metamorphosis) is particularly significant in insects where only the final instar is sexually mature. In the lepidoptera (butterflies and moths) there are four instars of the larval (caterpillar) form followed by an immobile non-feeding fifth instar (pupa) during which the final winged insect is formed.

This type of development and metamorphosis has no counterpart in vertebrate animals and is controlled by two hormones which are specific to insects. One, the so-called "moulting hormone" (MH) controls the process of development of a new integument and shedding of the old at each instar which takes place without change of structure. The other, the so-called "juvenile hormone" (JH) controls the process of metamorphosis. The chemical structures of both have been determined. MH is a steroid, ecdysone,and JH is methyl *trans, trans, cis*-10-epoxy-7-ethyl-3,11-dimethyl-2,6-tridecadienoate, although there may be minor variations in structure between different species.

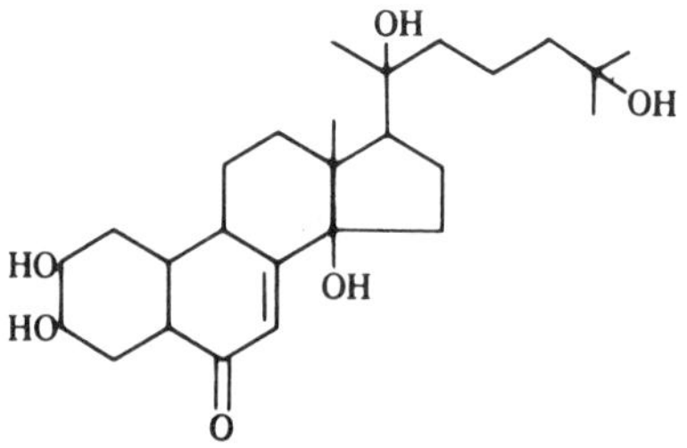

Moulting Hormone (MH)

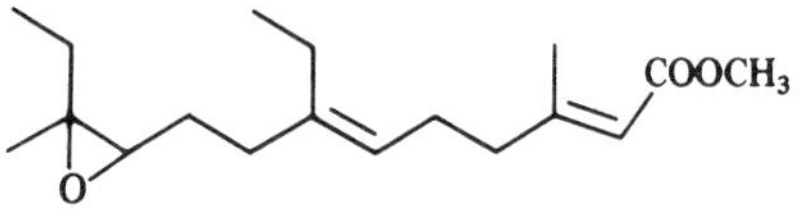

Juvenile Hormone (JH)

Experimental studies indicated that insects die or become sterile if one or other of these hormones is in excess at the wrong time. The possibility of using them, or, preferably, cheaper synthetic analogues, to control insect pests was apparent. A substantial number of compounds have, in fact, been discovered which have MH or JH activity. In the case of MH these are mainly steroid substances extracted from various plants, especially ecdyster-one which is ecdysone with an OH group in position 20. Some steroids with MH activity have been synthesised from the readily available starting materials ergosterol and stigmasterol.

A considerable number of long chain unsaturated aliphatic compounds have been found to possess JH activity. The most easily accessible are those based on farnesol. The natural hormone is, in fact, essentially the epoxide of farnesol but with two methyl groups replaced by two ethyl groups.

Farnesol

One of the problems of using MH or JH or their "mimics" for insect control is that the compounds apparently cannot pass through the cuticle and are therefore not active when applied externally. This has, so far, proved a complete stumbling block in the case of MH mimics but some JH mimics have been discovered which are active by topical application and some of these are now being produced commercially, namely hydroprene, kinoprene, triprene and methoprene.

$(CH_3)_2CH(CH_2)_2CH_2CH(CH_3)CH_2CH{=}CHC(CH_3){=}CHCOOC_2H_5$ Hydroprene

$(CH_3)_2CH(CH_2)_3CH(CH_3)CH_2CH{=}CHC(CH_3){=}CHC))CH_2C{\equiv}CH$ Kinoprene

$(CH_3)_2C(OCH_3)(CH_2)\ CH(CH_3)CH_2CH{=}CHC(CH_3){=}CHCOSC_2H_5$ Triprene

$(CH_3)_2C(OCH_3)(CH_2)\ CH(CH_3)CH_2CH{=}CHC(CH_3){=}CHCOOCH(CH_3)_2$ Methoprene

It has been found that synthetic mimics, in which part of the natural hormone is altered, are far more effective in disrupting insect growth and development than is an overdose of the natural hormone. One problem with their commercial development is that the compounds are difficult to synthesize and consequently expensive, although, if they were active enough, they might be cost-effective. Another disadvantage of JH is that its application retains the insect in the larval stage, which is often the one which does most damage to crops so, if it does not die rapidly, losses will continue. Hormones may, therefore, be most suitable for control of insects which are most damaging in their adult state and in which the larvae are exposed rather than hidden. Moreover, application of hormones has to be carefully timed and can be effective only when the development of the insect pest is synchronous across the whole of the area to be treated, i.e. that all insects in the area reach the same stage of development at the same time. The hormone mimics appear to be very non-toxic to men and animals and also have little potential for environmental damage but there is no assurance that they would be specific and not harm beneficial insects. It has been argued that resistance is unlikely to develop because the compounds used are analogues of natural hormones but there is no theoretical reason to believe that this is so and some cross-resistance to JH mimics has already been observed in some insects resistant to certain conventional insecticides.

Inhibitors of Chitin Synthesis

Another point of difference between animals and insects is that insects have to form a new integument at each moult and, to do this, they have to synthesize chitin, a glucosamine polysaccharide, which is the main component of their horny shells. Some synthetic compounds have been discovered which inhibit chitin synthesis and deposition and leave the larvae with a fragile, malformed shell which easily ruptures and causes death.

The most promising compounds so far are N-(4-chlorophenylamino-carbonyl)-2,6-dichlorobenzamide and the corresponding 2,6-difluoro compound, now commercially available as diflubenzuron. Complete control of gypsy moth larvae has been obtained at the low application rate of 30 g/ha but, in order to be effective by ingestion, the particle size in the formulation must be less than 2 microns. Diflubenzuron has very low mammalian toxicity.

Diflubenzuron

Recently a large number of synthetic compounds with widely varying and unrelated chemical structures have been found to disrupt insect growth to varying degrees. An example of a compound which inhibits pupal growth is shown below, but the precise mode of action of most of these compounds is as yet unknown.

Other Possibilities

A further difference between the metabolism of animals and that of insects which might be exploited for pest control is that insects are incapable of synthesizing steroids, which they require for larval growth and pupation. They have to obtain these from extraneous sources and herbivorous insects can transform plant sterols such as sitosterol and stigmasterol into the cholesterol they need. If compounds could be discovered which would prevent assimilation of these essential steroids from the insect's food they might provide very specific means of insect control. So far no such compounds have been discovered, but there is some indication that this is not beyond the bounds of possibility in the observation that some antibiotics, such as filipin, are known to be insecticidal and are also known to form stable complexes with steroids, which may destroy their biological availability.

One difficulty in the way of recognizing and exploiting differences between animals and insects is that, although much is known about the physiology of most insect species, relatively little is known about their biochemical processes. Whereas most of the hormone and enzyme systems responsible for the major metabolic processes in man have been identified and characterized there is much less detailed knowledge of insect hormone and enzyme systems. Without this knowledge it is difficult to select targets for attack by synthetic chemicals.

The whole subject of the nature and function of amino acids in insect biochemistry and of the enzyme systems associated with them, such as monoamine oxidase, is currently being intensively studied and these studies may suggest methods of approach to new insecticides. Some advances have already been made in this direction and an example of a compound which kills insects by interfering with metabolism of 5-hydroxytryptamine and which may be suitable for insect control in the field, is shown below.

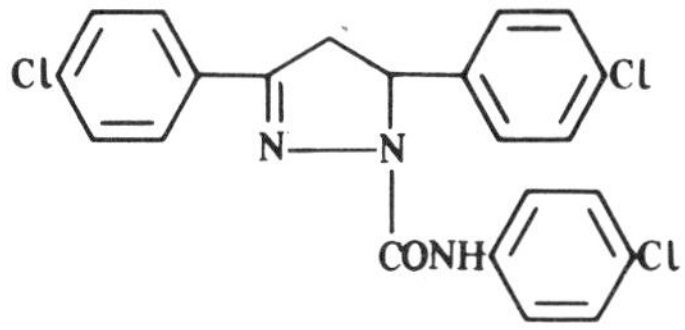

An attractive target for interference by synthetic chemicals is γ-aminobutyric acid (GABA). This is now known to be a major neurotransmitter in insects which acts at inhibitory chemical synapses. One of its main functions is to regulate the opening and closing of chloride channels through cell membranes. The insect GABA system is distinctly different from that of the mammalian central nervous system so there is potential for discovery of compounds with selective toxicities.

With respect to hormones, the insect clearly utilizes a great many more than the moulting hormone and juvenile hormone which have already been identified. Excretion in many insects is controlled by release into the blood of a powerful diuretic hormone. Water conservation is critical for insects because they have a large surface area to volume ratio. Their impermeable cuticles and excretory and respiratory systems are designed to keep water losses to a minimum. If compounds could be discovered which stimulated release of the diuretic hormone or which had diuretic hormone activity their application might lead to death by desiccation. It is interesting to note that pyrethroids cause instantaneous onset of diuresis in insects. Many insects take enormous amounts of food at one time and these appear to secrete a hormone which platicises the abdominal cuticle and allows it to expand to accommodate these giant meals. Application of compounds which stimulated producted of this hormone or which had plasticising hormone activity might lead to death literally by bursting. Such hormone-stimulators or hormone mimics might well be highly specific for the target species and thus environmentally safe.

There is no doubt that compounds which interfere with insect growth or development or which affect biochemical processes peculiar to insects — the so-called "third generation" insecticides — are a potentially very fruitful area for future research and will certainly lead to development of new insecticides with commercial utility, but their development will require a much greater knowledge of insect biochemistry than we have at present, and their effective use a greatly increased understanding of insect ecology and behaviour.

Further reading

American Chemical Society, *Symposium on Natural Pest Control Agents*, Advances in Chemistry Series, No. 53, Washington, D.C., 1966.

Crosby, D. G. *Natural Pest Control Agents*, American Chemical Society, Washington, D.C., 1976.

Nakanashi, K. *Recent Advances in Phytochemistry* **9** 283–297, 1978.

12

Repellents, Attractants and other Behaviour-Controlling Compounds

Repellents and attractants might seem to be compounds evoking directly opposite responses. In fact neither response is simple. Repulsion is the less complex behaviour. It is much more frequently evoked by synthetic compounds and is much less specific than attraction. It is partly for this reason that repellents are already made in large amounts and widely used with good effect, while attractants are still in the development stage. There are, however, two other good reasons for the much more advanced state of repellents.

The most important is that repulsion, if efficient enough, is itself a useful means of pest *control*, which need not be identified with pest *destruction*. If we could stop the mosquito from biting us, the carrot fly from laying eggs near our carrots or the deer from stripping bark from our forest trees, we should have done all we need in our local interest. If the pests are far-ranging, like pigeons or deer, the use of an effective repellent, were one known, could be strategically better than killing, unless killing were carried out over a wide area. A repellent can be useful in itself. An attractant, on the other hand, can serve no direct control purpose unless the pests attracted are killed or sterilized. It must form part of a combined operation. A very useful auxiliary role has been to bait traps for population assessment in order to decide the right time to apply insecticidal sprays with maximum effectiveness and economy and minimum undesired effects.

Another important difference is that a repellent need not be effective over a great distance from its site of application. It would be preferable to drive the mosquitoes out of range of sight and hearing but the only really necessary effect is to stop them biting. Only a very small proportion of the population of mosquitoes within flight range may come near enough to be attracted to blood or repelled by repellent. An attractant, to be useful, must lure a high proportion of the population to its destruction, and therefore must be effective over a long range. It has a more difficult task to perform.

Practical Use of Repellents in Agriculture

Repellents can act at such short range that it becomes difficult to decide in some cases whether an olfactory or tactile response is involved. Coal-fire soot scattered along the row of seedlings is a very effective deterrent to slugs. Its effect is probably mainly mechanical, providing a very unsuitable surface for the crawling process of the animal. Pepper, as a repellent for cats, is effective only when it is disturbed by scraping. Evil-tasting oily products smeared on tree-boles, in so far as they are effective in preventing damage by deer and rodents, are distasteful to tongue and lips and even this may be partly mechanical.

The fungicides tetramethylthiuram disulphide and zinc dimethyldithio-carbamate-cyclohexylamine complex are used to stop deer and rabbits from stripping bark, and *tert*butylsulphenyl dimethyldithiocarbamate is incorporated into rubber and plastic insulation for electric cables to stop rodents from gnawing them.

Although public sentiment views destruction of insects, or even of rodents, with equanimity, killing of birds and other "pleasant" animals provokes strong public opposition. Some use is made in agriculture of chemical repellents for birds and small mammals which cause tremendous damage to growing crops. The response is probably gustatory. For example, 9,10-anthraquinone is used as a seed dressing to deter birds. An interesting compound is 4-aminopyridine which does not kill birds at the concentrations used for repellence but causes those which eat bait containing it to behave in a manner which alarms the whole flock and makes them leave and not return. In some way not understood, this compound creates a disturbance in birds and produces in them fear of treated areas. It was found, incidental to its normal use, that the insecticide methiocarb deterred birds from picking fruit, causing some sickness if the deterrent effect did not operate quickly enough. Fear of public objection has tended to restrict use of this insecticide rather than to extend the market and promote search of analogues for more active compounds.

Insect repellents have found little use in modern agriculture for protection of growing crops. The large areas involved would probably make their use uneconomical even if it could be made effective. Their use is also incompatible with monoculture in large fields, within which there can be no choice of food for the insect. Under these conditions, only a repellent which also completely inhibited feeding, could be effective.

Insect Repellents for Man and Livestock

Insects, of course, can be repelled in flight by response initiated by olfaction. Oil of citronella certainly works this way. If objects contaminated with it are interspersed in a large chamber, or out of doors, with similar but adsorbing objects (for example, gauze, cylinders, some filled with cotton wool moistened with the oil, others with active charcoal), mosquitoes do not merely not stay on the oil-scented surfaces, but clearly avoid them before they are within alighting distance. It will be seen below that the mosquito repellents now most widely used appear to act at a distance by cancelling the signals of attraction.

There are many species of biting insects. At best they are a nuisance, sometimes almost intolerable, but many also carry diseases. The best known example is the transmission of malaria by anopheline mosquitoes, but there are other serious diseases, prevalent in the tropics, which are carried by biting insects. In the case of an obligate parasite which lives as well as feeds upon its host, for example the body louse (the carrier of typhus), attention throughout the community to personal hygiene is the best treatment. With many free-living flies, however, especially when man is only one of many host species, personal hygiene is much less effective.

It is against the free-living biting insects outside urban area that repellents are mainly used. The problem became particularly acute for military personnel in jungle warfare. Most of the casualties were through insect-borne diseases. Oil of citronella was first used as a repellent but was too short-lived. Also, its aggressive smell indicated the presence of hidden personnel and was objectionable to many wearers. Intensive search for alternatives was undertaken and dimethyl phthalate became widely used.

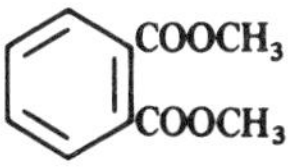

Dimethyl phthalate 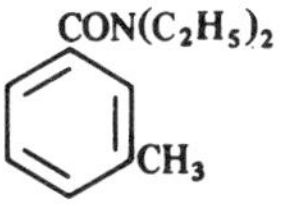   DEET

Dimethyl phthalate was not, however, effective against all inimical species and thousands more compounds were tested. Two, in admixture with dimethyl phthalate, produced a broader spectrum of action. These were 6-butoxycarbonyl-2,3-dihydro-2,2-dimethylpyran-4-one (butopyronoxyl), made from mesityl oxide and dibutyl oxalate, and 3-hydroxymethylheptan-4-ol (ethohexadiol), made by hydrogenation of butyraldol. A third compound, the most generally effective of all and the one most used today, came too late for World War II. It is N,N-diethyl-3-methylbenzamide (DEET), manufactured from 3-methylbenzoyl chloride and diethylamine. The 2- and 4- methyl compounds are also active, but less so than the 3-methyl isomer. Dibutyl succinate, dipropyl isocinchomeronate and butoxypolypropylene glycol have also found some use as insect repellents.

These compounds do not steer the mosquitoes away in flight as does oil of citronella. Although a tangible smear produces a departure reaction in an alighting insect, particularly in the case of DEET, their most important effect seems to be to cancel out the attractant properties of the animal body. If flat copper bars are laid on the floor of a cage and heated at one end and cooled at the other, they are ignored by the mosquitoes as long as they are dry. However, when covered with dampened cloth (black was found to be better than white), mosquitoes alighted very much more frequently on the warm part of the bar; in fact they seldom landed on the cold part. When the air was permeated with molecules of a repellent by hanging a sheet of filter paper moistened with the particular repellent in the upper part of the cage, the behaviour of the mosquitoes was completely changed. The number alighting on the bar was very greatly reduced and instead of being concentrated near the warm end they appeared to be distributed along its length.

Repellents are formulated as oils, creams or gels for hand application, or put up in self-dispensing aerosol packs. Creams and aerosols incorporating a sun screen with the repellents are marketed.

Pyrethrum deposits have considerable repellent effect, as well as being insecticidal. After use of a pyrethrum aerosol, flies tend to avoid the treated room for some time. The burning of pellets or coils containing pyrethrum is practised in various parts of the world to repel mosquitoes from rooms, particularly bedrooms. Although a sufficient dose of pyrethrum rapidly renders an insect immobile, the first effect of slight pick-up is to produce a state of great excitement. The mechanism of repellence in this case may be a direct consequence. There is some parallel to the behaviour of gases according to the kinetic theory. Concentration decreases in a part of the gas volume which is heated. The effect of a low dosage of pyrethrum on flying insects is somewhat equivalent to several thousand degrees temperature rise on gas molecules.

General Disorientation

Many insects are attracted to light, especially ultra-violet, and to sweet, fermenting foods and these behaviours are useful to collectors and, occasionally, for trapping pests. Localized trapping within the crop is of little use and may bring in more flying pests than are trapped, depending on distance response. A highly specific attractant or one more powerful than the food source is necessary. Useful delay of build-up of whitefly infestation can be achieved, however, by placing sticky, bright yellow surfaces just above a young crop early in the season, a method more successful in glass houses than in the open. Some protection of young crops can also be obtained by laying bright reflecting material between the rows, which disorients some laying females normally conditioned to movement away from the sky.

Specific Insect Attractants

It has long been known that the females of some species of insect can excite an approaching response in males at a distance, in favourable cases, of miles. It is clear that volatile substances of extremely high physiological activity must be responsible. Now that something is known about these sex "pheromones", it has been estimated that the threshold quantity for response can be as low as about 30 molecules or 10^{-14} μg. The molecules are picked up by the antennae of the males where they produce electrical impulses in the nerves which initiate a muscular response. This reponse is produced only by the specific pheromone.

Interest in the sex-pheromones has recently been intensified by two developments. Firstly, the exploitation of modern microtechniques — chromatographic separation and nuclear-magnetic-resonance, infrared, and mass-spectrograph analysis — has made possible the chemical identification of some of the compounds responsible, available only in minute quantities. Secondly, public pressure for more selective methods of pest control and the increasing importance of insect resistance, have directed attention to this most specific of all responses and one without which reproduction would appear impossible.

Many of the natural insect sex pheromones have now been isolated, identified and synthesized and are available commercially. In general, they tend to be long chain unsaturated aliphatic alcohols or ketones or related compounds, but activity for a particular species is critically dependent on precise structure and configuration. For example, only the 10-trans-12-cis isomer of the silkworm moth attractant shown below is effective. The insect can distinguish geometrical isomers and enantiomers.

$$CH_3(CH_2)_2CH{=}CHCH{=}CH(CH_2)_8CH_2OH$$
Natural silkworm moth attractant

$$CH_3(CH_2)_5CH(OOCCH_3)CH_2CH{=}CH(CH_2)_5CH_2OH$$
Natural gypsy moth attractant

$$CH_3(CH_2)_5CH(OOCCH_3)CH_2CH{=}CH(CH_2)_7CH_2OH$$
Synthetic gypsy moth attractant

Nevertheless, provided the structural and steric features essential for activity are retained it is possible to produce synthetic compounds which have attractive properties similar to the natural pheromones. For example, the synthetic compound 12-acetoxy-1-hydroxy-9-octadecene, which can be manufactured economically from ricinoleic acid obtained from castor oil, has similar properties to the natural gypsy moth attractant.

The sex pheromones are not always produced by the females. In the case of the cotton boll weevil it is the male which produces four pheromones that attract the female.

Nor is a sexual response the only one which can be produced by pheromones. The name is used in general for any chemicals secreted by an animal to stimulate some form of physiological or behavioural response from another member of the same species. Ants, for example, secrete pheromones as a trail to guide other members of the colony back to the nest. "Alarm pheromones" are emitted by some insect species to warn other members of danger. Tree bark beetles secrete "aggregation pheromones" to bring them together for a concerted onslaught on a pine-tree.

The attraction of the egg-laying female of some phytophagous species to the food plant is at least in part determined by volatile chemicals produced by that plant and called "phytomones". They have not been so much investigated as the more highly specific and more active pheromones.

It appears, therefore, that much of the behaviour of insects is mediated by chemical stimuli and it is an attractive thought to synthesize natural stimuli or active analogues and to use these to interfere with natural behaviour of insect pests in a way which could be used to control them. Such a method of control would be environmentally safe, specific to a particular pest and free from the possibility of toxic residues.

So far no successful control (as distinct from useful population studies) has been achieved by use of sex pheromones. The most likely application is to distribute synthetic pheromone or an effective equivalent in sufficient quantity to saturate the male's response. In an experiment with cis-7-dodecenylacetate and the cabbage looper moth, Trichoplusia ni, in California, Shorey reduced the effectiveness of traps baited with virgin females from a nightly collection of 125 males per trap to less than two. The lure was evaporated from 36 sites in a 144 ha plot at a total rate of 3.6 g/night. Such success is certainly worth following up as are the reasons for relative failure in other cases. The same "male confusion" has given more variable, usually unsuccessful, results with the gypsy moth.

The most spectacular success so far has been achieved neither with a pheromone nor a natural phytomone but with a compound discovered by empirical testing to be very attractive to the male tropical fruit fly, Dacus dorsalis, which seeks out and avidly feeds on wafers impregnated with this lure even when laced with the insecticide naled. Distribution of these wafers from the air achieved complete depopulation of this pest on a Caribbean island too remote for rapid repopulation of the feeble fliers. The active lure was 1-allyl-3,4-dimethoxy benzene (methyl eugenol). Sec.butyl 2-methyl-benzoate was found to be effective with the mediterranean fruit fly.

Chemical Control of Insect Behaviour

The behaviour of insects, particularly of the social insects such as bees and ants, has long been a challenge to human understanding. Much of the behaviour makes no sense at all in terms of human motives, emotions or intelligence. The directionally accurate homing flight of a honey-bee from a distant foraging expedition arouses wonder and admiration and yet, if the hive is moved a few feet during the bee's absence, the behaviour of the returning bee appears incomprehensibly stupid. It will fly about to exhaustion near the old location of the alighting board, apparently unable to detect the conspicuous hive in the immediate vicinity.

Insect behaviour requires completely impartial and objective study: no interpretation should ever be based on human behaviour. It is being studied very deeply by the knowledgeable few, but their work is very little known to the intelligent layman or the worker in related fields. Certainly until recently little interest was taken by practical agricultural entomologists. The natural-product chemist confines his resourcefulness to identifying characteristically olfactory substances available in extremely minute quantities. Yet, without presentation of basic knowledge of insect behaviour to the agricultural research worker, the discoveries of the chemist are not likely to become of much practical value.

Attraction and repulsion are essentially vector (directional) behaviour patterns. Concentration of a chemical substance is essentially a scalar (non-directional) quantity. No substance can attract or repel *per se*. A very steep concentration gradient, which is met only close to some source, as at the edges of a small thermal up-current of air, or in extreme form at an interface between liquid and air, has been shown to produce a vector response, but this cannot explain attraction from great distances. In the only cases where the mechanism of such attraction has been clearly demonstrated, it was found that the chemical "command" is "fly upwind". The vector part of the response thus depends on wind direction, not on concentration gradient. The insect flies in such direction that, judged by visual marking on the ground, it makes slowest progress. If it cannot make progress at all in the slowest direction (i.e. the wind is too strong), it does not fly. This response is perfectly suited to natural conditions but, by suitable tricks with moving light patterns on the floor of a wind tunnel, the behaviour of the insect can be made totally inappropriate and it is by such experiments that the detailed response can be analyzed.

The command may be "fly upwind". It may be "turn sharply". It may be "fly faster". It may, as with a contact repellent, be simply "fly" or, as on contact with a suitable host surface, "don't fly". More than one command may be involved and one stimulus may cancel another. Many of the commands responsible for feeding control and other activities are chemical in origin. Their definite "stop-go" nature has been shown by many experiments in which insects have been caused to eat, suicidally, non-food which tastes right, to starve in the presence of food or even to engorge to the point of actual bursting.

The successes mentioned in the previous section open up possibilities of very economic and specific means of insect pest reduction. Despite many failures, more intensive research is well worth funding. Indeed it is research on the failures which is most needed to increase the successes.

A remarkable case of apparent cancellation of response appeared when the sex pheromone of the corn earworm moth, *Heliothis zea*, was identified as (z)-11-hexadecenal and shown to elicit response in caged males. Not only did it fail to attract males into traps in the field but eliminated the attractive effect of virgin females when present in the same traps. A second unidentified compound may be solely responsible for remote search-stimulation of flying males and be countermanded by too high a concentration of the identified copulatory stimulus.

Local Attraction and Repellence

Field research on the use of attractants may have been too concerned with the idea of opposed behaviours used separately. More might be made of interaction and localized effects. Concentration gradients must play a part. Insects are certainly able to detect gradients, temporal and spatial, much more sensitively than mammals, doubtless partly due to their olfaction receptors being situated on dry extended organs, rather than in wet tube walls. The mucous fluid covering receptors in the nasal passage introduces diffusive delay between change of concentration in air and at the receptor site. Insects have a better smell memory than man and the sense is less rapidly fatigued. The human is fairly sensitive to the arrival of a new smell but becomes oblivious to it, at different rates for different stimuli, if it persists. A fall of concentration is much less well detected than a rise. The rapid reaction of an insect to flying out of a smell plume is an important factor in "homing in" on a source.

The food-plant searching of the female butterfly strongly suggests that local gradients are important. Although the population of the conspicuous flying white butterfly over a cabbage field is higher than over a neighbouring wheat field, observation in a mixed garden indicates a different mechanism of local selection. Food and non-food leaves are almost indiscriminately visited but the stay on non-food leaves is much shorter. This may be due to a chemotactile response to a different chemical than the one responsible for remote attraction but could also be due to a steep gradient of a single messenger substance, negative near an absorbing non-food leaf and *relatively* greater (i.e. greater value of d log C/dx) than the opposite gradient in higher concentration near the food leaf. The important message conveyed by a steady low concentration remote from the cabbage field is "fly upwind". When the concentration becomes high and confusing random trial begins and the important message may be "wrong" as the non-food leaf is visited. Whatever the mechanism, local choice is clearly involved and we should exploit it as an alternative to trying to eliminate remote attraction. Modern knowledge of behaviour control by chemicals could well be applied to improve the old established practice of trap cropping.

The housewife is said to be increasingly demanding of unblemished fruit and vegetables now that so much produce is marketed in transparent packaging for convenience, preservation and hygiene, although she may be, in another capacity, a vocal opponent of chemical contamination. It would seem therefore good sense for the grower to use a method which might sacrifice say 10% of his crop in a predetermined layout in order to have the other 90% unblemished and uncontaminated rather than to have the whole crop requiring more detailed examination at harvest and at risk of higher rejection rate for exceeding a chemical residue level.

We mentioned in Chapter 2 that different cultivars are known in some cases to have less attraction for egg-laying pest insects than others. This has been called "non-preference" resistance. It has not been found sufficient to give useful pest-avoidance by itself. Plant-breeding may be able to achieve this, but it would have to be done without detriment to yield or quality. Success could more likely come from combining cultivar choice and band treatment with a repellent or attraction-cancelling chemical. Intervening, narrower bands would be treated with a non-repellent insecticide, and the crop from these destroyed.

Anti-feeding Compounds

The feeding of insects is initiated by chemoreception in the appropriate organ. The initiating compound is characteristic of the host range of species and is usually a token without significant nutritional value. The token substance applied to paper may even initiate feeding on this totally unsuitable food. The feeding initiator is not usually identical with the compound which leads the insect to the host. The signal to cease feeding is more complex. "Surgical" procedures can cancel this signal so that the insect feeds until it bursts, and at least one compound, methyl eugenol, is known which has the same effect without surgery in the tropical fruit fly.

Inappropriate or excessive feeding has not so far been considered, outside the laboratory, but compounds which appear to cancel the signal to initiate feeding are known and research in this field to find better "antifeeding" compounds has been pursued. No repellent action need be associated with the anti-feeding action. In the presence of the anti-feeding compound the insect may starve to death while remaining on its host plant.

Possible application in agriculture seems to be opened up by the discovery that 4-(dimethyl-triazeno)-acetanilide (DTA) inhibited the feeding of south-

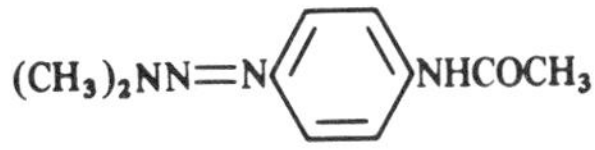

$$(CH_3)_2NN = N\langle\bigcirc\rangle NHCOCH_3$$

DTA

ern army worms when applied at dosage rates in the range of commercial insecticides. The screening tests showed that the compound was not effective against aphids or mites, but was effective against army worms and Mexican bean-beetle larvae. The non-toxic compound left the predators unaffected and their appetites did not seem to be influenced. It was not highly toxic to honey-bees and did not inhibit them from feeding on treated sugar solutions. It showed some systemic behaviour in the host plant.

A limited field test was organized mainly to ascertain the effectiveness and possibilities, of the antifeeding concept as a method of insect control. Although the compound was ineffective against chewing insects which fed inside the fruit, such as the plum curculio, corn earworm and cornborer, the first season's results were promising in that most of the leaf-feeding caterpillars and beetles were controlled by the material. However, more extensive field tests on some cotton insects, boll weevil, bollworm and leaf-worm, did not give any useful results. It appeared that when low insect population was present the effect of the deterrent compound was dominant, but under heavy pressure from an increasing population the deterrent ceased to be effective. No further compounds of this type have been developed, and this is no longer considered a very promising area of research.

Azadirachtin, mentioned under insecticides (Chapter 11) is a powerful antifeedant and another natural product from *Polygonum hydropiper*, polygodial prevents aphis-probing at very low application rate. It has a much simpler molecule and has been synthesized but its action is very dependent on its stereochemistry. The natural product has the configuration shown but the racemic mixture obtained by synthesis is highly phytotoxic. Resolution must remove the phytotoxic + isomer very completely to leave the antifeedant-isomer safe to apply.

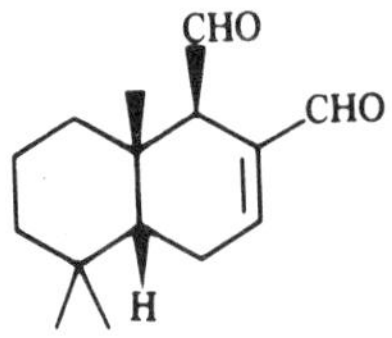

(−) polygodial

Oviposition Inhibitors

It has been found that, after the female boll weevil has deposited her egg in a cotton bud, she cements the hole with her frass. This frass releases volatile compounds, which appear to be specific monoterpene alcohols or aldehydes, which deter other females from depositing an egg in the same bud. If the deterrent compounds could be identified and synthesized or if synthetic analogues which were effective could be discovered, spraying a cotton crop with these might be an effective method of controlling the pest.

Further Reading

American Chem. Soc. Symposium, *Insect Pheromone Technology*, 190, 1985.
Copper Development Association, *Copper Compounds in Agriculture*, London, 1957.
Evans, E. *Fungal Diseases and Control by Chemicals*, Blackwell, Oxford, 1968.
Finch, S. Chemical attraction of plant-feeding insects to plants. In *Advances in Applied Biology*, vol. 5, ed. T. H. Coaker, Academic Press, 1980.
Large, E. G. *The Advance of the Fungi*, Jonathan Cape, London, 1958.
Nordlund, D. A., Jones, R. L. and Lewis, W. J. *Semiochemicals, their Role in Pest Control*, Wiley, 1981.
Pickett, J. A. *Phil. Trans. Roy. Soc*, **B310**, 235–239, London, 1985.
Roy. Soc. of Chemistry, Monograph. *Recent Advances in Chemistry of Insect Control*, 1986.
Torgeson, E. C. *Fungicides*, Vols. I and II, Academic Press, London and New York, 1967.
Wright, R. H. *The Sense of Smell*, CRC, 1982.

13

Chemicals used against other Invertebrates

It has become usual to refer to chemicals effective against the small phytophagous mites as acaricides, distinguishing them from insecticides. The mites belong to the order arachnidae which includes the enormous number of species of spider of all shapes, sizes and feeding habits. They differ from the insects in having unsegmented bodies, eight legs instead of six and no antennae. The differences in response to toxic chemicals must arise mainly from differences in biochemistry, but whether the difference in average response between the two orders is greater than the differences within the orders has never been fully investigated. The difference between most pest insects and most phytophagous mites would probably not have given rise to the separate classification of the pesticides had not DDT, the first synthetic insecticide to have very widespread use, been rather untypically ineffective against mites. Its use in orchards brought the mites from a level of not very great importance to the status of a major damaging pest, not simply because it did not kill them but because it killed off their insect predators. Two other factors caused the miticides to remain a separate class — the upsurge of mites necessitated great research effort to find chemicals highly toxic to them and their very rapid breeding rate caused them to develop resistant strains rapidly so that new compounds had to be found. Had some other synthetic pesticide — e.g. chlordimeform — been the first to be used on a very large scale, we might never have made so definite a separation of acaricides and insecticides.

The first compounds effective against phytophagous mites were in the bridged diphenyl group, mostly with both phenyls having 4 chloro substitution. Many compounds with different bridging groups were made and used. Four are still in use though in some areas one or more have become ineffective through resistance development. They are:

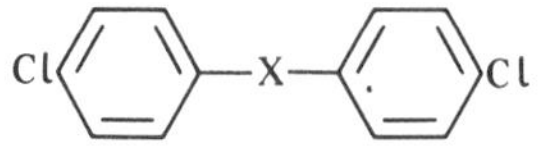

$X = -O-SO_2-$ Chlorfenson

$X = -\underset{\underset{CH_3}{|}}{\overset{\overset{OH}{|}}{C}}-$ Chlorfenethol

136

$$X = -\underset{\underset{\text{OC.OC}_2\text{H}_5}{|}}{\overset{\overset{\text{OH}}{|}}{C}}- \qquad \text{Chlorbenzilate}$$

$$X = -\underset{\underset{\text{CCl}_3}{|}}{\overset{\overset{\text{OH}}{|}}{C}}- \qquad \text{Dicofol}$$

It will be noted that DDT, the origin of all the trouble, is clearly in this chemical group, differing from dicofol only in having H in place of OH. The most likely source of the difference in mode of action between DDT and the acaricide members is the presence of a hydrophilic group in all the acaricides. Some compounds had other substituents in the rings and the most widely used, until defeated by equally widely generated resistance, was tetradifon, in which one ring had 4-chloro and the other 2,4,5-trichloro substitution. The bridge was sulphone.

Many mites infesting deciduous orchards overwinter in the egg stage. The relatively large eggs are laid in crevices in the bark and are vulnerable to winter-washes containing oils and rather general poisons which the trunk can tolerate during the dormant period. DNOC and dinoseb are used for this purpose and have the added advantage of killing off lichens. Other dinitrophenol derivatives having more selective action against mite eggs and adults are dinocap and binapacryl, both used at lower dosage on fruiting trees to kill powdery mildew.

The chemicals now mainly in use for control of mites on green crops are organotin compounds, particularly tricyclohexyltin hydroxide, cyhexatin and tris (2 phenyl-2-methylpropyl) tin oxide (fenbutatin), which are to date the most effective compounds. These tin compounds are not very active against insects and therefore cause less reduction of predation than chlordimeform and amitraz which are good general insecticides and significantly systemic. Benzoximate has good activity against mites in orchards.

The most important predators of phytophagous mites are some sarcophagous mite species which makes the distinction between acaricides and insecticides a not very helpful one.

Spider mites rasp the tissues of leaves and suck up the cell contents. They take up in this way a relatively large volume of cell sap and consequently tend to be vulnerable to the water-soluble systemic organophosphorus aphicides as well as to the specific acaricides mentioned, which have only a very limited systemic action.

It should be noted that other members of the Arachnidae, especially the cattle tick and sheep scab mite, do extensive damage to agricultural animals.

Various chemicals are used in their control but a discussion of animal health products is outside the scope of this book and the reader should consult the books indicated at the end of this chapter for further information.

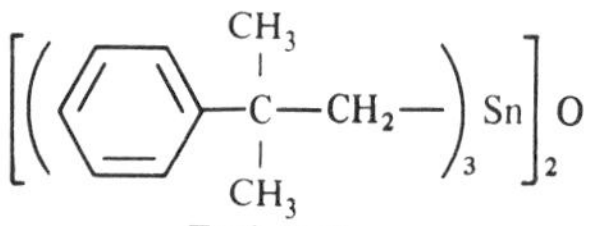

Fenbutatin

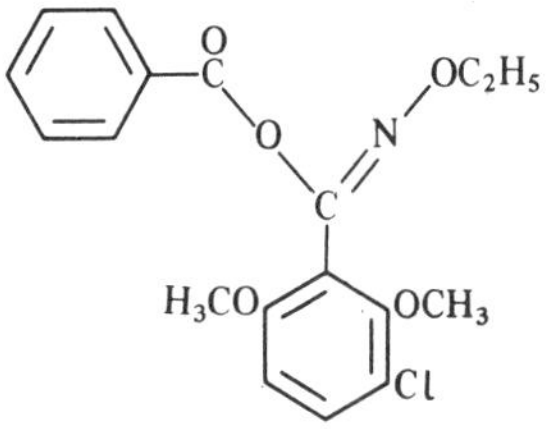

Benzoximate

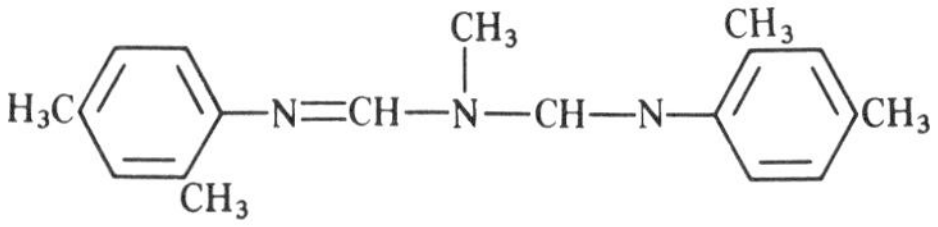

Amitraz

Nematicides

Nematodes are small worm-like organisms, generally about 1 mm long, which either live on plant roots as ectoparasites or enter the plant tissues via the roots and become endoparasites in leaves and stems. There are very many species which are ubiquitous and do vast damage to crops, not only by feeding on the plants and causing them to become stunted, unyielding and less resistant to diseases, but also by actively transmitting virus diseases and allowing entry of fungi and bacteria through the damaged roots. Many produce galls. Their eggs remain dormant in the soil for long periods and often hatch out only under the influence of chemical substances secreted from the roots of the growing plants. The full nematode fauna of soil and the precise damage they do are imperfectly known as yet.

Because the eggs are often protected by cysts they are very invulnerable to attack of any kind and so chemical control is a difficult problem. The principal method of control is still crop rotation but this has its limitations, and the modern tendency towards monoculture has exacerbated the problem. An attractive method of control would be chemicals which would cause the eggs to hatch in the absence of host plants, but this has not yet been achieved. The natural hatching factors are complex oxidized sugars, quite unsuitable for commercial production.

The most widely used methods for controlling nematodes involve rather drastic and expensive treatment of the soil before sowing or planting. They are application of heat, generally in the form of live steam, or volatile chemicals having a wide spectrum of toxicity. In both cases almost complete sterilization of the treated soil results, but it is virtually impossible to achieve this in the whole depth of soil, even in glasshouse practice. However, most soil nematodes are not deep-dwelling and are usually eliminated, so the results in practice are better than might be expected. Some nematodes have seasonal migratory habits and it is important in these cases that treatment is carried out when they are not in the deep layers of the soil. The damage done by nematodes to crops is much more serious if they are present during the early life of the transplant or seedling so elimination from the initial rooting zone may give the most satisfactory results.

All the fumigants used to control nematodes are toxic to plants and must be applied from one week to several months before planting. The rate of application is usually 200-450 kg/ha. The compounds most widely used are methyl bromide, ethylene dibromide, 1,3-dichloropropene, methyl isothiocyanate, formaldehyde, carbon disulphide and chloropicrin. The first four are generally used when nematodes are the primary target and the last three when control of soil fungi is also required, but they are all effective general sterilants in sufficiently high dosage. 1,2-Dibromo-3-chloropropane has sufficiently low phytotoxicity to permit its use under favourable and controlled conditions for control of nematodes in citrus orchards. The toxicant is introduced into the soil along one side of each row of trees in one year and along the other side in the next in order to reduce direct chemical damage.

If good control is to be achieved distribution of the chemical in the soil must be very good. The fumigants listed above are automatically dispersed by diffusion in the soil air spaces, but if a non-volatile nematicide is to be used this distribution must be achieved mechanically or by the use of heavy irrigation following treatment with a water-soluble compound. The first method involves introduction of a dust formulation into the soil and stirring to the necessary depth with a powerful rotary hoe. This method is effective only on easily-worked, friable soils, and is expensive. It has been applied to good potato land using an inorganic mercury salt as the nematicide. The second method can be applied only to good-structured, free-draining soils in which the compound can be washed down quickly and uniformly. If slow downward leaching under natural rain is to be relied on, the compound must not be significantly adsorbed on soil colloids. This imposes an almost impossible condition for complex non-ionized substances.

Two organophosphorus and two oximecarbamate insecticides have been useful in some soil situations and crops for control of nematodes by drenching. They are illustrated below.

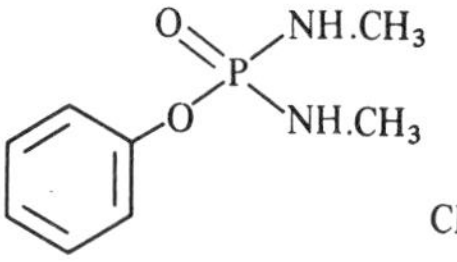

Diamidafos 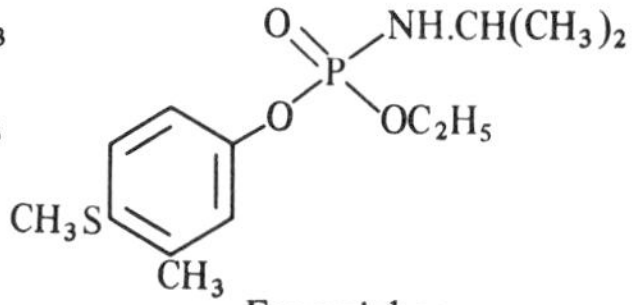   Fenamiphos

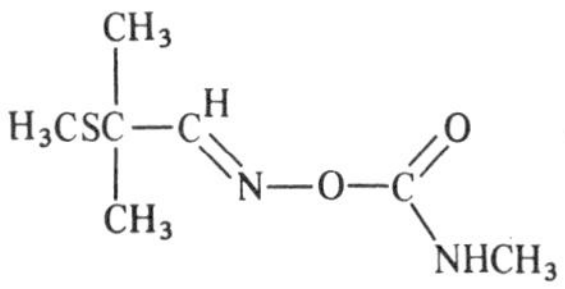

Aldicarb 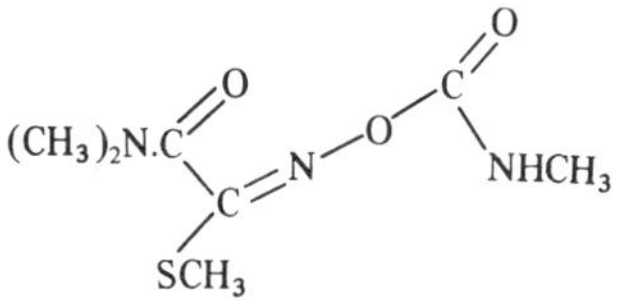   Oxamyl

All have adequate water solubility for this purpose. Oxamyl is very soluble and the solubility of aldicarb is increased by oxidation of the S atom. The sulphone form, aldoxycarb, is commercially available. It is now the most widely used. The restrictions on all these are the necessity for free-draining soil structure and undesirably high toxicity to mammals.

The leaf- and stem-dwelling nematodes may be controlled by several organophosphorus pesticides. Parathion is effective on chrysanthemums. Acephate and dimethoate have the advantage of better systemic behaviour.

Several nematodes are parasites of farm animals, but the compounds above are too toxic to be of interest for veterinary applications for which other compounds are available that have not found use in crops. Recently, however, there has been interest in some complex compounds called avermectins produced by the fungus *Streptomyces avermitilis*, which are very active against veterinary targets, and some active metabolites have been found to be sufficiently persistent in soil to offer some prospect of agricultural use. The molecules are complex ring structures including several pyrane rings and one 16 atom macrocycle. They are one group of several natural products which are subjects of active research but their practical use for control is uncertain.

Finally, it should be mentioned that not all nematodes are inimical to man's interests. Some are parasitic on insects and at least one, multiplying rapidly in a stem boring caterpillar, is under test as a control measure.

Molluscicides

Slugs and snails cause serious damage to crops, especially to potatoes. In a wet spring they can reduce the market value of many green and root vegetables, and, in the case of wheat, may devour much autumn-sown seed before emergence. No really satisfactory method of chemical control has yet been found. The most effective chemical known, much used in bait form among garden crops, is a tetramer of acetaldehyde known as metaldehyde or simply "meta". It is made by polymerization of acetaldehyde in solution in alcohol below 30°C in the presence of sulphuric acid, which catalyses the interconversion of the monomer and the various polymers. Meta is considered to be predominantly one stereoisomer of the eight-membered ring formed from four molecules of acetaldehyde. A poison bait of metaldehyde mixed with bran is broadcast thinly or placed in small heaps in the evening when the soil is moist. Ingestion of the poison by the mollusc induces increased production of slime and causes death by desiccation.

Because meta does not give fully satisfactory control under field conditions many other compounds have been tried. Amongst those which are reasonably effective are carbaryl, methiocarb, phorate, aldicarb and thiocarboxime. However, because of the toxicity of these compounds to man, animals and wildlife, their use is restricted and there is a need for discovery of safer compounds. It is interesting to note that beer and cider are very attractive to slugs but also very lethal to them.

Methiocarb

Thiocarboxime

Poison baits are curative treatments applied after damage has been done. Preventative methods would be better but those which are currently available kill too few of the pests and those deep in the soil survive and rapidly restore the population in the surface layers. Much more needs to be known about behaviour and population dynamics and about the mechanism of slime secretion.

Water snails are a problem because they harbour a phase in the life cycle of the *Schistosoma* organism which is responsible for one of the most debilitating and widespread tropical diseases in man, bilharzia.

Aquatic species of snail, like all aquatic animals, must be adapted to make good molecular contact with a great volume of water in order to obtain sufficient oxygen. It is therefore understandable that they are more vulnerable to lipophilic substances dissolved at only low concentration. Most of the compounds effective against aquatic snails are lipophilic (or are salts of lipophilic acids) with the exception of copper sulphate which is still used in large quantity, and is the only common agent for both land and water species. Water containing 2–3 ppm of cupric ion kills nearly all snails after 24 hours' exposure. Even at present copper prices, few organic molluscicides can compete for cost but several factors operate against the successful use of copper. It is toxic also to aquatic vegetation, particularly algae, and can therefore upset the complex ecology of streams and ponds. It is also toxic to fish. It is rapidly inactivated in alkaline hard waters by precipitation as the basic carbonate and in muddy waters by adsorption on base-exchanging clay particles.

Pentachlorophenol (PCP), introduced into the water as a concentrated solution of the sodium salt, is also effective at a few parts per million and has been extensively used. It is much less strongly adsorbed than copper and is also more toxic to snail eggs, but is just as toxic to fish and some vegetation. Handling the concentrate is a considerable toxic hazard to man. Acrolein (acrylic aldehyde, $CH_2 = CH - CHO$) has also achieved some success as a poison for river-dwelling snails. It is sufficiently water soluble not to evaporate excessively over the period required for action, but its lachrymatory property makes handling the concentrate unpleasant.

While the newer, more active organic compounds are not adsorbed by clays, they are adsorbed by organic constituents of mud and therefore share with copper the difficulty of adequate penetration of stagnant water along vegetated river margins. None is yet known which has a satisfactorily low toxicity to fish. Their chief advantage over copper and PCP is their lower phytotoxicity. A compound which has had some success is 5,2'-dichloro-4'-nitrosalicylanilide (niclosamide), prepared by reaction of 5-chloro-salicyloyl chloride with 2-chloro-4-nitroaniline.

Niclosamide

Other Invertebrate Pests

Woodlice cause some damage but are easily controlled with DDT or lindane. Millipedes cause sporadic and unpredictable damage to root crops but can be controlled with lindane, methiocarb or aldicarb. Symphylids cause damage to young vegetable seedlings and are best controlled with aldicarb.

A related aquatic problem is the economic loss caused in marine transport by barnacles which attach themselves to the hulls of ships and seriously increase power-to-speed ratio. Special antifouling paints are used to combat these organisms. These paints generally contain sparingly soluble copper compounds, especially cuprous oxide, but some more complex organic compounds are now being introduced as antifouling paint constituents. Organo-tin compounds are useful constituents but no treatment is completely effective. Water is, unfortunately, a much better solvent than air for most physiologically active chemicals (except oxygen).

Further Reading

Dickson, D. W. *Nematode Control Guide*, University of Florida, 1969.
Jones, F. G. W. and Jones, M. G. *Pests of Field Crops*, Arnold, London, 1974.

14

Chemicals used against Vertebrates

While there are many voices raised against the possible long-term or side-effects of the use of insecticides, few are raised against the actual killing of harmful insects. There is, however, much damage done to human interests by creatures which are closer to man in the scale of evolution. Birds and small mammals are, unlike insects, warm-blooded, so they can cause losses throughout the year. Also, because of their highly developed central nervous systems, they can be more purposeful, and their greater mobility makes them less dependent on environmental conditions. Agriculture has greatly modified their way of life and provided them with an abundance of food. Some birds, like the sparrow, have become completely dependent on man.

In the countries with the highest standard of living, much opposition is met to killing these animals, especially by poison. Gin traps were made illegal in England and Wales by the Pests Act of 1954 but even humane traps are completely unselective. In a musk-rat campaign in Scotland, 1,000 musk-rats were trapped together with 6,000 other animals. Certain poisons such as red squill and phosphorus have been prohibited by the Cruel Poisons Act of 1962. As a result of the Protection of Animals Act of 1911 only rats, mice, voles, shrews and moles may be poisoned in England, although it is legal to gas rabbits, and there is somewhat more freedom in Scotland. Under the Agriculture Act of 1972, poisons may be used against squirrels and coypus in certain circumstances. The Protection of Birds Act of 1954 protects wild birds generally but specifies those that may be killed, including wood-pigeon, sparrow, rook, jackdaw, crow, magpie, jay and bullfinch. In all, there are about 30 Acts in the UK which govern destruction of birds and small mammals, and any control measures must be in accord not only with these, but also with public sentiment. This sentiment arises from greater leisure in developed countries for altruistic interest in animal life and particularly from the remoteness of most of the population from the hard facts of agricultural life. The housewife buying plums in a city shop does not appreciate the problems of the grower who has to shoot bullfinches in order to provide them.

This type of public sentiment does not occur in countries where most of the population is engaged in, or closely in contact with, agriculture and where food is short. In parts of Africa, flocks of weaver birds, running into millions, completely devastate vast areas of cereals. There are few weapons, however indiscriminate, which have not been tried against this pest, but they have had remarkably little success.

Rats and Mice

In developed countries, public sentiment varies widely from species to species, possibly as a result of conditioning by childhood stories and toys — many babies have a cuddly bunny but few have a cuddly rat. Rats are so universally loathed by man that few communities object to attacking them by poison. The rat devours growing and stored crops, it often fouls more food than it eats, it carries diseases such as bubonic plague, which is transmitted by the rat flea, and Weil's disease, its excreta contains bacteria which cause food poisoning, and it is destructive to buildings, embankments, drains, cables, etc. The rat population of the U.K. is estimated to be the same as the human population — 55 million. The field mouse and domestic mouse do similar damage and are also generally disliked, especially by women. Field mice dig up newly-planted seeds such as peas and sugar beet and feed on soft fruits and cereals.

In closed situations such as warehouses and ships' holds rats and mice can be controlled by sealing and fumigating with self-dispersing poisons such as sulphur dioxide, hydrogen cyanide or methyl bromide.

In farms and urban buildings rats and mice are controlled by poison baits. Most of these are fairly toxic to other animals and to humans but restriction of their action to rats and mice is usually achieved by placement of baits containing a general poison in situations frequented by the pests but inaccessible to domestic animals. Ideally a rodenticide should not be unpalatable to rats and mice, should not arouse their suspicions and cause them to become "bait shy" if more than one feed is required to give a lethal dose, should cause them to seek the open air before dying so as to avoid hygiene and odour problems, should not act so rapidly that the rodent perceives warning symptoms before a lethal dose has been ingested and should be much less toxic to domestic animals, especially to cats and dogs which may catch and devour affected rats or mice. No known rodenticide meets all these requirements. The safety of domestic animals must depend on the placement of baits where and when these animals cannot gain access. Some operators seal the baits in plastic sachets which the rats, with mistaken curiosity and cunning, gnaw open.

For a long time zinc phosphide, arsenious oxide and a natural plant extract, red squill, were the most common rodenticides. Red squill is safe because it is rapidly decomposed in the body of the rat and, if taken directly by most other animals, it rapidly acts as an emetic; rats, however, cannot vomit. The odour of zinc phosphide is repulsive to most animals but is accepted by the rat.

The first synthetic organic rat poison of commercial importance was 1-naphthyl thiourea (antu), manufactured by reaction of 1-naphthylamine with ammonium thiocyanate. Another earlier organic rodenticide was 2-chloro-4-dimethylamino-6-methylpyrimidine (crimidine).

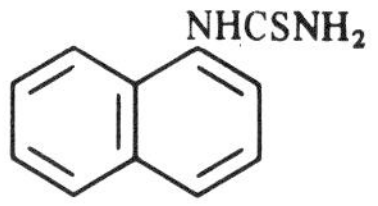

Antu

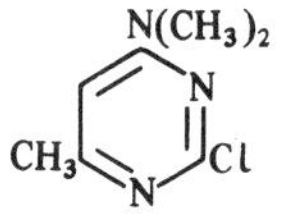

Crimidine

A particularly successful and widely-used compound, especially against mice was chloralose; manufactured by reaction of chloral with glucose.

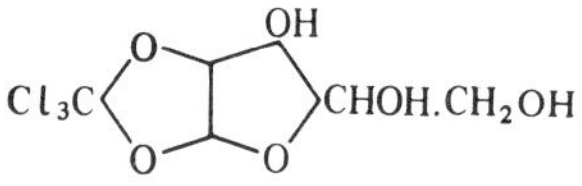

Chloralose

Fluoroacetic acid, prepared by high temperature reaction of chloroacetic acid and sodium fluoride, was used either as sodium salt, the amide or the anilide. Its use is now mainly restricted to ships and sewers because of its high mammalian toxicity. In the U.S.A. it may be used only by licensed operators.

All the above compounds are accepted by the rat but are also highly toxic to other animals. They are acute poisons intended to be lethal in a single dose and to kill quickly. As rats may not take sufficient of an acute poison bait immediately it is usual to "prebait" by offering unpoisoned bait until the rodents are feeding freely.

Chronic poisons, which are used at concentrations which kill only after several doses, were introduced around 1950. The most widely-used and successful was 3-(1-phenyl-2-acetylethyl)-4-hydroxycoumarin (warfarin), which is manufactured by reaction of hydroxycoumarin with benzalacetone.

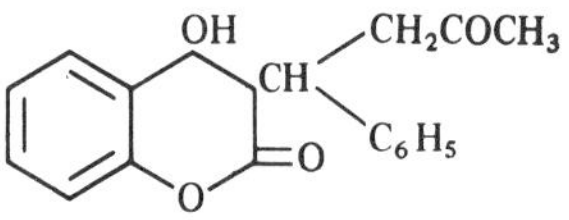

Warfarin

Warfarin has the effect of arresting coagulation of blood and, with strict control of dosage, is used for this purpose in human medicine. Non-coagulation appears to be induced more easily in rats and mice than in most other animals and to have more drastic effects, but safe use is mainly dependent on placement of baits. The rodents die of internal haemorrhage after coming into the open in search of water. Warfarin has no tendency to produce poison-shyness.

Unfortunately, anticoagulant resistant strains of rats and mice have spread alarmingly throughout the U.K., Europe and the U.S.A. so that some of the older poisons have had to be brought back into use. A number of other coumarins and related indanediones have been introduced, such as coumachlor, coumafuryl, coumatetralyl, valone, pindone, diphacinone and chlorphacinone, in order to try to control warfarin-resistant rodents, but have not been very successful in meeting this objective.

X =	
1- (4-chlorophenyl) -2-acetylethyl	Coumachlor
1- (2-furyl) -2-acetylethyl-	Coumafuryl
1,2,3,4-tetrahydronaphth-1-yl-	Coumatetralyl

X =	
Isovaleryl-	Valone
Pivalyl-	Pindone
Diphenylacetyl-	Diphacinone
(4-chlorophenyl) -phenylacetyl-	Chlorphacinone

The breakthrough came when it was discovered that certain substituted 4-hydroxy-2H-1-benzopyran-2-ones are extremely toxic to both normal and warfarin-resistant rats. The commercial compounds are bromadiolone, difenacoum and brodifacoum. Of these, brodifacoum is the most useful and has revolutionized rat control. It is comparatively harmless to humans and domestic animals and is used as pelleted bait thus avoiding use of toxic whole grains which might be eaten by animals or, in developing countries, even by desperate humans. Unlike the warfarin type rodenticides, which need ingestion over a period to be effective, brodifacoum is effective in a single dose.

X =	
3- [3- (4'-bromo-1,1'-biphenyl-4-yl) -3-hydroxy-1-phenylpropyl] -	Bromadiolone
3- (3- [1'1'-biphenyl-4-yl] -1,2,3,4-tetrahydro-1-naphth-yl) -	Difenacoum
3- [3-(4'-bromo-1,1'-biphenyl-4-yl) -1,2,3,4-tetrahydro-1-naphth-yl] -	Brodifacoum

A more complex compound which has been introduced for control of rats and mice including warfarin-resistant strains is scilliroside. With an oral LD50 to rats of 0.43 mg/kg it is almost as toxic to rats as brodifacoum with an oral LD50 of 0.26 mg/kg.

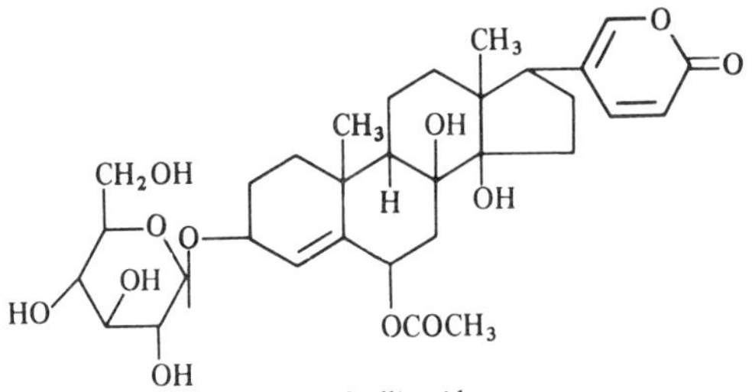

Scilliroside

There is need for new types of chemicals which have the properties for a successful rodenticide. Three recent developments are an organophosphorus compound, phosazetim, a urea, pyriminil, and a novel type of pesticide, a silicon compound, silatrane, but none of these has survived commercially.

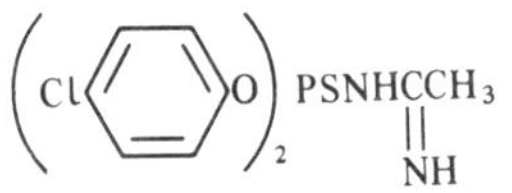

Phosazetim

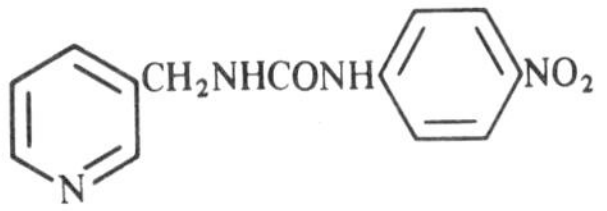

Pyriminil

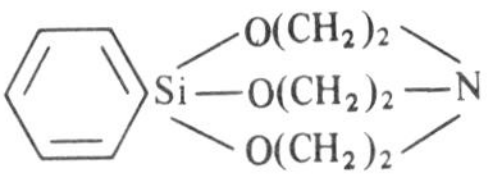

Silatrane

Economical, effective and safe use of rodenticides demands much more knowledge of the habits and behaviour of rats and mice.

Rabbits

Control of rabbits has been studied most extensively in Australia and New Zealand where they are major pests. Control by the myxomatosis virus has been very successful but the virus is becoming attenuated and resistant strains of rabbits are emerging. It was introduced into the U.K. with widespread effect but, as the public found the spectacle of dying rabbits distasteful, deliberate spread of this disease was prohibited by the Pest Act of 1954. Nevertheless, it must be realized that rabbit damage in the U.K. amounts to about £100m per year.

Poison baits containing rodenticides are used against rabbits in Australia and New Zealand but, in the U.K., poisoning of rabbits is illegal, although they may still be shot, snared, ferreted or trapped. Chemical control is generally by hydrogen cyanide introduced into burrows. Contractors may employ anhydrous hydrogen cyanide with special equipment and precautions, but, for general use, a powdered water-soluble cyanide is available. A suitable powdered formulation with good storage properties under reasonably dry conditions is a mixture of sodium cyanide, magnesium carbonate and anhydrous magnesium sulphate. It is placed in burrows with a long spoon or blown in with a dust gun. Chloropicrin is used instead of hydrogen cyanide in New Zealand but not in the U.K. Sodium fluoroacetate is extensively used in Australia and New Zealand in carrot or jam baits against rabbits and opposums. (See, however p. 5.) Although this very toxic compound, with no satisfactory antidote, is very stable *in vitro,* it is remarkably susceptible to enzymic hydrolysis by pseudomonas bacteria which are widely distributed in soil, and so its use gives rise to no long-term health or environmental hazards.

Moles

Moles eat insects and aerate soil but they can destroy seedlings by burrowing under them and their hills can damage machinery and degrade pastures. Moles are controlled by trapping and by gassing either by hydrogen cyanide or more primitively, but cheaply, by fitting a flexible pipe adaptor to a tractor exhaust and leading the gas into openings made in the runs. Baiting is also used and the poison employed is invariably strychnine which is injected into the bodies of earthworms which are then dropped back into the runs.

Squirrels

Squirrels do extensive damage to field crops and trees. In the U.K. use of rodenticide baits is now permitted in areas where the aggressive grey has displaced the shy and timid red squirrel.

Coypu and Mink

These two animals were introduced into closed farms in the U.K. for fur-raising but escaped and colonized. The coypu has established itself in East Anglia where it eats sugar beet and cereals and damages river banks. Rodenticides such as warfarin may now be used against them.

Other Mammals

Control of game animals such as hares, deer, etc., is a problem because of legal restrictions, public sentiment and private interests. An interesting new chemical approach is based on the fact that animals have an acute sense of smell and use chemical secretions — pheremones — from exterior glands to convey various messages to other members of their species. One of the purposes is to demarcate the individual's territory, and other members of the species will not cross such a "scent barrier". Some of the natural pheromones have been isolated, identified and synthesized, and others will follow. The hope is that they can be used for artificial marking to protect cultivated lands, but a considerable knowledge of the behaviour of the species will be needed if they are to be used effectively.

Birds

Public sentiment is strongly against poisoning birds, even those which it is legal to kill and even when they are seen to do extensive damage. In the U.K. the wood-pigeon is a major pest. It causes about £5m per year agricultural loss. One approach to chemical control is to use a bait containing a non-lethal narcotic. For this purpose chloralose is almost exclusively used. Shortly after feeding on the treated grains, birds become stupid and sleepy. If left alone, they recover completely. The farmer can kill all the wood-pigeons and put the pheasants in a safe place to recover. Use as a bait of large grain, such as field beans, which smaller birds cannot swallow, helps to make the operation automatically selective. The wood-pigeon is, however, a very mobile pest and destruction on one isolated farm is of little value. Labour-costly use of chloralose can therefore be effective only in a co-operative campaign carried out by all farmers in an extensive area. Consequently it has been little used.

Chemical repellents would be useful. Sprays that, while harmless, would make buds unpalatable to bullfinches, seeds unpalatable to rooks and pigeons, bark unpalatable to rabbits and deer, would satisfy every interest. Unfortunately there has been little progress along these lines. Products based on impure anthraquinone are used successfully in seed dressing to reduce consumption by rooks, but they are not effective with most bird species.

4-aminopyridine (4-AP) causes individual members of a flock of birds to utter vocal signals of distress which act as an area repellent to the rest of the flock. It is widely used in orchards and market gardens as it is harmless to the birds. The insecticide methiocarb is an effective bird-repellent which is extensively used in the U.S.A. and is probably the best product currently available to protect ripe fruit. Despite a certain amount of suspicion from ornithologists it has been approved for this purpose by the Environmental Protection Agency.

It is salutary to realize that by far the most significant aspect of the bird pest problem nowadays is the danger they present to jet aircraft and consequently to life and safety of passengers, a risk which grows as aircraft get bigger and more numerous. Methods of dispersing birds from airfields are badly needed.

General

It is noteworthy that, apart from modern rodenticides, the chemicals used to control vertebrates are very primitive compared with those used to control insects. Mainly they are inorganics such as arsenates, thallium, phosphorus and cyanide or natural products such as strychnine or red squill. This compares with the state of the art in insecticides 100 years ago when the main compounds used were arsenates and nicotine. There are very strong pressure groups, particularly in the U.S.A., to prevent chemical control of mammals and birds so that they can be shot for "sport".

Control of vertebrates is an example of the need to develop systems of total pest management, in which chemicals will play merely one part. An essential prerequisite for developing such systems is a detailed knowledge of the ecology of the pest species, and of its population dynamics. Most control methods currently used depress numbers for a short time only, which has the effect of reducing competition and increasing breeding success, so the population rapidly reestablishes itself. Shooting and trapping in particular effect only minor local improvements. Effective control requires understanding of habits and behaviour, for example, it may be much more effective to shoot or trap when numbers are low instead of waiting, as is customary, until numbers are high. There is obviously scope for "second-generation" chemicals which do not kill directly but provide control by affecting some aspect of behaviour. If the pest can be deterred from the crop there may be no need actually to kill it.

Further Reading

Davis, R. A. *Control of Rats and Mice*, Ministry of Agriculture, Fisheries and Food Bulletin, No. 181, H.M.S.O., London, 1961.
Murton, R. K. and Wright, E. N. (Eds.) *The Problems of Birds as Pests*, Institute of Biology Symposium, No. 17, Academic Press, London and New York, 1968.

15
Fungal Diseases and Protection by Heavy Metal Compounds

Fungal Diseases

The fungi form a very large group of primitive plants which cover a wide range of size and habit, from the field mushroom and its larger relatives to unicellular yeasts. Most fungi have a complex life cycle. They are propagated by means of asexually produced spores which, in many species, are of more than one type. A sexual stage is also known in most species, but many, including potato blight, can persist through thousands of generations without it. Some spores are very short-lived and must quickly reach a favourable environment to survive. Other spores, usually from the sexual stage, can remain viable in a dormant condition for a long period in a dry or cold environment. This resting stage is often essential for survival of the species from one season to the next. Some species go through many cycles in one season. Others, like those living inside mature trees and forming fruiting "brackets" outside the bark, take many years from one fruiting stage to the next.

Fungi are devoid of chlorophyll. They must therefore obtain their energy-food from other organic matter. The saprophytes live on dead matter and are largely responsible for the breakdown of animal and plant remains in the soil. In this role they are essential in agriculture but they can also attack structural materials of natural origin — timber, and fabrics based on vegetable or animal fibres. Such materials are more at risk in an agricultural than in an urban situation — fencing posts more than roof timbers, stack covers more than household linen. Protection of timber against fungi has been touched on in Chapter 7.

A few fungi, for example the several species causing "ring-worm", are parasitic on animals, including man. Within the chemical industry the manufacture of compounds for the treatment of these diseases is accepted as belonging to the pharmaceutical branch and will not be dealt with in this book. The fungi causing plant diseases are accepted as targets for the pesticides industry. These fungi are the most effective competitors of man for the products of his agricultural labour. Chemical control and selection of immune varieties are the only alternatives to indirect practices of good husbandry — crop rotation, general hygienic measures and evasive tactics. Often these indirect practices are in conflict with efficient business organization of simple cropping systems.

A few fungal species, notably of the genus *Botrytis*, can be either saprophytic or parasitic. The soft rots of strawberry and raspberry fruits, for example, overwinter on ground litter and usually spread on to the fruits from adhering dead leaf or calyx fragments. Many parasitic fungi are, however, highly specialized, and can develop only on living tissues of a single, or few, host species.

Often there are two quite different hosts, each harbouring a different phase of the complex life-cycle. The rust disease of wheat has the barberry as an alternate host and the rust of white pine the currant. Drastic manual weeding-out of barberry in the wheat areas of France, and later of the U.S.A., led to a considerable reduction in the incidence of rust. Control of pine rust by eradication of currant species in forest areas of U.S.A. is not yet so successful, probably because there are too many small wild plants. Herbicides are now being used in this indirect attack on a fungus. In the U.K., where currant is abundant and cultivated, the planting of white pine has been abandoned. One side-result is a minor export trade in blackcurrant juice from the U.K. to the U.S.A.

Many other examples could be quoted where the prevalence of a parasitic fungus has prevented the cultivation of a crop in an area otherwise suitable. Fungus attack is more damaging in large-scale monocultures than in a natural mixed stand where sensitive host individuals are widely spaced. Increasing level of parasite population is the chief reason for the adoption of crop-rotation practices. For these reasons it is very difficult to assess the economic damage done by parasitic fungi, much of this damage being hidden and indirect. Even the direct damage is enormous.

Host and Parasite

The big problem in the chemical attack on parasitic fungi is that of toxicity to the host. Host and parasite are too close biochemically. The biggest difference is the presence of a photosynthetic mechanism in the higher plants. Photosynthesis is localized in the small chloroplasts inside the leaf cells. These produce the sucrose, which the rest of the plant uses by similar biochemical reactions to those operating in a fungus for metabolic energy and as the source of combined carbon. A higher plant can, in fact, almost be considered, from the biochemical point of view, as a fungus parasitic on its own chloroplasts. This is not far from the truth even from the anatomical viewpoint. The primitive green lichens consist of a non-green fungus species enveloping a separately reproduced population of unicellular green algae, living in intimate and necessary association (symbiosis). Most higher plants show a relic of this behaviour in that the chlorophyll is carried in the cytoplasm of the seed-germ and is not genetically controlled by the chromosomes.

Several important herbicides inactivate an essential step in photosynthesis and are lethal to higher plants without much affecting fungi. The fact that this major biochemical difference is the wrong way round makes the search for safe fungicides more difficult. Once the parasitic fungus has gained entry to the host tissues, the discrimination must be biochemical and the compound must be systemic. However, many practical "fungicides" act only prophylactically. They must be applied before the fungus invades so that they can lie on the outside of the tough leaf cuticle of the host ready to attack the fungus spore at the germinating stage, when it is most vulnerable.

Disinfection of Seed

Some diseases overwinter as dormant spores on the seed of the host. The host and parasite germinate together and the parasite lives internally in the host without killing it. Its spores are either produced alongside the seeds of the host or replace these seeds and then infect healthy seed through the air. The most important of such diseases are the smuts and bunt of wheat, but many others are in this class. They are controlled by chemicals applied to the crop seed before sowing. The spores are not affected while in the dormant state but are killed as they germinate. The germ tube of the parasite must move over the host seed surface seeking entry, while the host radicle grows more rapidly and downwards, away from the seed. Selective toxicity to the parasite is largely dependent on this geometrical difference.

The "dressing" of seed protects the future crop not only against seed-borne diseases but also against soil-borne fungal diseases and voracious insects. Its effectiveness is necessarily limited because of the very localized application and the need for biochemical selectivity. The convenience and economy of seed-dressing makes it, however, a clear choice when the disease can be controlled this way.

Protective Fungicides for Growing Crops

If a purely protective, rather than systemic, fungicide is to be effective it must stop the infection from "taking" on the crop. At this stage the fungus spore is exposed and vulnerable and a compound applied to the leaf surface has the best chance of being taken up into the germ tube of the spore while not penetrating significantly into the tissue of the mature leaf. Once the fungal hyphae have penetrated into the internal cells of the host a protective fungicide ceases to be effective. It is significant that the only fungi which are fairly effectively dealt with after establishment — the powdery mildews — penetrate only into the superficial leaf cells. These diseases are caused by a very high population of very small individuals.

Much the largest tonnage of protective fungicides used in agriculture consists of inorganic compounds of copper of low solubility and either elementary sulphur or organic compounds containing sulphur. Some of these products are only a little younger than the knowledge that most plant diseases are caused by fungi.

Potato blight hit Europe, particularly Ireland, in 1842. About ten years later, due mainly to the work of a great amateur in the U.K. the Rev. M. J. Berkeley, and a great professional in Germany, Anton de Bary, it was becoming recognized that a parasitic fungus could be responsible. It took another ten years at least, after much academic polemics, for this idea to be generally accepted. Sulphur dust had already been used successfully against the powdery mildew of vines, and first salt, then later copper sulphate dried off with lime, had been found to give a cleaner crop of wheat after application to the seed. The use of salt was suggested by the clean crop resulting from seed salvaged from a shipwreck.

It was not till 1882 that Millardet in France saw the significance of another accidental discovery. A paste of lime and copper sulphate had been painted on vines by the roadside in the Bordeaux district solely to discourage local boys from stealing the fruit. Millardet realized that this "Bordeaux mixture" had discouraged a far more deadly enemy than schoolboys. The downy mildew which had been building up to disastrous levels in France was not attacking the roadside vines.

There have, of course, been developments in the inorganic copper and sulphur products made available by the industry, but the changes have been more concerned with cost, packaging and convenience factors than with biological efficiency. Many plant pathologists consider that the original Bordeaux mixture made up in the field is frequently found to be more effective in comparative tests and never less efficient than the more convenient modern products.

It is very difficult to decide whether one product is generally a more efficient protective fungicide than another. The comments in the next section refer directly to copper fungicides and potato blight but are relevant to protective applications of "insoluble" fungicides in general against diseases which infect the foliage from the air.

Efficacy of Protective Treatment

The reason for the difficulty is that the biological and climatic variables may have an over-riding influence. These include local intensity of source of infection, many aspects of climatic conditions including weather *after* treatment, nutritional status of the crop, predisposing damage to the crop by wind and insects. In the case of potato blight, if the sprayings have been perfectly timed, almost any copper product will be effective. At the other extreme, if spraying is left until symptoms are already present, no practical field treatment is of any real value. Unfortunately, choice of timing cannot be made entirely on facts known at the time of choice, since future weather, and therefore "luck", is important.

Intermediate conditions can occur where, in well laid-out trials, formulation X can be shown to be significantly more effective than formulation Y, but other conditions can occur where the reverse is true. It is important for the chemist to realize this kind of limitation on the improvements he can make at the chemical end, and some brief explanation is therefore justified of how these differences can arise. It is possible to state the significance of some factors clearly, while admitting that there are others whose significance may be as great but not known. Only the influence of solubility and adhesion will be discussed here.

At one extreme, some copper compounds are too soluble. If a solution of the sulphate is sprayed and the weather remains dry, the crop will be severely damaged or even killed. If sufficient rain follows soon enough to save the crop, there will not be an effective residual deposit to prevent the germination of incoming spores. Copper sulphate cannot, therefore, be used alone as a fungicide. At the other extreme, some copper compounds, e.g. cuprous iodide or cupric ferrocyanide, are so insoluble that they have no effect on either host or parasite. An intermediate solubility, like that of the hydroxide or many basic salts, and some degree of adhesion of the solid to the leaf are necessary. These factors enable surface moisture (without which the spore cannot germinate) to let the copper migrate to the spore but prevent total loss in the first shower of rain.

It is evident that there is no absolute optimum either for solubility or adhesiveness. If heavy rain is going to occur a few days after spraying, the only product which may give any degree of residual control is one of very low solubility and high adhesion. If only dew or drizzle is experienced after spraying, a better residual deposit will be obtained from a more soluble product. It is true that a deposit which will survive heavy rain will be at least as active after light drizzle, but the pressure of infection is likely to be much greater in the second case, since the heavy rain washes off most of the spores it brings. There is thus a different optimum set of physical properties for the two weather conditions.

One answer to this problem is to use formulations with a range of properties so that the behaviour is at least adequate under a wide range of weather conditions. This accounts for the success of products which include other fungicides (dithiocarbamates and organotin compounds, see below) along with low-soluble copper compounds.

By careful addition of aqueous ammonia (3 equivalents) to well-stirred aqueous cupric chloride (4 equivalents) and subsequent dialysis through cellulose, an indefinitely stable colloidal solution of the oxychloride can be obtained. It has been claimed that products of this type can produce a more complete and uniform cover by spraying. While this is true under idealized laboratory conditions, the property confers doubtful advantage in the field. As the suspension concentrates by evaporation after spraying, coagulation of the colloidal matter occurs, particularly if hard water has been used to dilute the concentrate. Moreover, the fine structure of the deposit within any small area is usually of less significance than the gross pattern which results from the wetting and drainage behaviour of the diluted suspension as a whole and its redistribution by the action of dew and rain.

In the case of potato blight, the conclusions drawn from laboratory and field experiments seem widely at variance. In the laboratory a very uniform coverage of finely divided fungicide is necessary to give efficient protection against a heavy artificial inoculum. In the field, a relatively poor deposit, even that produced by low-volume spraying from the air, appears to give as good a protection as that obtained by high-volume spraying. No spraying is of much value once the disease is active within the crop. The last sentence gives a useful clue to the general explanation of the discrepancy. The field spraying protects the crop only against the incoming inoculum from distant sources. This test is not made in the laboratory. After "ideal" application in the laboratory, which cannot even be approached in the field, protection can be secured against a dense inoculum of fresh spores.

Why the high population of fresh spores is so much more resistant is not clearly understood, but the reason why the spores which have travelled for a distance are killed by a not very uniform deposit is probably that they need liquid water to germinate. The infection therefore starts within the portion of the leaf covered by the pendant drops at the lower margins. The water forming these drops has collected both copper and spores.

"Fixed Coppers"

Bordeaux mixture is prepared by mixing a slurry of lime in water into a solution of copper sulphate in water. This is often done in the actual spray tank. Originally, quicklime was employed but it is now possible to supply slaked lime packaged so as to avoid carbonating. Calcium carbide has been used as a source of lime slurry, but explosion, probably initiated by cuprous acetylide, has occurred. The lime is added in considerable molecular excess, about equal in weight to the hydrated "blue vitriol". The final product contains about 12.75% of metallic copper. It is very safe to use because its toxicity to men and animals is low. The rather gelatinous nature of the fresh precipitate (and Bordeaux mixture should be made immediately before use) helps to increase the deposit by delaying drainage from high-volume application. The carbonation of the excess lime during exposure on the leaf probably assists the adhesion of the final deposit.

Bordeaux mixture was rapidly followed by Burgundy mixture, in which the lime is replaced by washing soda. In *eau celeste* excess ammonia was used to hold the copper in solution in the sprayer but liberate it on exposure. Much more risk of plant damage was incurred by its use, not only because the copper is transiently more available but because a high concentration of free ammonia is itself phytotoxic. Neither of these two products is used today. They have been replaced by the single package "fixed coppers" in which a finely divided low-soluble copper compound is packed in a form stable in storage and readily dispersible in water only. The copper compound is usually a basic cupric salt.

The solubility of these compounds is not easily defined nor is its significance simple. The free cupric ion concentration present in a suspension in distilled water should be less than about 5 ppm. The solubility is, however, inevitably dependent on pH. While water on a leaf surface is likely to be slightly alkaline, potassium carbonate being excreted more freely than organic acids, the germinating fungus spores often excrete other compounds, of which the simplest is glycine, which form soluble chelates with cupric ions. The fungus spore therefore generally accumulates copper within itself at a much higher concentration than that of free ionic copper in a water suspension of the fungicide.

Nearly all the copper is precipitated from aqueous solutions of cupric salts by less alkali than corresponds to a simple stoichiometric equation — e.g. $CuCl_2 + 2NaOH \rightarrow Cu(OH)_2 + 2NaCl$. Precipitation is usually complete with about three-quarters of this amount of alkali, and the existence of some definite crystalline compounds has been demonstrated by X-ray analysis. The most widely used compound is the oxychloride, of approximate composition $3Cu(OH)_2 . CuCl_2$. It is usually prepared by reaction of hydrochloric acid on scrap metallic copper in the presence of blown air.

The oxychloride forms as a very fine suspension which is filtered off, dried and mixed with a small proportion of wetting agent and a sticker such as starch or glue. The particle size in the final suspension remains finer if the concentrated product is marketed without drying, but packaging of suspensions is troublesome and their behaviour on storage unreliable. It is generally sold as a 50% wettable powder or 10%-25% dusts.

Other copper compounds of a similar type which have been used include basic copper sulphate, $CuSO_4 . 3Cu(OH)_2 . H_2O$, basic copper carbonate, $Cu(OH)_2 . CuCO_3$, tetracopper calcium oxychloride, $4Cu(OH)_2 . CaCl_2$, and basic cupric zinc sulphate complex. All these compounds, like the oxychloride, have low toxicities to men and animals.

Products containing yellow cuprous oxide can be used in place of the many basic cupric salts available. This compound is obtained as a fine precipitate during reduction of cupric salts in buffered solution. It is best known to most chemists as the solid produced in Fehling's solution by reducing sugars. Such processes are, of course, far too costly for a commodity product to be used in agriculture, and, industrially, an electrolytic oxidation is used. Cuprous oxide is therefore mainly produced in countries with cheap water power. Cuprous oxide is much less soluble in distilled water, in the absence of air, than are the basic cupric salts but it is slowly brought into solution by oxidation on exposure. As in the case of the cupric compounds, the reaction with leaf and spore exudates is important.

There is no clear evidence of advantage for either cuprous oxide or basic cupric salts for control of any one fungus disease. Preference depends more often on local prejudices and the impact of effective salesmanship than on technical performance. Even colour has had an influence on the choice. The blue-green cupric products leave a less noticeable deposit on foliage (an advantage perhaps to the seller of the crop but a disadvantage for the spray operator) but the yellow colour of cuprous oxide has the merit in Buddhist countries of a holy and healing significance. One of the authors has been asked in all seriousness during his technical career to colour cuprous oxide green and to colour cupric oxychloride yellow.

Substantially different copper formulations are those in which an organic salt is formed and applied in oil solution. The mixed naphthenic acids (carboxylic acids of alicyclic hydrocarbons) obtained from petroleum oxidation are the most widely used but salts of fatty acids, particularly linoleic and oleic, are also oil soluble and, in this state very fungicidal. These compounds have been mentioned in Chapter 7 for wood preservation. They have been tried in agriculture but are too phytotoxic to be acceptable for most applications.

Other Inorganic Fungicides

Mercury

Many heavy metals are highly toxic, especially to micro-organisms. The decoration with silver of some foodstuffs available to the wealthy minorities in the Indian subcontinent probably has its justification in protection against microparasites of the gut. This metal has also been used in the treatment of ringworm. The metals other than copper which have found fungicidal use in agriculture are zinc, chromium and nickel used in inorganic forms, mercury, used both in inorganic and organic compounds and tin, used only in organic compounds. Germanium and lead compounds analagous to those of tin have also been tried but without showing any advantage. Cadmium succinate is used as a fungicide on turf.

Zinc and copper complex chromates have been found useful against potato blight but have not survived long comparison with the standard copper products and later developments. In practice, therefore, other inorganic usage is confined to mercury and nickel salts. Of the former, the almost insoluble mercurous chloride is used by soil application, particularly against club-root disease of the cabbage tribe. It is also effective against fungi which damage fine turf. Mercury salts are toxic to most organisms and these dressings also control the cabbage-root-fly, other soil insects and nematodes. For effective control of the latter, however, the toxicant must be dispersed through several inches depth of soil. Although it has been claimed that the vapour of elementary mercury, to which the salt may be reduced in the soil, is able to diffuse in the soil air-space, too high a dosage is required to be economic.

Mercury is an inherently toxic element and some concern has been felt about the possible environmental effects of slow build-up of soil residues. Fears on this score may not, however, be well-founded, since all heavy metals tend to get locked up in insoluble forms among the soil minerals. Many soils contain more unavailable native mercury than is applied as a pesticide. Nevertheless, in the present climate of public concern about possible environmental effects of pesticides, even if unproved, the use of mercury compounds has come into disfavour and all registrations for use on food crops in the U.S.A. have been cancelled.

Nickel Salts

Water-soluble nickel salts, such as the chloride, are far from non-toxic to higher plants if used in excess, but they are sufficiently more active against some fungal parasites, particularly wheat rusts, to permit their use for effective control. Some degree of curative action (i.e. killing of the established parasite) and systemic effect is claimed. The observation is of particular interest because wheat rust is very erratic in its incidence. In most years there is negligible damage. Occasionally, about one year in six, very serious loss of crop can result. To insure the crop, considerable stock-piling of fungicide is necessary and this is much more feasible when a heavy inorganic chemical with many other uses is the one which has to be called into action.

Organomercury Fungicides

Mercury, more easily than most other metals, forms stable organic compounds in which it is linked to carbon. Such compounds are all fungitoxic, many of them much more so, under practical conditions of application, than inorganic salts. The advantage is often associated with greater volatility, which permits a more uniform redistribution among dressed seeds during storage than can be obtained in initial mixing. It also permits some desirable movement in the soil air space.

Excessive volatility, can however, give rise to user-hazard. Casualties have occurred in factories handling ethyl mercury chlorides (EMC). These probably arose from disproportionation

$$2C_2H_5HgCl \rightleftharpoons (C_2H_5)_2Hg + HgCl_2$$

yielding the more volatile mercury diethyl (b.p. 160°C). For this reason, and because the toxicity of EMC to men and animals is high, it is little used nowadays and the main mercury compounds which are still used in agriculture are phenylmercury acetate (PMA) and methoxyethylmercury silicate (MEMS) or acetate (MEMA). They are used exclusively as seed dressings or for fungal control in turf.

It should be noted that mercury and organomercury salts have much more covalent character than those of most metals and one cannot assume that these salts are effectively involatile. Mercuric chloride, for example, has a boiling point of 301°C and mercuric oxide is noticeably volatile in steam. The choice among the wholly covalent and partly electrovalent substituents on the mercury atom is largely determined by solubility, volatility and stability rather than by inherent fungitoxicity. There is a general tendency towards larger substituents than ethyl in the organic part. Phenylmercury and methoxyethyl mercury compounds are now more widely used for the reasons given above.

Synthesis of Organomercury Compounds

The compounds can almost always be prepared by the Grignard synthesis, but for the two main classes of organomercury compounds, cheaper industrial routes are available. The Kharasch method for diethylmercury chloride reacts lead tetraethyl with mercuric chloride. Lead tetraethyl is made in large tonnage as a motor fuel additive and is itself prepared by reaction of a sodium-lead alloy with ethyl chloride. Schematically,

$$Na_4Pb + 4C_2H_5Cl \longrightarrow 4NaCl + Pb(C_2H_5)_4$$

(in fact the alloy must be much richer in lead and the excess reused), followed by

$$2HgCl_2 + Pb(C_2H_5)_4 \longrightarrow 2C_2H_5.HgCl + (C_2H_5)_2PbCl_2.$$

The reactions are general for alkyl substituents, but the availability of lead tetraethyl directed chief attention to ethylmercury compounds. Other anions can be left attached to the ethylmercury cation by choice of the appropriate mercuric salt or a mixture of mercuric oxide and the appropriate acid. Thus, ethylmercury acetate (EMA) can be made by reaction of mercuric oxide, acetic acid and lead tetraethyl at 90–95°C.

In the preparation of ethylmercury compounds by this route, the reactants are usually ball-milled in the dry state with an inert mineral diluent. The lead compounds remain in the mixture, which is further diluted if necessary with inert powder and wetting agent to give the formulated product directly. If a pure product is required, soluble ethylmercury acetate is first produced which is extracted with water from the insoluble lead compounds. From this solution a less soluble ethylmercury compound can be precipitated.

Use of a higher proportion of tetraethyl lead enables mercury diethyl to be formed. Ethylmercury salts can be prepared by heating the appropriate acid and mercury diethyl, e.g.

$$Hg(C_2H_5)_2 + CH_3CO_2H \rightarrow C_2H_5HgOCOCH_3 + C_2H_6$$

By reaction of aniline with 4-toluene sulphonyl chloride at 80–90° to give 4-toluene sulphonanilide, followed by treatment with ethylmercury acetate at 20–30°C, ethylmercury 4-toluenesulphonanilide is obtained. This is a somewhat less toxic compound than ethylmercury chloride and has been used as a seed dressing.

Ethylmercury 4-toluenesulphonanilide

Some organomercury compounds can be obtained more directly by displacement of hydrogen in aromatic compounds or addition of ethylenic compounds.

Thus the important phenylmercury acetate (PMA) can be obtained in 90% yield by heating benzene and mercuric acetate in glacial acetic acid under pressure at 110°C for 2 hr.

$$C_6H_6 + Hg(O.CO.CH_3)_2 \longrightarrow C_6H_5.Hg.O.CO.CH_3 + CH_3CO_2H$$

The more reactive ring in 2-chlorophenol can react even with mercuric oxide to give hydroxymercury-2-chlorophenol which has also been used as an agricultural fungicide for seed dressing.

Hydroxymercury-2-chlorophenol

A suspension of mercuric acetate in methanol absorbs 1 mol of ethylene to give methoxyethylmercury acetate (MEMA).

$$CH_3OH + CH_2{=}CH_2 + Hg(O.CO.CH_3)_2 \longrightarrow$$
$$CH_3OCH_2CH_2{-}Hg{-}O.CO.CH_3 + CH_3CO_2H.$$

Less soluble methoxyethyl mercury salts, such as the silicate (MEMS), are effective seed dressings.

Phenylmercury salts can add on to tertiary amines to give quaternary nitrogen compounds in which one of the four valences of the N atom binds it to Hg. Such a compound is phenylmercury triethanolammonium lactate, a water-soluble compound with a high affinity for wool which has found more application for moth-proofing than for control of fungi on crops.

Organotin Compounds as Fungicides

In 1950 a fruitful collaboration began between the International Tin Research Council in London and the Institute for Organic Chemistry in Utrecht. The research on fungitoxic properties of organotin compounds has been reviewed by van der Kerk. A review by Ascher and Nissim on the potential value of these compounds as insecticides can also usefully be consulted.

The organic compounds of tin have advantage over those of mercury in that tin is not an inherently toxic element. The toxicity arises from reaction of the molecular compound. It is much greater in those compounds of tetravalent tin in which three covalent Sn–C links are present than in compounds of the type R_2SnX_2 or SnR_4 where R as usual signifies a hydrocarbon radical and X an anionic group.

The biggest usage of an organotin compound is for stabilization of some transparent plastics against photochemical attack, for which purpose tributyltin oxide, $(C_4H_9)_3Sn–O–Sn(C_4H_9)_3$ is preferred. This compound has considerable biocidal properties and has found much use in rot-proofing of fabrics and as a constituent of anti-fouling paints which prevent the growth of barnacles and algae on ships' bottoms. Although expensive for timber preservation, it is to date the most effective compound for protecting wood piles in marine harbours against the destructive attack of the toredo worm.

Despite the non-toxicity of elementary tin, the development of organotin compounds suffered a serious set-back through one of the worst incidents involving death by poisoning in recent history. It happened in France in 1954 when a number of innocent users of a new skin disinfectant were fatally poisoned. The compound was nominally the relatively harmless diethylin diiodide but was found to contain a high proportion of the very toxic triethyltin iodide. It is not rational for an error of ignorance or carelessness to bring into disrepute all related compounds — but it was inevitable. Only now have safer compounds, with proper knowledge of their risks, become accepted. In most countries agricultural use is restricted to ornamentals and root crops.

The compounds now of most importance are triphenyltin salts. These are less toxic to mammals than the trialkyl, particularly triethyl, tin salts and it is perhaps an advantage that the desired compounds are more toxic than the associated impurities. If appropriate precautions are taken in handling triphenyltin acetate, the presence of diphenyl and tetraphenyltin will create no new problem.

The trialkyltin compounds are too phytotoxic for safe use on growing crops. Success for tin compounds in this field came with the introduction of triphenyltin acetate (fentin acetate) and triphenyltin hydroxide (fentin hydroxide).

Fentin acetate

This compound has been used for control of leaf spot diseases of sugarbeet and celery and blight of potatoes. There is use in other crops too, but on others again the compound is too damaging. Although more phytotoxic than "fixed coppers" at the same dosage, it is used, for successful fungus control, at only about one-tenth of the dosage. Higher yield increases of the crops mentioned have been found to follow control with triphenyltin than have followed control with copper. It has been suggested that triphenyltin has some growth stimulant effect at low dosage, but the view is more generally held that "copper shock" produces a growth depression, without visible damage, which partly off-sets the effect of fungus control.

Two related compounds which have found use as protective foliar fungicides are decyltriphenylphosphonium-bromochloro-triphenylstannate (decafentin) and di-|tri-(2-methyl-2-phenylpropyl)tin|oxide (fenbutatin oxide).

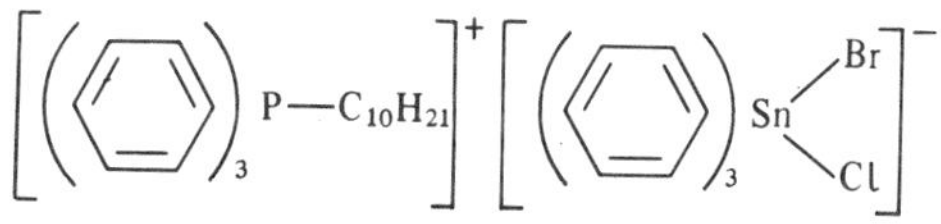

Decafentin

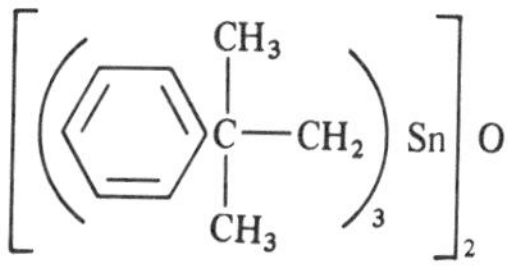

Fenbutatin oxide

A tin compound which has found extensive use, not as a fungicide, but as an acaricide, is tricyclohexyltin hydroxide (cyhexatin).

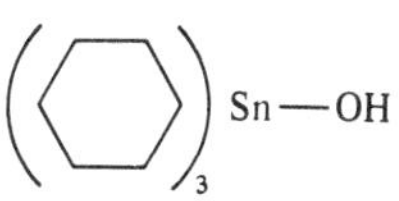

Cyhexatin

A related compound, also used as an acaricide, is 1-tricyclohexylstannyl-1,2,4-triazole (azocyclotin).

Chemistry of Organotin Compounds

Trialkyl and triaryl tins are fairly stable cations forming salts with strong acids. Weak acids form salts which are extensively hydrolysed in water. Thus triphenyltin acetate, a white solid, soluble to about 20 ppm of water, is fairly rapidly converted, in contact with water, to the much less soluble oxide. There is some degree of covalent behaviour but not so extensive as with corresponding mercury compounds, and ionic replacement reactions are very rapid. All the compounds form sulphides of very low solubility and react rapidly with mercaptans. Affinity of the triorganotin radicals for–SH groups in biochemical systems is probably the basis of their toxic behaviour.

Tin can be effectively combined with hydrocarbon radicals only by the use of Grignard intermediate. The preferred industrial procedure is to use the alkyl or aryl magnesium halide in slight excess so as to obtain first the neutral non-polar tetraalkyl or tetraaryltin which can be removed by extraction with non-polar solvents or by distillation. The tetra compound is then reacted back with stannic chloride, a reaction which, in the case of tin, gives preponderantly the compound having the average composition, thus:

$$3SnR_4 + SnCl_4 \rightarrow 4R_3SnCl$$

The desired salt is then obtained by metathesis.

The organotin compounds are inevitably expensive, because of the scarcity of available elementary tin and the rather expensive reaction process. They are however very active. The big demands in the plastics field for organotins has stimulated work on conditions for maximum production efficiency.

Further Reading

See page 206.

16

Sulphur, Organosulphur and Other Organic Fungicides

Sulphur

Elemental sulphur — in the form of flowers of sulphur, produced by sublimation and applied as dust — was the first successful protective fungicide. It was used against the powdery mildew of vines. It is also toxic to spider mites and a single treatment often has both effects, since mite and powdery mildew attacks are at their worst during hot, dry weather. About 75,000 tonnes of sulphur are still used annually as a pesticide in the United States, 13,000 as an acaricide on citrus and the rest as a fungicide on apples, peaches, cherries, vines and sugar beet. It is interesting to note that the 13,000 tonnes used on citrus compares with a total of 2,000 tonnes of all other insecticides and acaricides, although it must be realized that sulphur is applied at 20–40 lb/acre compared with 2–4 lb/acre for organic compounds. The reason why sulphur is still used on such a large scale is that it is cheap and is very safe to handle and poses no risks to human and animal health or to the environment. Also, it does not produce resistance and many growers are turning back to it after disillusion with the short effective life of many organic acaricides.

Elemental sulphur is now usually ground to a finer powder than "flowers" with the addition of a mineral diluent (see Chapter 22), particularly when the product is made wettable and intended for application by spraying after suspension in water. Modern techniques of manufacture now favour production of micronized wettable sulphurs which contain no diluent but just wetting agents. These can be produced with 100% of particles in the range 1 to 6 microns and 95% between 2 and 3 microns. They mix instantaneously with water to give a suspension which is stable even in hard water and is completely compatible with Bordeaux mixture and with all organic pesticides Because of the even particle size adhesion to leaves tends to be greater and the coverage is more uniform so that the effect, which is entirely one of contact activity, is enhanced.

Liquid sulphur at 99.9% pure is filtered hot and mixed under pressure with an aqueous solution of a dispersing agent and stirred while hot and passed through a colloid mill to give an emulsion in which the liquid sulphur is dispersed as fine droplets. This is passed through filters so that the final dispersion contains only droplets in the particle size range of 1 to 6 microns. The dispersion is then cooled so that the droplets solidify. More dispersing agent and antifoam is added and the suspension is then spray-dried.

Sulphur is one of the substances which can be brought into a "classical" colloidal suspension and has particular interest in this state since remarkably monodisperse material can be made, usually by the slow reaction of sodium thiosulphate in dilute solution with mineral acid. A much cheaper way of producing a concentrated suspension is by the interaction of hydrogen sulphide and sulphur dioxide simultaneously introduced into water containing stabilizing agents. Colloidal sulphur concentrates prepared in this way are still obtainable, but they have the usual storage and transport difficulties of this type of formulation.

A previously much used liquid sulphur product is the so-called "lime-sulphur". This is a clear reddish-yellow liquid, stable in the absence of air and light, obtained by adding elementary sulphur to a boiling water slurry of slaked lime. Both lime and sulphur pass into solution, concentrates with as high a density as 1.3 being easily obtained. The sulphur is mainly present as polysulphide ions, $-S- (S)_x -S-$, where x represents a scatter of numbers in the neighbourhood of 2. The oxygen of the lime appears mainly as thiosulphate. A very approximate representation of a typical reaction, in which 50 kg of calcium oxide and 100 kg of sulphur are finally brought into solution in 1000 litres is

$$6\,CaO + 21\,S \longrightarrow 6\,Ca^{++} + 2\,S_2O_3^= + 3\,S_4^= + S_5^=.$$

There is a slight residual alkalinity and the polysulphide ions are stable in absence of light and air. The corresponding free acids deposit sulphur and liberate hydrogen sulphide. This decomposition occurs when the diluted spray takes up atmospheric carbon dioxide on exposure, the initially clear pale yellow spray liquid becoming milky over a period of a few minutes after spraying.

The alkalinity and salinity of lime-sulphur sprays and the evolution of hydrogen sulphide make them more aggressive and more phytotoxic than sprays of suspended sulphur. Phytotoxicity is increased by the presence of oil, and lime-sulphur should not be tank-mixed with emulsified pesticides. On chemical grounds it is also a rather incompatible product. Its alkalinity contra-indicates its admixture with easily hydrolyzed organic pesticides, such as parathion. The hydrogen sulphide evolved inactivates heavy metals present so that it cannot be used with lead arsenate or with sprays intended to contribute deficient trace-metals, such as manganese or iron. Lime-sulphur is therefore usually employed by itself. It is effective for the control of powdery mildews on vines, hops and some other fruit, apple scab and some leaf-spot diseases. Used at sufficient dilution, damage to the crop can be avoided except on particular varieties known to the grower as "sulphur-shy". More concentrated lime-sulphur sprays are used against the overwintering spores of some diseases, such as leaf-curl of peach, during the dormant period of the host. However, because it is caustic and disagreeable to use, lime-sulphur is mostly being replaced by products more easy and pleasant to handle.

Lime-sulphur is, of course, chemically incompatible with copper sprays because of the precipitation of cuprous sulphide. There is also something complementary, and perhaps antagonistic, in the biological action of these fungicides. The spread of some diseases can be arrested by *either* copper or sulphur treatment, but, against most diseases, one or the other is clearly advantageous. Thus powdery mildews are much more susceptible to sulphur than to copper, while the reverse is true of the downy mildew diseases. When choice is made between them, sulphur is always used against the Oidium disease of rubber trees but copper always against potato blight and blister blight of tea.

Copper is one of the minor elements essential for all forms of life. Either excess or deficiency can be lethal, but, for most forms of life, including man, the right internal adjustment is made over a wide range of availability in the environment. The fungi appear to be more critically dependent on the external availability of copper than most organisms. A rather obvious theory of the fungicidal action of sulphur products held that they produced critical copper deficiency by insolubilizing copper as the sulphide or a mercaptide. No clear evidence in support of this theory has, however, been brought forward. Another theory drew a parallel between the action of elementary sulphur in cross-linking ("vulcanizing") raw rubber and its fungicidal effect. This theory was cruder and even more improbable, since the conditions of reactions are widely different. Nevertheless is was very productive in causing tests to be made of the various sulphur compounds developed in the rubber industry to accelerate and control the vulcanization reaction. This led to the discovery of what have been to date the most widely used of organic fungicides, produced on a scale comparable with that of the herbicide 2,4-D and the insecticide DDT at its peak. These are the dithiocarbamates.

Dithiocarbamates and Related Compounds

Chemistry
Carbon disulphide reacts with primary or secondary alkylamines to form alkylamides of dithiocarbonic acid. The half amides are formed very readily. They are acidic and usually called dithiocarbamic acids. The free acids are

not stable but the salts are much more stable and so the reaction is normally carried out in the presence of aqueous alkali to give a solution of the alkali metal salt:

$$RR'NH + CS_2 + NaOH \longrightarrow RR'N.CS.SNa + H_2O$$

If the reaction is carried out with excess amine in place of alkali and the resulting alkylammonium salt of the dithiocarbamic acid is heated, a thiourea is formed, H_2S being liberated. If the alkali salt is reacted with an alkyl halide, a rather stable ester is formed. Many such compounds have been prepared but have no importance as fungicides. Their formulae are given to illustrate the structures.

Tetraalkylthiourea   Alkyl ester of dialkyl
                            dithiocarbamic acid

The dithiocarbamates are very reactive compounds and it is impossible here to deal with all the reactions which they can undergo involving oxidation and loss of sulphur. *The Dithiocarbamates and Related Compounds* by Thorn and Ludwig should be consulted for further information on chemistry, biochemistry and fungicidal action. Two reactions of great importance must, however, be mentioned.

When dithiocarbamate salts are oxidized under mild conditions, a reaction occurs analogous to the formation of disulphides from mercaptans. The products are called thiuram disulphides.

$$2\ RR'N.CS.SNa + I_2 \longrightarrow RR'N.CS.S - S.CS.NRR' + 2NaI$$

In the laboratory preparation of these compounds, iodine is the preferred oxidizing agent since there is no danger of the oxidation proceeding too far, but, for industrial preparation, chlorine is preferred for economic reasons. It must be introduced slowly under conditions of good agitation.

Oxidation of dithiocarbamates to thiuram disulphides can occur on exposure to air as can the formation of monosulphides, with liberation of sulphur. Most thiuram disulphides are crystalline compounds. They are neutral in reaction, soluble in organic solvents and of low solubility in water. The tetramethyl compound (thiram) was the first compound in the whole class to find use as a fungicide and is still valuable as a seed dressing against soil fungi.

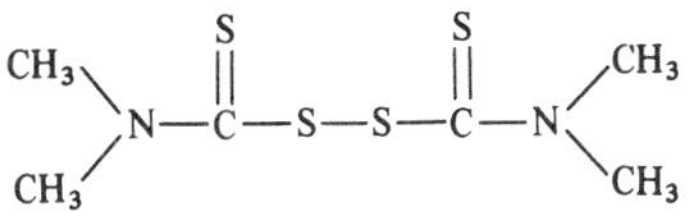

$$CH_3\!\!\diagdown\atop CH_3\!\!\diagup N\!-\!\overset{\overset{S}{\|}}{C}\!-\!S\!-\!S\!-\!\overset{\overset{S}{\|}}{C}\!-\!N\!\diagup CH_3\atop \diagdown CH_3$$

Thiram

The other reaction which must be mentioned is confined to the compounds where only one alkyl group is attached to an N atom. This is decomposition into hydrogen sulphide and the alkyl isothiocyanate

$$RNH.CS.SH \rightarrow RNCS + H_2S.$$

This reaction occurs, along with more complex side reactions, whenever a solution of dithiocarbamate is acidified, although, as a laboratory route to isothiocyanates, it is preferable first to react the dithiocarbamate with a chloroformate. It is generally considered that the excellent soil fungus control which can be achieved by solutions of sodium monomethyldithiocarbamate (metham-sodium) is due to the action of the methylisothiocyanate slowly liberated. The evidence for this is that the effect is more widely distributed through the soil than could be explained by slow diffusion in soil water and that it is similar to the effect of injected methylisothiocyanate itself or of other compounds which can generate this volatile substance.

Metham-sodium is used at high dosage, in the range of 50–200 kg/ha for sterilization of soil to be used for very high value crops, such as glass-house beds and land favourably situated for very early cropping. The liberated isothiocyanate is effective against nematodes, many soil insect pests and weed seeds as well as fungi. The more stable and less phytotoxic zinc salt (ziram) and ferric salt (ferbam) have been used as agricultural fungicides and the nickel salt has been used to control bacterial diseases in rice. Some use has also been made of zinc propylene bisdithiocarbamate (propineb).

However, by far the most important dithiocarbamates for use as protectant fungicides on growing crops are those derived from ethylene diamine, known as the ethylene bisdithiocarbamates

$$H_2NCH_2CH_2NH_2 + 2CS_2 + 2NaOH \rightarrow$$
$$NaS.CS.NHCH_2CH_2NH.CS.SNa.$$

Nabam

The sodium salt (nabam) is fungicidal but tends to damage the host leaves and has no useful persistence as a fungicide under wet conditions. The persistence was found to be greatly increased by addition of zinc sulphate and lime in the spray tank. The insoluble zinc salt (zineb) and the manganous salt (maneb) were then prepared in the factory by the obvious methods and marketed in wettable powder form.

Nabam is usually manufactured by running a 20–60% solution of ethylene diamine and sodium hydroxide in water down a packed column up which carbon disulphide vapour is ascending. The reaction is highly exothermic and use of equipment with no moving parts obviates fire hazard from the extremely inflammable carbon disulphide. A solution of nabam, ready for use, is withdrawn from the bottom of the column and excess carbon disulphide is condensed from the top of the column and returned to the base.

Maneb is made by adding manganous chloride to the solution of nabam and filtering off the precipitated solid and drying it at 50°C in a forced draught.

Zineb is usually made by reacting the ammonium salt of ethylene bisdithiocarbamic acid with zinc oxide at 20–30°C. This gives crystals with an average size of one micron. If zineb is prepared from nabam and a zinc salt the product is colloidal and amorphous and not as stable as the crystalline material.

The heavy metal salts of dithiocarbamates are all of low solubility in water. Chemically they are not simple salts. They have greater solubility in some organic solvents than in water and the zinc salt of dimethyldithiocarbamate has been distilled in short-path vacuum apparatus. These facts, together with absorption spectra differing from those of the separate ions indicate a considerable degree of covalent or chelate structure.

Since a divalent metal can therefore link two dithiocarbamate groups which can also be linked by oxidation to the disulphide structure, it is evident that, in the products formed from ethylene bisdithiocarbamates, there are possibilities of polymeric structure. In some commercial products, such polymerization has been claimed to confer greater stability of deposits.

Zineb and maneb now rank in tonnage alongside elementary sulphur and fixed coppers. They are used as spray or dusts against a wide variety of fungus diseases of foliage. They have partly displaced fixed coppers for potato blight control, although they are more advantageously used in admixture with copper compounds. They have a wide spectrum of activity but are, curiously, least active against the diseases susceptible to elementary sulphur. They are extremely safe to use and have very low toxicities to men and animals.

Two variants which have found widespread use are the mixed manganous and zinc ethylene bisdithiocarbamates (mancozeb) and a mixture of the ammoniates of zineb and ethylene bisdithiocarbamic acid with bi- and trimolecular cyclic anhydrosulphides and disulphides (metiram). A vast number of mixed formulations and combinations of maneb and zineb with other fungicides have been introduced as proprietary products.

Substituted Phenols

Most phenols, particularly chlorinated phenols, are toxic to microorganisms. Cresols and higher homologues contribute to the fungicidal action of creosote oils in timber and solutions of pentachlorophenol (PCP) have replaced creosote impregnation when the colour and odour of the latter are objectionable. Some alkylchlorophenols are widely used constituents of household disinfectants. All these compounds are, however, too phytotoxic to permit their use for fungus control in agriculture.

A substituted phenol which has long been used to prevent mould growth on stored cotton goods is the anilide of salicylic acid.

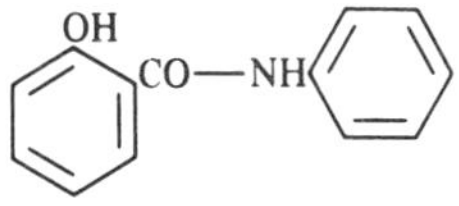

Salicylanilide

Another phenolic compound of value in rot-proofing of cellulose textiles is dichlorophen prepared by condensation of 4-chlorophenol with formaldehyde with sulphuric acid as catalyst. It is also used to control moss in high quality turf.

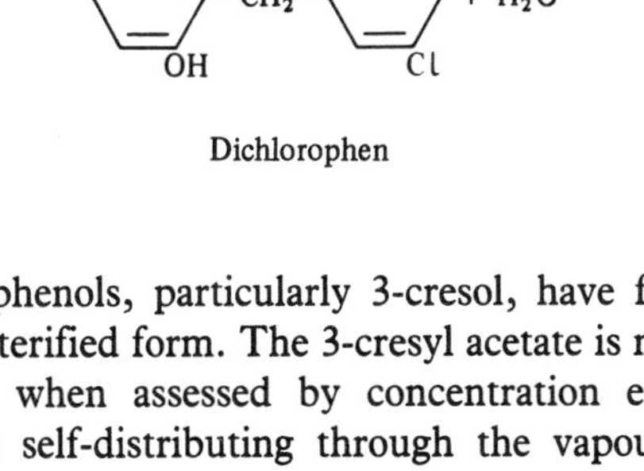

Dichlorophen

Relatively simple phenols, particularly 3-cresol, have found a specialized fungicidal use in esterified form. The 3-cresyl acetate is not among the most active compounds when assessed by concentration effective in culture medium, but it is self-distributing through the vapour phase and non-corrosive and has been used for prevention of mould development in electrical and optical apparatus in tropical use. The total amount of mould growth which accidental nutrients can support inside a pair of binoculars may be extremely small, but a very thin spread of mycelium over lens surfaces can have a serious effect.

A phenol of interesting properties and having minor use on crops is 8-hydroxyquinoline (oxine).

Oxine

This compound was the first to show any significant systemic effect, is the elm tree against the Dutch elm disease, but it does not give adequate control. Oxine has considerable chelating powder for heavy metals, particularly copper, and the cupric oxine complex has shown greater fungicidal power in some situations.

2-Phenylphenol is used in the preservation of packed fruit against moulds, but for this use the unsubstituted diphenyl is used more extensively although of lower activity in culture medium tests. The explanation is that the preservative is desirably applied to the wrapping medium only and the more volatile compound is more rapidly redistributed. This usage has, of course, also to meet a very critical standard with regard to off-flavour and residues.

Dinitrophenol Derivatives

Substituted 2,4-dinitrophenols, especially 6-methyl-2,4-dinitrophenol (DNOC), were earlier used as rapid-acting selective herbicides. These compounds are very toxic to men and animals and so their use has been largely discontinued. They were also found to be very toxic to spider mites, which infest fruit trees, but were too phytotoxic to be used for control except in winter washes in the dormant season to kill the spider mite eggs (see Chapter 7, on oils).

However, by increase in size of the alkyl group adjacent to the OH, and by esterification of the OH, useful selectivity against mites with adequately reduced phytotoxicity was obtained. Similar substitutions also appeared to promote activity against some fungi, particularly the powdery mildews.

It is probable that the esters are not active as such, their activity being consequent on release of the free phenol by hydrolysis. In addition to changes in absolute solubility and in partition ratio between oily and aqueous biophases the rate of hydrolysis introduces another factor which can modify the toxicity. No simple correlation is observed with rates of hydrolysis in simple solutions, and it is probable that enzyme-catalyzed hydrolysis is of major importance.

The most successful compounds for mite control have been the substituted acrylic esters. In particular, 6-*sec*.butyl-2,4-dinitrophenyl-3,3-dimethyl-acrylate (binapacryl) has been shown to be an effective acaricide of very low phytotoxicity, having some activity also against apple mildew. Some carbonates have also been used such as isopropyl 6-*sec*.butyl-2,4-dinitrophenyl carbonate (dinobuton).

Binapacryl   Dinobuton

The product in this class which has proved to be most useful as a fungicide and which has been used extensively for many years for the control of powdery mildews is a mixture of about 65–70% of 2,6-dinitro-4-octylphenyl crotonate (dinocap-4) and 30–35% of 2,4-dinitro-6-octylphenyl crotonate (dinocap-6).

Dinocap-4   Dinocap-6

A related product is a mixture of methyl 2,6-dinitro-4-octylphenyl carbonate (dinocton-4) and methyl 2,4-dinitro-6-octylphenyl carbonate (dinocton-6).

Dinocton-4   Dinocton-6

It has been found that the fungicidal activity of dinocap, especially towards powdery mildews, is mainly due to the dinocap-4 whereas the acaricidal activity is mainly due to the dinocap-6. This appears also to be true for dinocton-4 and dinocton-6. In general, 2.6-dinitro-4-alkylphenol derivatives tend to be fungicidal whilst 2,4-dinitro-6-alkylphenol derivatives tend to be acaricidal.

The situation is made more complex because the octyl side chain is dinocap and dinocton is not a single species but a mixture of the isomeric 1-methylheptyl, 1-ethylhexyl and 1-propylpentyl groups. The products are made by condensing commercial secondary octanol, which is a mixture of species, with phenol which gives a mixture of 2-octylphenols and 4-octylphenols. This is then dinitrated to give a mixture of 2,4-dinitro-6-octylphenols and 2,6-dinitro-4-octylphenols.

In biological studies, it was shown that, in the 2,6-dinitro series the compounds having more compact alkyl substituents were more fungicidally active than those with more nearly straight chains whereas, in the 2,4-dinitro series, they were less fungicidally active.

The story now revealed is an interesting object lesson in the desirability of establishing the biological performance of chemicals in the first place with isolated pure materials. It is not, of course, in most cases practicable to supply the agricultural market with purified chemicals but it is desirable first to find out what compound to aim at.

The general method used for the preparation of alkylphenols is addition of an olefine and a phenol under rather drastic reaction conditions using sulphuric acid, an activated clay or a Friedel-Craft catalyst. These catalysts can also function to produce the olefine from an alcohol by elimination of water so that, if an alcohol and the phenol are used as starting products, the overall reaction appears to be a condensation. That direct condensation is not a true representation is shown by the non-formation of an n-alkylphenol from an n-alcohol and by the fact that cresols cannot be made by this route. From butanol, sulphuric acid and phenol a mixture of 2- and 4-s-butylphenols is obtained.

$$CH_3CH_2CH_2CH_2OH \xrightarrow{\ H_2SO_4\ } CH_3CH_2CH{=}CH_2 + H_2O$$

$$CH_3CH_2CH{=}CH_2 + C_6H_5OH \xrightarrow{\ H_2SO_4\ } \underset{CH_3}{\overset{CH_3CH_2}{>}}CH{-}C_6H_4OH$$

It will be evident that the same product would be obtained if secondary had been used in place of n-butanol. From higher secondary alcohols there are, of course, more possible isomers. From isobutanol the *tertiary*-butylphenols are obtained.

It is possible to obtain some control of the 2:4 ratio by choice of catalyst and reaction conditions. In particular, if a large excess of strong sulphuric acid is used, the phenol is sulphonated, mainly in the 4-position, before addition of the olefin. Further heating, after dilution with about 20–30% of water, causes desulphonation and this procedure gives a high yield of the 2-alkylphenol. The 2- and 4-alkylphenols are, however, easily separated by distillation, the 2- having significantly lower b.p. In the case of the *sec*-butylphenols the 4-compound has sufficient use as a plasticizer to make this separation of mixed products economical.

Chloronitrobenzenes and Related Compounds

Nitration of chlorobenzenes increases the reactivity of the C-Cl groups and compounds of this type are often lachrymatory and irritant. Many show activity on vegetative growth, of which scorch of leaves and arrested development of buds are the most frequent symptoms. They are toxic to most fungi in culture tests.

Pentachloronitrobenzene (quintozene) has the longest established usage of all these compounds. It is applied as a seed dressing. In massive dosage, up to several hundred kg per hectare, it has been incorporated by rotovation as a soil sterilant particularly against virus-carrying nematodes.

Another seed-protecting fungicide of this type is 1,2,4,5-tetrachloro-3-nitrobenzene (tecnazene). When used to control dry rot (*Fusarium caerulum*) in stored potatoes, it was found also to inhibit sprouting. It must not, of course, be used on seed potatoes and is suspected by some authorities of producing off-flavour. A mixture of 1,2,3-trichloro-4,6-dinitro and 1,2,4-trichloro-3,5-dinitrobenzenes has been used against soil fungi.

A related compound, which has cyano groups instead of nitro groups, is tetrachloroisophthalonitrile (chlorthalonil) which is manufactured by chlorination of isophthalonitrile in the vapour phase at 400–500°. It has been used as a foliage spray on some crops and also as a soil fungicide.

Compounds which may also be included in this group are 2,6-dichloro-4-nitroaniline (dicloran) which is mainly used against the grey mould of lettuce, and 4,5,6,7-tetrachlorophthalide (fthalide) which is used against rice blast.

Chlorthalonil   Dicloran   Fthalide

Quinones

Exploration of quinones as fungicides was initiated by the identification of the natural product juglone from rot-resistant walnut heartwood. Two simple chloro-substituted quinones found considerable use as seed-dressings and are still in demand. They are 2,3-dichloronaphthoquinone (dichlone) and tetrachlorobenzoquinone (chloranil).

Dichlone is manufactured by reaction of 1-naphthol with chlorine at 80–120°C. The reaction is exothermic and better yield and purity are obtained if the first exothermic part of the reaction is carried out at less than 40°C followed by completion of the reaction at 80–120°C than if the whole reaction is carried out at 80–120°C. Reaction is carried out in a solvent mixture of 25 parts 96% sulphuric acid, 71 parts glacial acetic acid and 4 parts water.

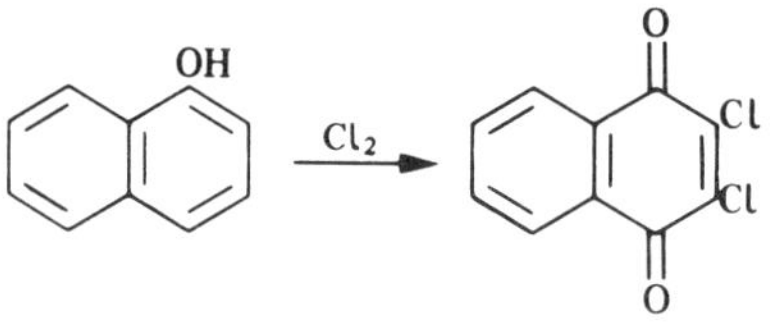

Dichlone

Chloranil can be manufactured by a number of methods but the only economical process is reaction of cyclohexane with hydrochloric acid and oxygen. The reactants are mixed and passed at 220–240°C over a catalyst of copper chloride, cobalt chloride and ferric chloride deposited on alumina.

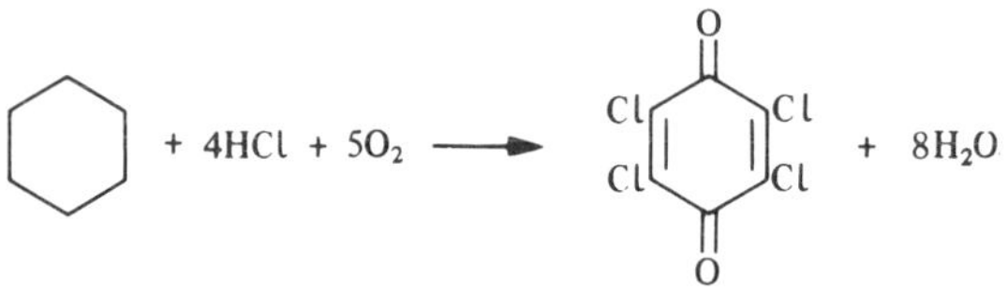

Chloranil

A fungicide of more complex quinone structure is 2,3-dicyano-1,4-dihydro-1,4-dithia-anthraquinone (dithianon) which is active against apple scab and other pome fruit diseases, except apple mildew.

The dioxime, benquinox, is also a quinone derivative and, like the simpler quinone compounds, is mainly useful as a seed dressing.

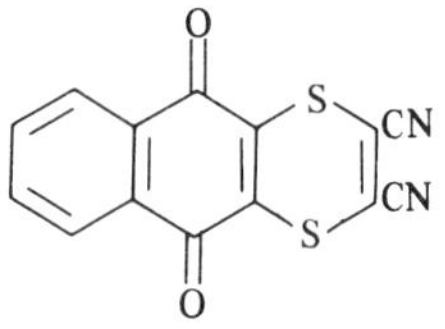

Dithianon 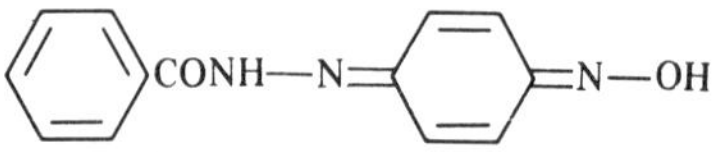   Benquinox

Trichloromethylmercapto Compounds

A very widely used fungicide is N-trichloromethylthio-4-cyclohexene-1,2-dicarboximide (captan). The very reactive perchloromethyl mercaptan can be condensed with various imines to give quite stable compounds having the -N-S-CCl$_3$ group, all of which show fungicidal properties. In captan, the imine is that of tetrahydrophthalic acid, the anhydride of which is first prepared by condensation of maleic anhydride with butadiene.

Captan

Captan is a high-melting crystalline solid, formulated as a dust or wettable powder. It is used in seed dressings and also by application to foliage for protection against many leaf-spot diseases. It is widely used against apple scab and is considered to improve the appearance of apple skin as well as reduce the incidence of this disease.

The corresponding derivative of phthalimide itself, folpet, has also been used for similar purposes, but less successsfully. There appears to be more risk of damage to fruit and, although the product is more effective than captan against potato blight, it is not competitive with fixed coppers, dithiocarbamates or, more recently, triphenyltin salts. Its main use has been on ornamentals.

A later related compound is captafol, in which the trichloromethyl group of captan is replaced by 1,1,2,2-tetrachloroethyl. In some quarters this is considered the most effective compound to date against potato blight, but is at an economic disadvantage with the more widely used products mentioned above.

Two related compounds which contain the -SCFCl$_2$ group instead of the -SCCl$_3$ group, have found some use. These are dichlofluanid and tolyfluanid.

Dichlofluanid   Tolylfluanid

Cationic Surfactants and Relatives

Surfactants are compounds in which a large hydrophobic group (usually a paraffin chain) is attached to a strongly hydrophilic group which may be anionic, neutral or cationic. In the latter class it may be a quaternary nitrogen group, cationic at all pH, or an amine group requiring at least slight acidity to make it functional.

During investigations of cationic surfactants as formulation constituents (wetting, emulsifying, etc, agents) it was soon evident that they had, as a class, rather powerful bactericidal action. This is widely exploited in their use, officially approved in many countries, as alternatives to steam for the sterilization of dairy equipment. The most active of easily prepared compounds for this purpose is dodecylbenzyldimethyl ammonium chloride, prepared by methylation of dodecylamine and addition of benzyl chloride.

Compounds of this type are less effective against fungi than against bacteria and there is considerable risk of leaf damage if they are used against crop diseases. Compounds in which a strongly basic, but not quaternary, group terminates the paraffin chain have, however, shown useful activities against some fruit diseases, notably apple scab.

The most widely used and effective is dodecyl guanidine acetate (dodine), usually formulated as a 65% wettable powder. It is used to combat scab on apples and pears and leaf spot on cherries and strawberries.

The compound is manufactured by reaction of dodecylamine with cyanamide in the presence of acetic acid at 140–160°C in an autoclave.

$$C_{12}H_{23}NH_2 + H_2NCN + CH_3COOH$$

$$\longrightarrow C_{12}H_{25}NH-\underset{\underset{NH}{\|}}{C}-NH_2 . CH_3COOH$$

Dodine

Another fungicidal product of this type is 2-heptadecyl-2-imidazoline acetate (glyodin) which is used for control of foliage disease on a wide variety of fruits. Ethanol and stearic acid are reacted to give ethyl stearate which is heated with ethylene diamine to give N-(2-aminoethyl)-stearamide which is then heated at 200°C under reduced pressure and the 2-heptadecyl-2-imidazoline distilled out. This is then reacted with acetic acid in isopropanol to give glyodin.

Imidazolines and oxazolines formed from fatty acids of a wide range of chain lengths have been made and tested but the optimum chain length has always been found to be in the range of C_{14} to C_{17}. For good fungicidal effect a high lipoid solubility may be necessary or perhaps a high degree of surface adsorption, either of which requires a long chain. That the effect does not

$$C_{17}H_{35}COOH + C_2H_5OH \rightarrow C_{17}H_{35}COOC_2H_5 + H_2O$$

$$C_{17}H_{35}COOC_2H_5 + NH_2CH_2CH_2NH_2 \rightarrow C_{17}H_{35}CONHCH_2CH_2NH_2$$

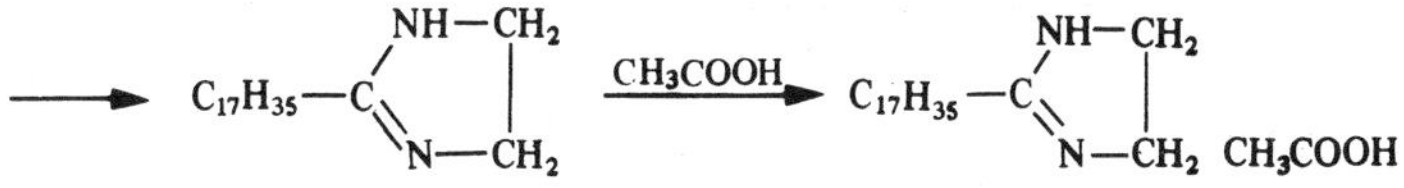

Glyodin

increase indefinitely with increasing chain length may well be due to decrease of absolute solubility.

A commercial fungicide related to dodine but which has two amidine groups and a chain containing nitrogen atoms is guazatine.

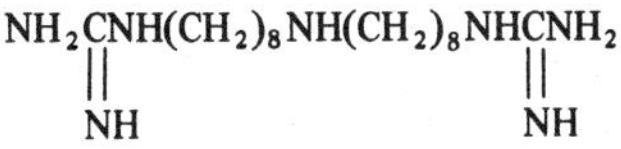

$$\underset{NH}{NH_2\overset{\|}{C}NH(CH_2)_8NH(CH_2)_8NH\overset{\|}{C}NH_2}$$

Guazatine

Imidazole and Triazole Derivatives

A number of derivatives of imidazoles and triazoles have been developed as fungicides. In general, the imidazoles were most effective against animal fungi and the triazoles against plant fungi. 1-(2-chlorophenyl-diphenyl)

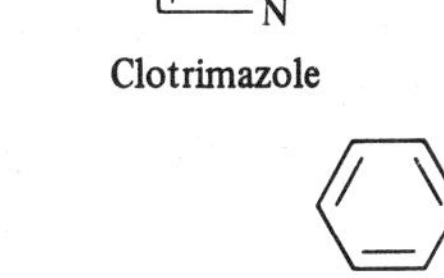

Clotrimazole

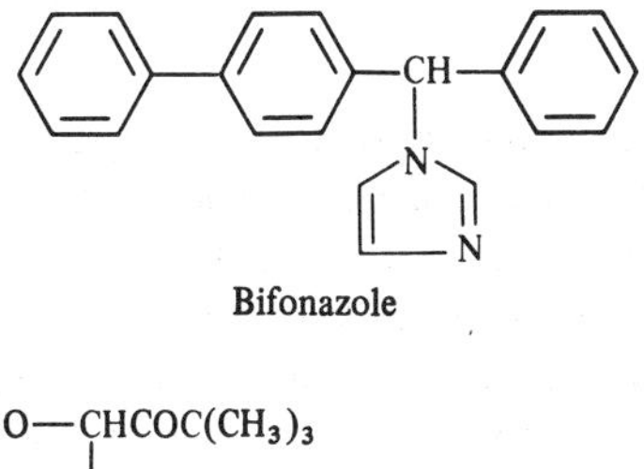

Bifonazole

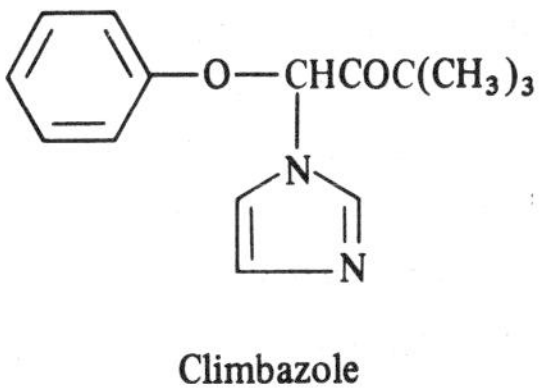

Climbazole

methylimidazole (clotrimazole) is very effective against dermatophytoses and candidal skin infections in humans and animals. 1-(1-1'-biphenyl-phenyl) methylimidazole (bifonazole) is a topical antimyotic of long life for use in humans and animals. 1-(4-chlorophenoxy)-3,3-dimethyl-1-imidazolyl-2-butanone (climbazole) is highly active against *Pityrosporum* species in humans.

β-(1,1'-biphenyl-4-yloxy)-α-(1,1-dimethylethyl)-1H-1,2,4-triazole-1-ethanol (bitertanol) is a highly active foliar fungicide with good penetration for eradication of powdery mildew, rusts, scabs and other pathogenic fungi on fruit, soybeans and peanuts.

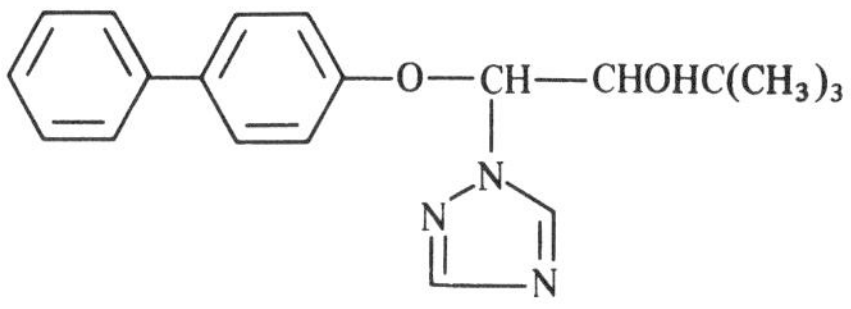

bitertanol

1-(3-trifluoromethylphenyl-diphenyl)methyl-1H-1,2,4-triazole, (fluotrimazole) is a highly active fungicide for control of powdery mildew in cereals, vegetables and beets. The real importance of this group of fungicides is that they led to the development of the useful systemic fungicides triadimefon and triadimenol.

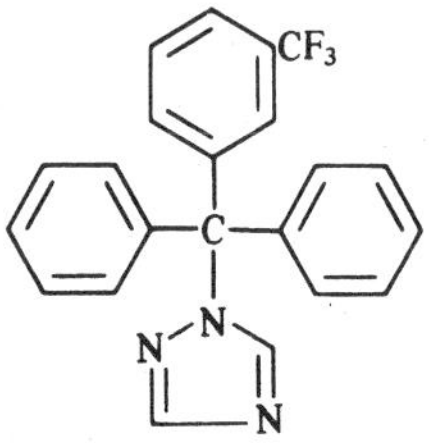

Fluotrimazole

These fungicides all act by interfering with the biosynthesis of fungal steroids and especially inhibit the synthesis of ergosterol which is essential for the viability of the cell wall.

Other Compounds

A number of derivatives of oxazoline have recently been introduced as protective fungicides. Dichlozine, 3-(3,5-dichlorophenyl)-5-methyl-2,4-dioxo-oxazolidine and dichlozinate, ethyl 3-(3,5-dichlorophenyl)-5-methyl-

2,4-dioxo-5-oxazolidine carboxylate, are used to control botrytis and sclerotinia. Of wider application is the imidazoline derivative iprodione, 3-(3,5-dichlorophenyl)-N-(1-methylethyl)-2,4-dioxo-1-imidazolinecarboxamide, which is a broad spectrum fungicide which controls a range of diseases on a wide variety of fruits, vegetables, vines and turf and is also an effective seed dressing for cereals.

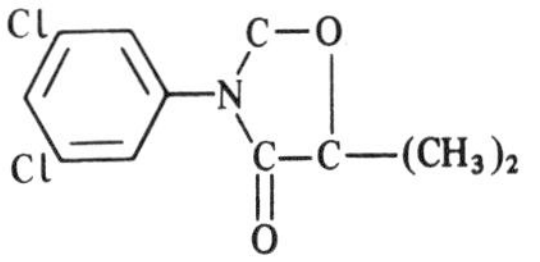

Dichlozine

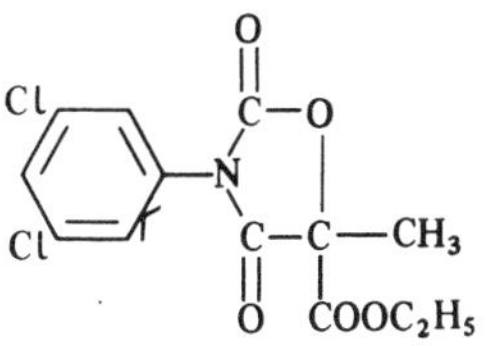

Dichlozinate

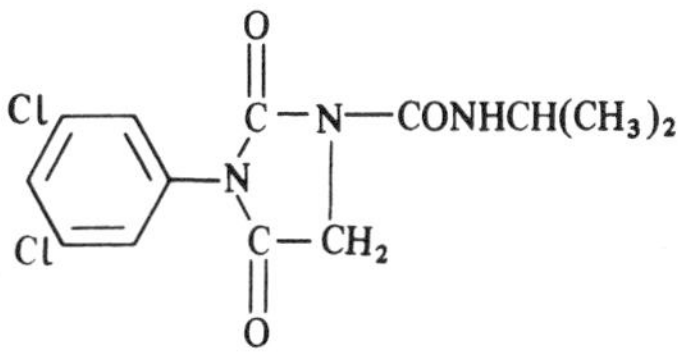

Iprodione

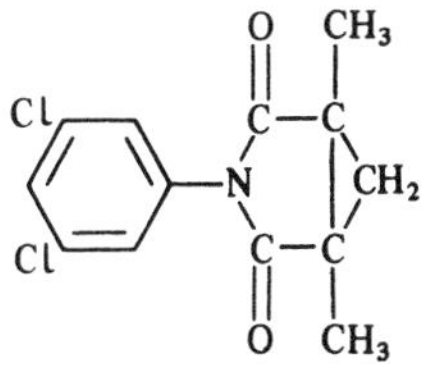

Procymidone

A related compound is procymidone, N-(3,5-dichlorophenyl)-1,2-dimethylcyclopropane-1,2-dicarboximide, which is used to control botrytis and sclerotinia in cereals, fruit and vegetables.

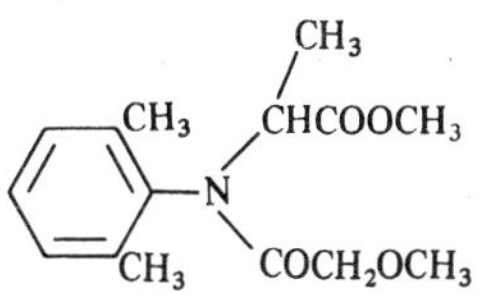

Metalaxyl

An interesting new compound is metalaxyl, N-(2,6-dimethylphenyl)-N-methoxyacetylalanine methyl ester, which is used to control soil-borne diseases caused by *Pythium* and *Phytophthora* and also downy mildews on a variety of vegetables, fruit, tobacco and turf.

It is impossible in a short general book to list all the compounds which have held at least a minor place or been subject to extensive field evaluation as protective fungicides. They include a diverse range of unrelated chemical types and some which have achieved commercial development are illustrated below.

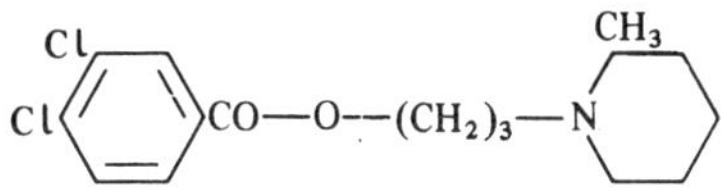

Piperalin

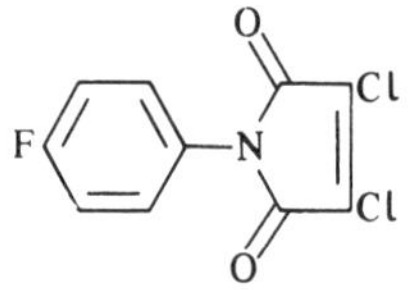

Fluoroimide 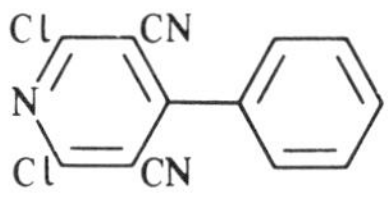   Pyridinitril

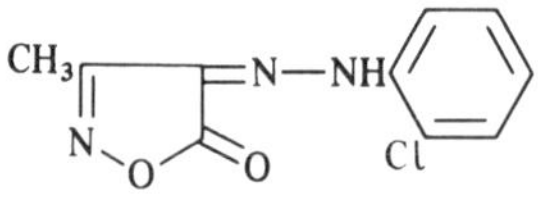

Drazoxolon   Phenaminosulf

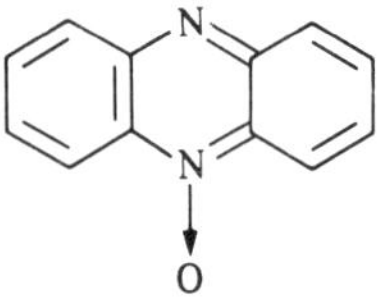

Phenazin oxide

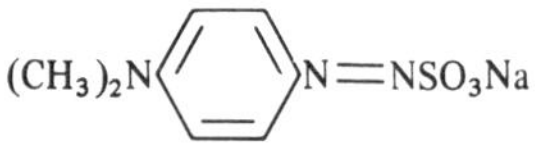

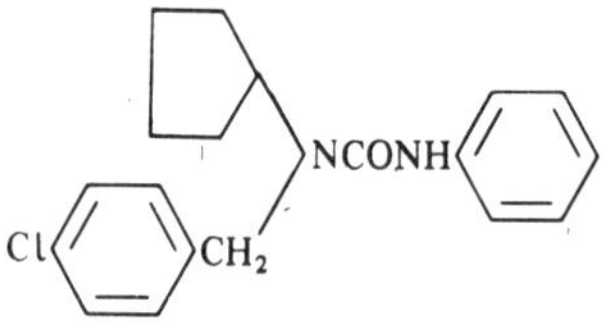

Pencycuron

However, the coppers, dithiocarbamates and captan provide adequate protective fungicidal effect against most fungi and they are cheap because they are manufactured on a very large scale from low-priced raw materials. The more complex organic compounds, which require several stages in their synthesis, cannot compete on the basis of "cost-effectiveness" even if they are more active and have, consequently, lower application rates. During the last decade the pesticides industry has therefore concentrated on discovery and development of fungicides which would be not just protective but would have eradicant or curative action on fungal diseases which had already become established in the plant. To do this the chemicals must be able to pass into the plant tissues and attack the fungus from within without injury to the host, that is, they must be systemic or, at least, partly systemic. A wide range of compounds of this type have now been produced and are dealt with in the next chapter.

Further Reading

See Page 206.

17
Systemic Fungicides

Introduction

The idea that it might be possible actually to cure a fungal disease by applying some chemical to the foliage or roots of an infected plant had occurred to agricultural chemists as early as about 1840 when the nature of fungal diseases was first recognized and the first inorganic protective fungicides such as Bordeaux mixture were introduced. Various attempts had some modest success — scab on potato tubers was controlled with mercuric chloride, anthracnose on vines with copper sulphate, and fireblight on pears with zinc chloride. Application of lithium salts to the roots of wheat and barley prevented development of powdery mildew. When organic protective fungicides such as the dithiocarbamates and captan were developed from 1940 onwards a vast number of organic compounds were tested to see if they could control established infections. In general, the compounds were either not sufficiently effective or, if they did kill the fungus, they also caused considerable damage to the host plant. This was not surprising because of the similarity of the biochemistry of the fungi and of higher plants, and the problem of selectively inhibiting a fungal infection within the living tissues of a plant without harming the plant itself was thought to be insoluble.

Nevertheless, two facts sustained the hopes of chemists in the post-World War II period. The first was that most plants are resistant to most fungi, and this resistance was shown in many cases to be due either to the presence within the plant of natural antifungal substances or to the production by the plant of antifungal chemicals — the phytoalexins — as a response to the invading organism. Some of these naturally occurring compounds were isolated but they did not give effective control when topically applied to the foliage because they did not penetrate to the appropriate sites of action — the plant produced them exactly where they were needed. Nevertheless, if plants could produce selective systemic fungicides which were not phytotoxic, there seemed no reason why chemists should not also eventually do so.

The second fact was the remarkable success of the medicinal chemists in this era in discovering synthetic chemicals which would control bacterial diseases in humans without harming the host. If systemic bactericides were possible, why not systemic fungicides? It was, in fact, from the field of chemotherapy that the first breakthrough came.

The isolation of penicillin in 1940 started the discovery of a whole range of chemotherapeutic antibiotics. The effects of many of these in plants were studied and it was found that streptomycin is readily translocated and would control some fungal diseases in plants such as the downy mildew of hops. The most interesting antifungal antibiotic was griseofulvin which was shown to be readily translocated, to have low phytotoxicity and to be effective systemically against a considerable number of fungal diseases of plants.

Griseofulvin   Epigriseofulvin

Griseofulvin has asymmetric centres at positions 2 and 6' and antifungal activity is confined to the (+)-isomer. The diastereoisomer, epigriseofulvin, is inactive. Griseofulvin does not inhibit germination of fungal spores but, at very low concentrations, causes stunting and distortion of the fungal hyphae, probably by affecting nucleic acids. It is broken down in plants and in soil so its use in practical agriculture is limited.

Other antibiotics have since been developed as systemic fungicides, particularly in Japan. Cycloheximide, obtained as a by-product in manufacture of streptomycin, is very active against a wide range of fungi but its use in agriculture is limited by its considerable phytotoxicity. Blasticidin has been used for control of paddy blast on rice, at concentrations as low as 5–10 $\mu g/cm^3$, and so is 100 times as active as organomercury fungicides. The polyoxins have been shown to be effective against a number of fungi. Kasugamycin, like blasticidin, controls paddy blast but has the advantage of being less phytotoxic and less toxic to men and animals. Cellocidin will control rice leaf blight and is interesting in having a very simple chemical structure for an antibiotic. It can be easily manufactured from 1,4-dihydroxybutyne or from fumaric acid.

Cellocidin

Cycloheximide, blasticidin and kasugamycin all act by inhibiting protein synthesis in the fungus. Antibiotics vary considerably in their toxicities to men and animals. Streptomycin is very safe; griseofulvin, kasugamycin and polyoxin are relatively safe but cycloheximid, cellocidin and blasticidin are rather toxic.

The search for relatively simple organic systemic fungicides which could be manufactured cheaply was continued, but it was not until the mid-1960s that success was achieved. Since then, a considerable number of synthetic products have come into commercial use and are having a profound effect on practical control of fungal diseases. This tendency will continue as new and more effective compounds are discovered, as they certainly will be.

Organophosphorus Compounds

Some organophosphorus compounds had been shown to be outstandingly successful systemic insecticides; they are readily taken up by and translocated in plants and they are, in general, not phytotoxic. These are two essential requirements for a systemic fungicide so it was logical for chemists to search in this group for a compound with the required fungicidal activity. This was eventually found in 5-amino-1-[bis-(dimethylamido)phosphoryl]-1,2,4-triazole, which was effective against the powdery mildew of barley. Many analogues were made and tested and this led to the first commercially successful systemic fungicide, triamiphos, 3-amino-2-[bis-(dimethylamido)phosphoryl]-5-phenyl-1,2,4-triazole which is manufactured by reaction of 3-amino-5-phenyl-1,2,4-triazole with bis-(dimethylamido)phosphoryl chloride.

Triamiphos

Triamiphos is very toxic to men and animals so its use was mainly limited to control of powdery mildew on ornamentals such as roses. Although its dermal toxicity is much less than its oral toxicity (LD50 oral 20 mg/kg, LD50 dermal 1500 mg/kg) it has now been withdrawn from commerce. However, non-phosphorus derivatives of 1,2,4-triazoles have given rise to some very useful systemic fungicides. The mode of action of triamiphos was to inhibit synthesis of DNA in the fungus.

All the various types of organophosphorus compounds have been searched to try to discover systemic fungicidal activity. Of the S-phosphorothioates, two compounds have been developed commercially and are used to control paddy blast on rice. They are kitazin, O,O-diethyl-S-benzylphosphoro-thioate, and kitazin P, O,O-diisopropyl-S-benzylphosphorothioate which are manufactured by reaction of sodium benzylthiolate with O,O-dialkyl phosphorochloridate.

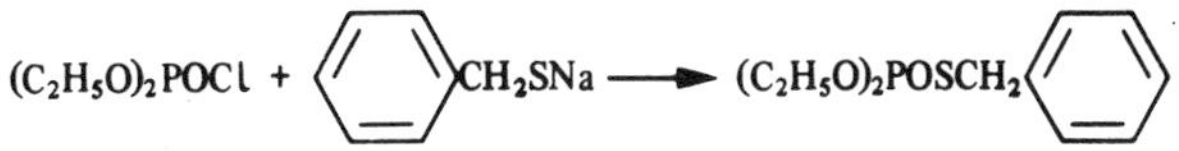

$$(C_2H_5O)_2POCl \ + \ \langle \bigcirc \rangle CH_2SNa \longrightarrow (C_2H_5O)_2POSCH_2 \langle \bigcirc \rangle$$

Kitazin

Kitazin is fairly water soluble so can be applied as a granular formulation to the water in the paddy fields from which it is rapidly absorbed through the roots and translocated in the plant. A single application lasts for three weeks and produces a remarkable increase in yield. The compound acts by inhibiting esterases in the cell wall synthesis system of the fungus. Both kitazin and kitazin P are very much less toxic to men and animals than triamiphos so they can be used safely.

Of the O-phosphorothioates, two compounds have achieved commercial success. Tolclofos-methyl, O,O-dimethyl-O-(2,6-dichloro-4-methylphenyl) phosphorothioate, is manufactured by reaction of 2,6-dichloro-4-methylphenol with O,O-dimethyl phosphorochloridothicate.

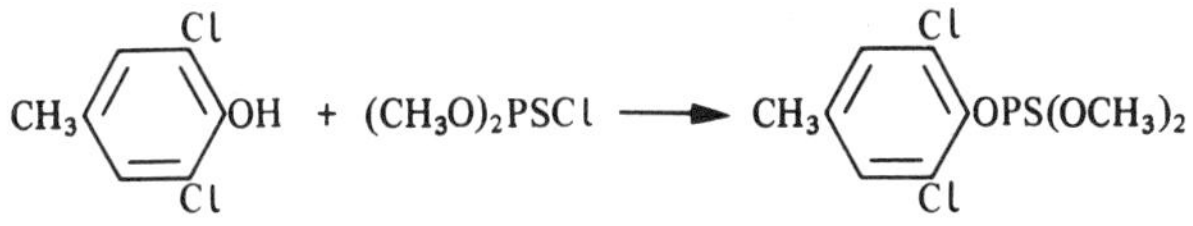

$$CH_3 \langle \bigcirc \rangle OH \ + \ (CH_3O)_2PSCl \longrightarrow CH_3 \langle \bigcirc \rangle OPS(OCH_3)_2$$

Tolclofos-methyl

Tolclofos-methyl is used to control soil-borne diseases caused by *Rhizoctonia*, *Sclerotinia* and *Typhula* on vegetables and cereals by both soil and seed treatment. It has very low toxicity.

Pyrazophos, O,O-diethyl-O-(6-ethoxycarbonyl-5-methylpyrazolo-|2,3,a|-pyrimidin-2-yl) phosphorothioate, is used to control powdery mildew on cucurbits, fruit and cereals.

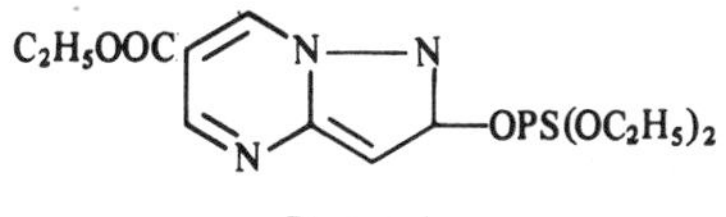

$$C_2H_5OOC \ \text{—} \text{—} \text{—OPS}(OC_2H_5)_2$$

Pyrazophos

The only phosphorodithioate which has been marketed is edifenphos, O-ethyl-S,S-diphenylphosphorodithioate which is manufactured by reaction of sodium phenylthiolate with O-diethyl phosphorodichloridate.

Edifenphos

Edifenphos has a specific action against the blast disease of rice. It is probable that all these organophosphorus fungicides act by interfering with chitin synthesis most likely by direct attack on some enzyme system in the cell wall of the fungus.

Captan is a widely used protective fungicide so it was logical to examine related phosphorus derivatives. This led to the development of ditalimfos, O,O-diethylphthalimidophosphonothioate which is manufactured by reaction of potassium phthalimide with O,O-diethylphosphorochloridothioate.

Captan   Ditalimfos

Ditalimfos is used to control powdery mildews on cereals, vegetables and fruit and scab on apples and pears. It has a very low toxicity. It is thought that the phosphonate moiety merely serves to transport the carboximide ring to the site of action where it acylates a vital enzyme system by opening of the ring.

A simple phosphonate which is systemically active against many diseases caused by *Oomycetes* on vines, hops, vegetables, tobacco and fruit is fosetyl-Al, aluminium tris(O-ethyl phosphonate). It is extremely mobile in the plant and has both preventive and curative action.

Fosetyl-Al   Inezin

A phosphonate which was introduced to control rice blast and stem rot was inezin, O-ethyl-S-benzylphenylphosponothioate, but its manufacture has now been discontinued.

Aliphatic Derivatives

The only commercial systemic fungicide which is entirely aliphatic is 2-cyano-N-(ethylaminocarbonyl)-2-(methoximino)acetamide   (cymoxanil). This compound is active against downy mildew of grapes and late blight of potatoes. Besides contact and local systemic action it has a post-infection curative effect. It also has antisporulant activity which greatly reduces the severity of the infection. One of the most interesting things about cymoxanil, apart from its being a unique type of systemic fungicide, is that the field application rate is only 10 g/ha.

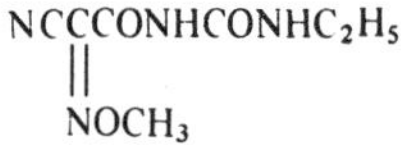

$$NCCCONHCONHC_2H_5$$
$$\|$$
$$NOCH_3$$

Cymoxanil

Alanine Derivatives

Interesting systemic fungicides have been obtained from the naturally occurring amino acid alanine. Methyl N-2,6-dimethylphenyl-N-furoylalaninate (furalaxyl) has both protective and systemic properties. It controls soil and air-borne diseases caused by *Phythium* and *Phytophthora*. It can be manufactured by reaction of 2,6-dimethylaniline with methyl α-choropropionate and treatment of the product with furoyl chloride.

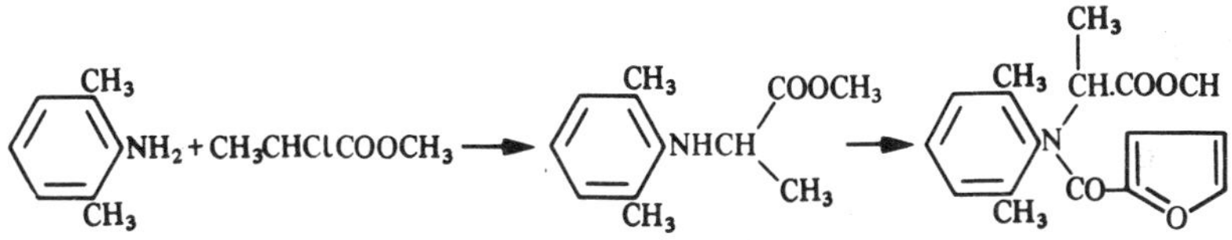

Furalaxyl

Methyl N-2,6,-dimethylphenyl-N-phenylacetylalaninate (benalaxyl) can be manufactured in the same way using phenylacetyl chloride in the final stage. It controls blue mould, late blight and downy mildew on potatoes, tomatoes and tobacco.

A compound which bears some structural resemblance to these derivatives of alanine is 2-chloro-N-(2,6-dimethylphenyl)-N-tetrahydro-2-oxo-3-furanyl) acetamide (ofurace). It provides good control of downy mildew of hops and grapes, late blight of potatoes and tomatoes and crown and root rots of tobacco by both foliar and soil application. It has both acropetal and basipetal systemic action.

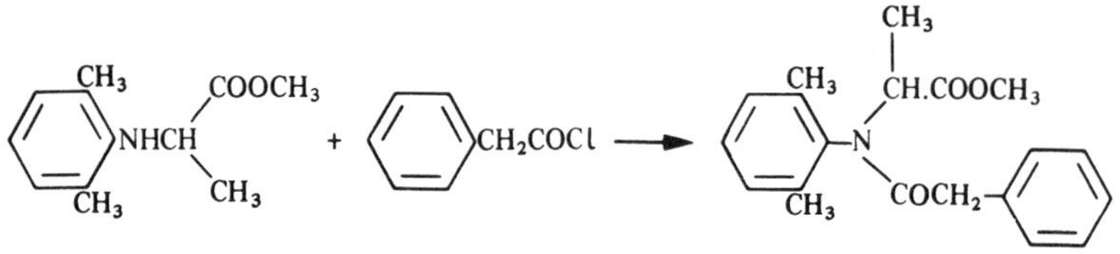

Benalaxyl

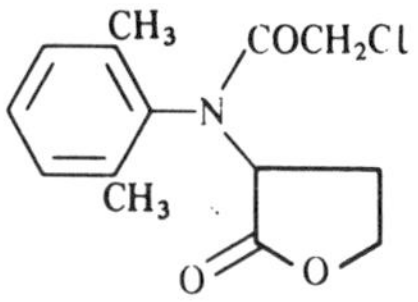

Ofurace

Benzene Derivatives

1,4-Dichloro-2,5-dimethoxybenzene (chloroneb), obtained by chlorination of hydroquinone dimethyl ether, is used as a seed treatment on sugar beet and as a soil treatment for beans and cotton. It is taken up by the roots and concentrated in them and in the lower parts of the stems, so it is not fully systemic. It is very specific and controls only the *Rhizoctonia* fungi. It acts by inhibition of DNA synthesis at the nucleotide polymerization stage. It is a very safe compound to use as its oral and dermal toxicities to men and animals are very low indeed.

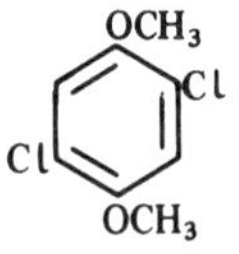

Chloroneb

Salicylanilide has been mentioned in the previous chapter as a protective fungicide for textiles. Two related anilides have been found to have some systemic activity but specifically against the brown rust of barley and the yellow rust of wheat. They are 2-methylbenzanilide (mebenil) and 2-iodobenzanilide (benodanil). Of these, benodanil has a greater margin of crop safety. 3'-isopropoxy-2-methylbenzanilide (mepronil) and 3'-isopropoxy-2-trifluoromethylbenzanilide (flutolanil) both have selectivity for *Basidiomycetes* and little activity against *Phycomycetes* and *Ascomycetes*. They are mainly used to control sheath blight in rice. Only 2-substituted benzanilides are systemically active. The compounds are easily manufactured by reaction of the appropriate aniline with the appropriate benzoyl chloride or ester.

Mebenil   Benodanil

Mepronil   Flutolanil

It has recently been shown that the benzoyl group in mebenil can be replaced by crotonyl. *Cis*-crotonanilide is active, but too phytotoxic for practical use, whereas *trans*-crotonanilide is inactive. It will be seen that the crotonanilide structure is essentially part of the mebenil molecule. Butyranilide is inactive.

cis-crotonanilide   n-butyranilide

Mebenil, flutolanid, benodanil and mepronil all act by interfering with the electron transport system in the fungus. They are very safe to use as they have very low oral and dermal toxicities to men and animals.

Two commercially important systemic fungicides are 1,2-bis-(3-ethoxy-carbonyl-2-thioureido)benzene (thiophanate) and 1,2-bis-(3-methoxy-carbonyl-2-thioureido)benzene (thiophanate-methyl). They are manufactured by reaction of phenylene diamine with isothiocyanoformic ester (obtained from methyl chloroformate and potassium thiocyanate) at room temperature in a non-hydroxylic solvent.

Thiophanate

Thiophanate and thiophanate-methyl are highly active systemically against barley and cucumber mildews but not against apple mildew. In the plant they are rapidly converted to ethyl benzimidazol-2-yl carbamate and methyl benzimidazol-2-yl carbamate respectively and these are, in fact the active fungicidal principles.

These benzimidazole compounds interfere with DNA synthesis and inhibit mycelial growth. Because cyclization is necessary to produce an active compound the 1,3- and 1,4- analogues of thiophanate are not active because they cannot undergo ring-closure. It is interesting to note some structural similarity of thiophanate with the ethylene bis-dithiocarbamates.

1-(3,4-Dichloroanilino)-1-formylamino-2,2,2-trichloroethane (chloraniformethan) is a systemic compound which is effective against mildew on spring barley. It has achieved considerable commercial success. It has a low toxicity to men and animals. It is manufactured by reaction of 3,4-dichloroaniline with $CCl_3.CHCl.NHCHO$, which is made from chloral and formamide.

Chloraniformethan

Furan Derivatives

2-methyl-3-phenylcarbamoylfurane (fenfuram) and 2,5-dimethyl-3-phenylcarbamoylfurane (furcarbanil) are carbanilides analagous to mebenil. They have a much wider spectrum of fungicidal activity and are effective against smut and bunt diseases of cereals and against some *Helminthosporum* and *Fusarium* species as a seed dressing. Fenfuram and furcarbanil have very low toxicities and are very safe compounds to handle.

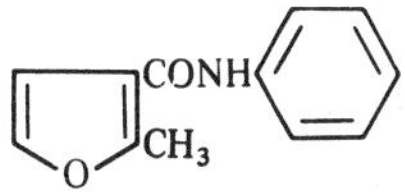

Fenfuram 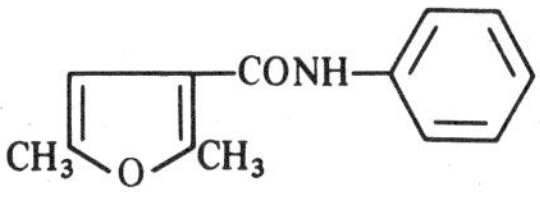   Furcarbanil

Pyran Derivatives

A carbanilide similar to furcarbanil but derived from pyran instead of furane is 2,3-dihydro-6-methyl-5-phenylcarbamoyl-4H-pyran (pyracarbolid). It is active against rusts, smuts and *Rhizoctonia* species. It is a compound of very low toxicity indeed.

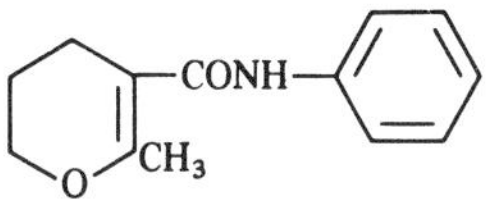

Pyracarbolid

Pyridine Derivatives

Bis-(4-chlorophenyl)-3-pyridine methanol (parinol) is very effective by foliar application in very low concentrations against powdery mildews on cucumbers, apples, roses and vines. It is not fully systemic but has what is called "translaminar" movement, that is, it protects the underside of the leaf when applied to the upper surface. A problem with purely protective fungicides is that they tend to be deposited only on the upper surfaces of the leaves so that mildew can grow unchecked on the undersides.

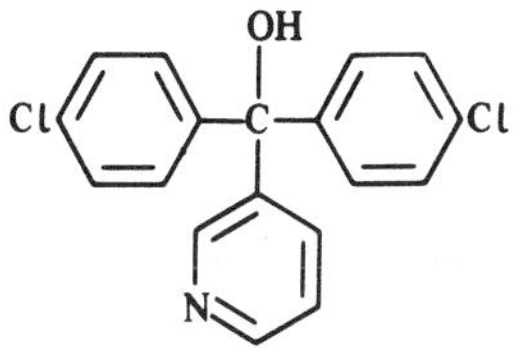

Parinol

The corresponding 2- and 4-substituted pyridines are not active.

Pyrimidine Derivatives

A pyrimidine analogue of parinol has very similar activity, and is particularly effective also for control of scab on apples. Like parinol, it is not fully systemic but enters the leaf and stops development of the fungus within it. It is 2,4-dichloro-α-pyrimidin-5-yl-benzhydrol (triarimol). However, the toxicity of triarimol, to men and animals is somewhat suspect and its production has been discontinued. Related compounds are α-(2-chlorophenyl)-α-(4-fluorophenyl)-5-pyrimidine-methanol (nuarimol) and α-(2-chlorophenyl)-α-(4-chlorophenyl)-5-pyrimidine-methanol (fenarimol). Fenarimol is safe to use and is active at low concentrations (40 ppm) against apple mildew. It also controls a wide range of other mildews. Its mode of action is probably to inhibit biosynthesis of lipids.

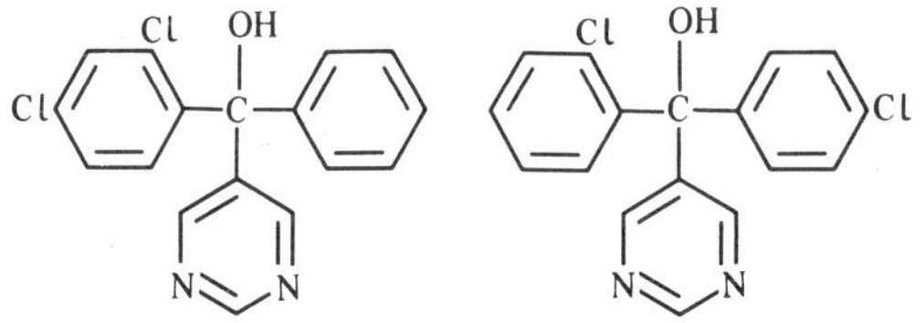

Triarimol   Fenarimol

The most important pyrimidine derivatives, which have had widespread commercial impact, are the 2-amino-4-hydroxypyrimidines. Two compounds are of particular importance, 5-n-butyl-2-dimethylamino-4-hydroxy-6-methylpyrimidine (dimethirimol) and 5-n-butyl-2-ethylamino-4-hydroxy-6-methylpyrimidine (ethirimol).

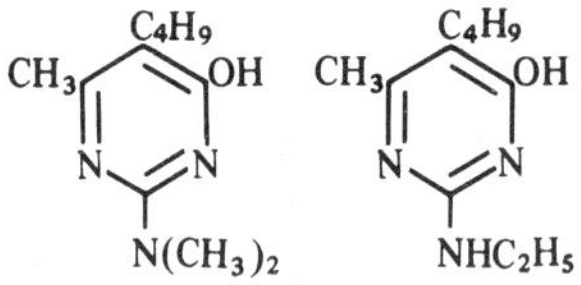

Dimethirimol   Ethirimol

Dimethirimol is particularly effective against the powdery mildew of cucurbits such as cucumbers while ethirimol is more active against the powdery mildew of cereals. They are fully systemic and move freely throughout the plants when applied to the roots. They act by inhibiting spore germination, probably by interfering with tetrahydrofolic acid metabolism. They are very safe compounds to use (LD50 oral 4,000 mg/kg, no effect dermally).

Fungicidal activity is affected by the size of the alkyl group in the 5-position and reaches a maximum at C_4H_9. Straight chain alkyl groups are better than branched chain. In general, the nature of the substituents on the amino group in the 2-position is not very significant.

Ethirimol is manufactured by condensation of ethyl butylacetoacetate (obtained from ethyl acetoacetate and butyraldehyde) with ethylguanidine (obtained from cyanamide and ethylamine). Dimethirimol is manufactured likewise from dimethylguanidine.

$$NH_2CN + C_2H_5NH_2 \qquad\qquad CH_3COCH_2COOC_2H_5 + CH_3(CH_2)_2CHO$$

$$NH_2.C.NHC_2H_5 \qquad\qquad CH_3COCOOC_2H_5$$
$$\overset{\|}{NH} \qquad\qquad\qquad \overset{\|}{CH(CH_2)_2CH_3}$$

$$\Big| H_2 \Big|$$

$$CH_3COCHCOOC_2H_5$$
$$\underset{C_4H_9}{|}$$

Ethirimol

The dimethylsulphamoyl ester of ethirimol (bupirimate) is active against apple mildew and against a number of mildews of soft fruits, whereas ethirimol is mainly active against cereal mildew. This widening of the spectrum of activity is probably due to effects on penetration and transport to the site of action. It is, in fact, broken down to ethirimol in the plant.

Piperazine Derivatives

N,N'-bis-(1-formamido-2,2,2-trichloroethyl)-piperazine (triforine) is a systemic fungicide effective by foliar application against powdery mildew on cereals, apples and cucumbers and against apple scab. It is an interesting compound in that it appears not only to move upwards to the leaves when applied to the roots but also downwards to the roots when applied to the leaves. This is an unusual effect because it is against the main flow of sap in the plant. It is an effect which would be required in any systemic fungicide which was to be active against root fungi by foliar application.

Triforine is chemically related to chloraniformethan and is manufactured by condensation of piperazine with $CCl_3.CHCl. NH.CHO$. It is safe to use as it has low toxicity.

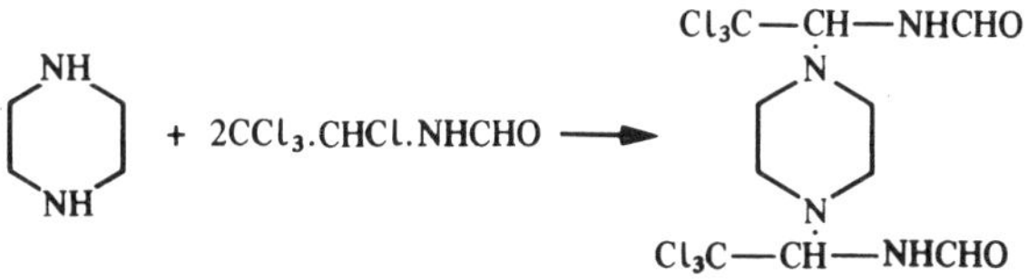

$$CCl_3-CH-NHCHO$$

Triforine

5,6,7,8-Tetrachloroquinoxoline (chlorquinox) appears to have limited systemic activity against mildew on spring barley.

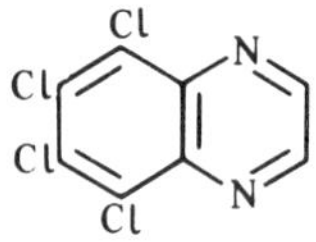

Chlorquinox

Oxazine Derivatives

4-Tridecyl-2,6-dimethylmorpholine (tridemorph) is active against barley mildew by root uptake but less so by foliar application. As the size of the alkyl group in 4-alkyl-2,6-dimethylmorpholines is increased both fungicidal activity and phytotoxicity increase to a maximum at C_{13}, so tridemorph has a low safety margin for crop damage. The 4-cycloalkyl-2,6-dimethyl-morpholines retain fungicidal activity but are much less phytotoxic. The best compound, which is used commercially, is 4-cyclododecyl-2,6-dimethyl-morpholine (dodemorph). They are made by reacting tridecyl chloride or cyclododecyl chloride with 2,6-dimethylmorpholine obtained from catalytic vapour phase ammoxidation of dipropylene glycol.

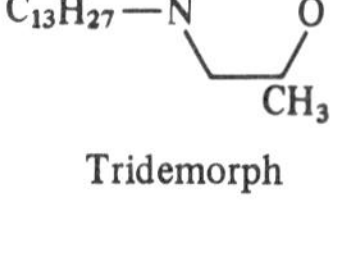

Tridemorph 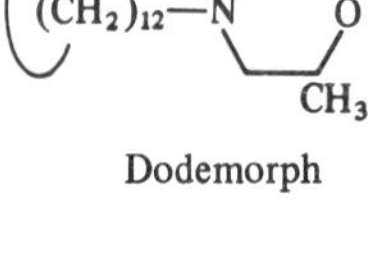   Dodemorph

Other alkyl groups in the 2,6 positions are less effective than methyl. Tridemorph and dodemorph are less active against wheat mildew than against barley mildew. They act by affecting the permeability of cell membranes to the fungus. They have low oral toxicities (LD50 oral tridemorph 1270 mg/kg, dodemorph 4,800 mg/kg) but they can cause fairly severe skin irritation.

A more complex oxazine derivative is 4-[3-(4-*tert*.butylphenyl)-2-methylpropyl]-2,6-dimethylmorpholine (fenpropimorph) which is used to control powdery mildew and rust on cereals.

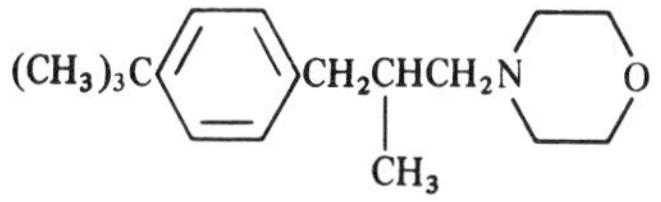

$(CH_3)_3C$ —⟨ ⟩— CH_2CHCH_2N ⟨ ⟩ O $\qquad$ $(CH_3)_2NCSSCH_2N$ ⟨ ⟩ O

CH_3

Fenpropimorph  $\qquad\qquad$ Carbamorph

N-dimethyldithiocarbamoylmethylmorpholine (carbamorph) is reported to have some systemic activity. It is related to the widely used dithiocarbamate protective fungicides.

Isoxazole Derivatives

3-Hydroxy-5-methylisoxazole (hymexazol) is a soil fungicide and seed dressing which is active against *Aphanomyces, Phythium, Corticium* and *Fusarium*. Hymexazole has only poor fungicidal activity *in vitro* but is very active in the field with an application rate of 250–500 g/100 kg seeds. This appears to be due to a potentiating effect of ferric and aluminium ions.

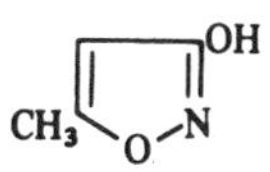

CH_3 ⟨ ⟩ O N OH

Hymexazol

Dithiolane Derivatives

Diisopropyl 1,3-dithiolane-2-ylidenemalonate (isoprothiolane) controls rice blast and also has some activity against planthoppers. It can be applied to the foliage or to the water in the paddy. It is manufactured by reaction of diisopropylmalonic ester with 2-oxo-1,3-dithiolane prepared from ethanedithiol and phosgene.

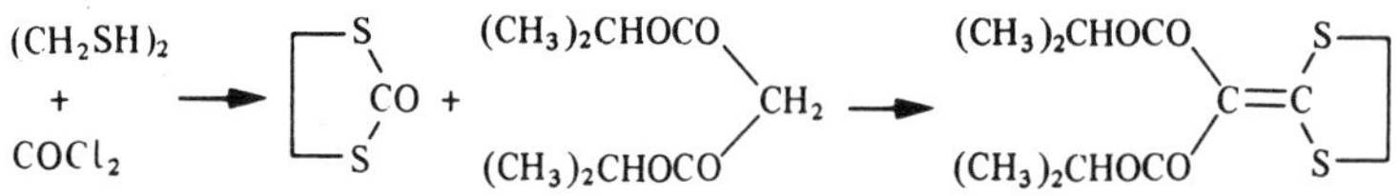

$$(CH_2SH)_2 + COCl_2 \longrightarrow \left[\begin{array}{c} S \\ CO \\ S \end{array} \right] + \begin{array}{c} (CH_3)_2CHOCO \\ (CH_3)_2CHOCO \end{array} CH_2 \longrightarrow \begin{array}{c} (CH_3)_2CHOCO \\ (CH_3)_2CHOCO \end{array} C=C \left[\begin{array}{c} S \\ S \end{array} \right]$$

Isoprothiolane

Oxathiin Derivatives

Two cyclic compounds closely related to salicylanilide which have good activity against the rusts, bunts and smuts of cereals and some soil fungi of cotton are 2,3-dihydro-6-methyl-5-phenylcarbamoyl-1,4-oxathiin (carboxin) and the corresponding sulphone (oxycarboxin).

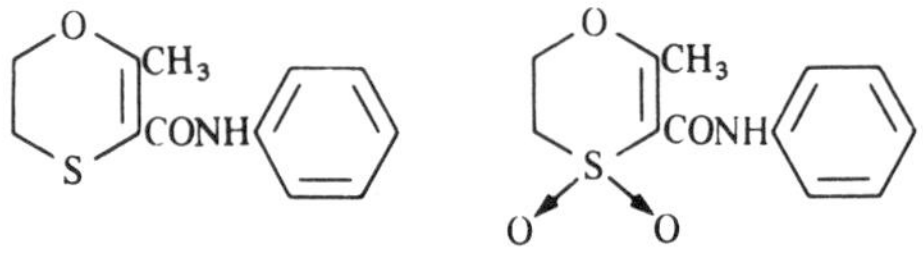

Carboxin   Oxycarboxin

Substitution in the phenyl group or its replacement by an alkyl group reduce activity. Carboxin and oxycarboxin probably act by interfering with the electron transport system in the tricarboxylic acid cycle. They have low oral and dermal toxicities and so are very safe compounds to use.

Carboxin is manufactured by reaction of α-chloroacetoacetanilide with 2-thioethanol.

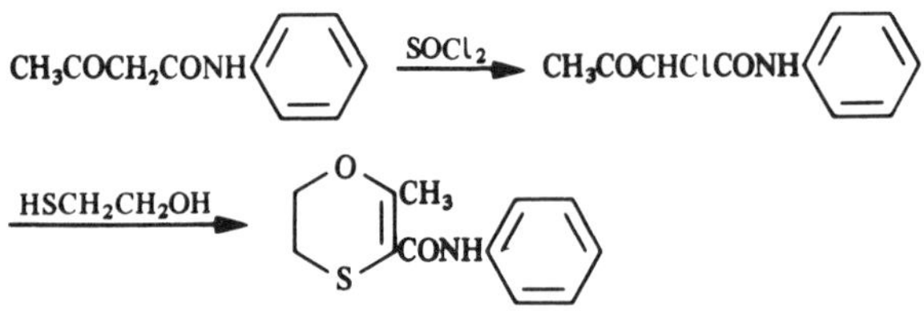

$$CH_3COCH_2CONH\!\!-\!\!\bigcirc \xrightarrow{\;SOCl_2\;} CH_3COCHClCONH\!\!-\!\!\bigcirc$$

$$\xrightarrow{\;HSCH_2CH_2OH\;}$$

Imidazole Derivatives

1-[2-(2,4-dichlorophenyl)-2-(2-propenyloxy)ethyl]-1H-imidazole, (imazalil) is active against root rot in wheat and barley and seed decay in cotton. It is also very effective in control of post-harvest decay of citrus, banana and stone fruits. It is active against fungi which are resistant to the widely used benzimidazole fungicides.

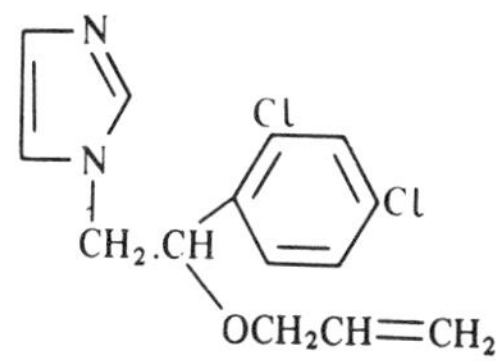

Imazalil

Triazole Derivatives

1-(4-chlorophenoxy)-3,3-dimethyl-1-(1H-1,2,4-triazol-1-yl)-2-butanone (triadimefon) controls powdery mildew and rust on cereals, vegetables, coffee, fruit, vines and sugar cane. Triadimefon is readily absorbed through the leaves and is translocated so it exerts a curative and eradicative as well as a protective action. It is manufactured by bromination of methyl *tert*.butyl ketone with bromine and reaction of the product with 4-chlorophenol. The intermediate thus formed is brominated with N-bromo succinimide, and the product reacted with 1,2,4-triazole.

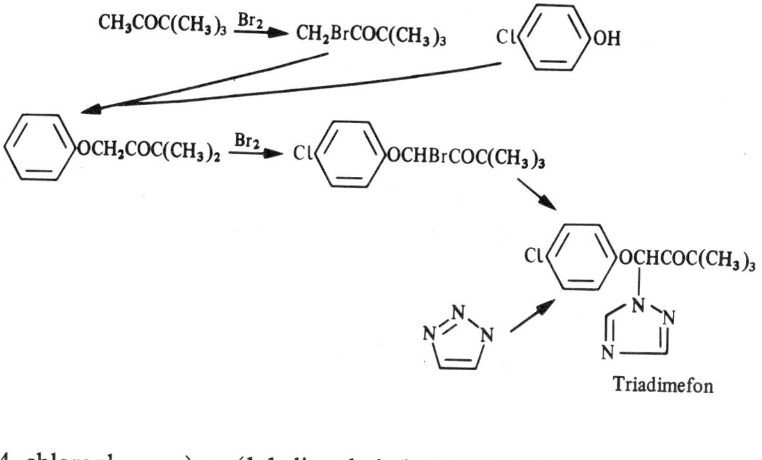

Triadimefon

β-(4-chlorophenoxy)-α-(1,1-dimethylethyl)-1H-1,2,4-triazole-1-ethanol (tridimenol) is a broad spectrum systemic fungicide for control of mildews, rusts and smuts in cereals by seed dressing. It controls virtually all seed-borne pathogens including those not suppressed by mercury seed dressings and is translocated from the seed into the seedling where it gives several weeks' protection. It is very active and 60 g suffice to treat sufficient seed for 1 hectare. It is manufactured by reduction of triadimefon.

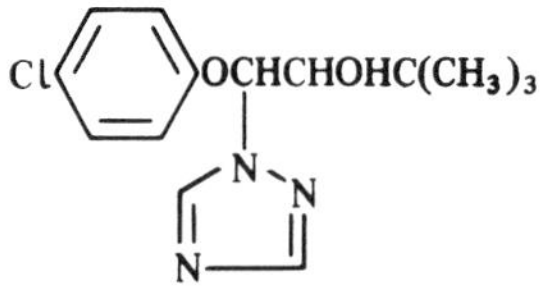

Cl⟨◯⟩OCHCHOHC(CH₃)₃

Triadimenol

1-[(2,4-dichlorophenyl)-4-propyl-1,3-dioxolan-2-ylmethyl]-1H-1,2,4-triazole (CGA 64250) is active against powdery mildew and rust in cereals.

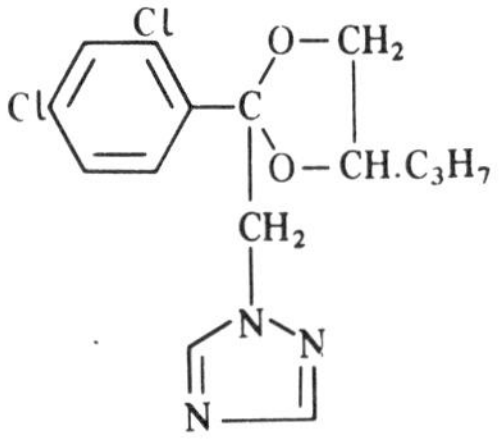

CGA 64250

1-(2,4-dichlorophenyl)-4,4-dimethyl-2-(1,2,4-triazol-1-yl) pentan-3-ol (diclobutrazol) is also very effective against mildews and rusts on cereals.

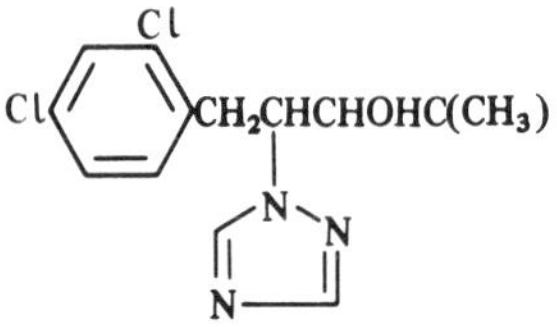

Dichlobutrazol

A more complex structure, which still contains the trizole ring, is 5-methyl-1,2,4-triazolo-(3,4-b)-benzothiazole (tricyclazone) which is used for the control of rice blast disease.

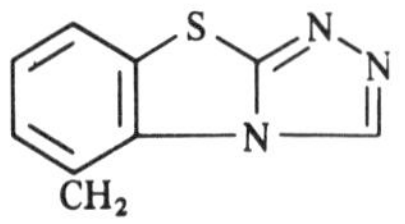

Tricyclazone

It appears that all the triazole fungicides act by interfering with the biosynthesis of fungal steroids especially by inhibiting the synthesis of ergosterol which is essential for viability of the cell wall. The probable site of action is hydroxymethylglutaryl-Co-A-reductase, a key enzyme in sterol synthesis.

$$\begin{array}{c} \text{N——N} \\ \text{CH} \quad \text{CH} \\ \text{N.C}_4\text{H}_9 \end{array} \qquad \text{Butrizol}$$

A comparatively simple triazole which was developed to control rust on cereals was 4-n-butyl-4H-1,2,4-triazole (butrizol) but its production has been discontinued.

Triazine Derivatives

3,5-dioxo-2,3,4,5-tetrahydro-1,2,4-triazine (azauracil) is systemically active against powdery mildews by root and foliar application at concentrations as small as 0.3–0.6 ppm. It is the only compound of 82 purines and pyrimidines tested which completely inhibited development of mildews. It appears not to prevent germination but stops the growth of the fungus during formation of the first haustorium, by inhibition of uridinemonophosphate.

Azauracil

Benzimidazole Derivatives

2-Substituted derivatives of benzimidazole are a class of systemic fungicides some members of which have achieved considerable commercial success.

Methyl 2-benzimidazole carbamate (carbendazim) controls a wide range of Ascomycetes and Basidiomycetes and is used world-wide on all kinds of fruits, vegetables, cereals and other crops.

Carbendazim   Benomyl

Methyl 1-(butylcarbamoyl)-2-benzimidazole carbamate (benomyl) is a derivative of carbendazim and is probably the most widely used world-wide of all the systemic fungicides. Like carbendazim, it controls a wide range of fungal diseases on crops of all kinds. In 1978 the main usages of benomyl in the United States were peanuts (750 tonnes), soybeans (100 tonnes), citrus (250 tonnes), apples (125 tonnes), peaches (100 tonnes) and cherries (20 tonnes). Benomyl is manufactured from phenylene diamine according to the following process:

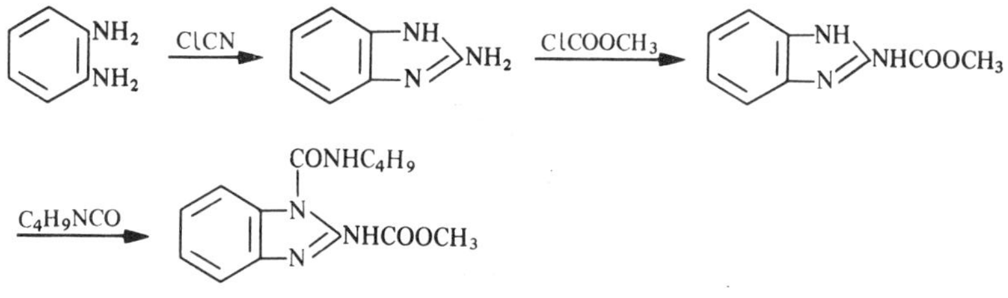

Two other derivatives of carbendazim which have achieved some commercial success are methyl 1-(2-methylthioethylcarbamoyl)-2-benzimidazole carbamate (mecarbenzid) and 1-(5-cyanopentylcarbamoyl)-2-benzimidazole carbamate (cypendazole).

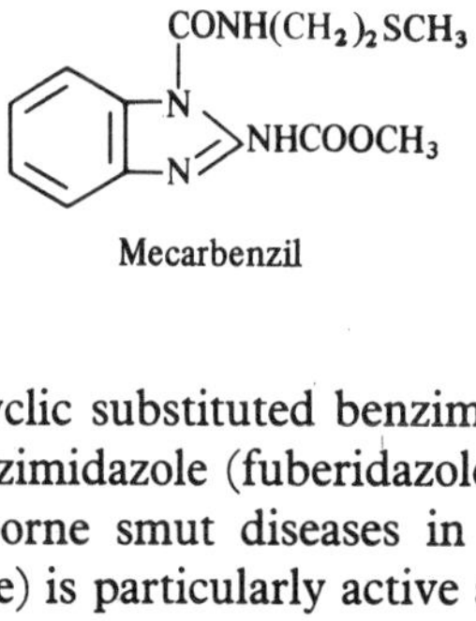

Mecarbenzil 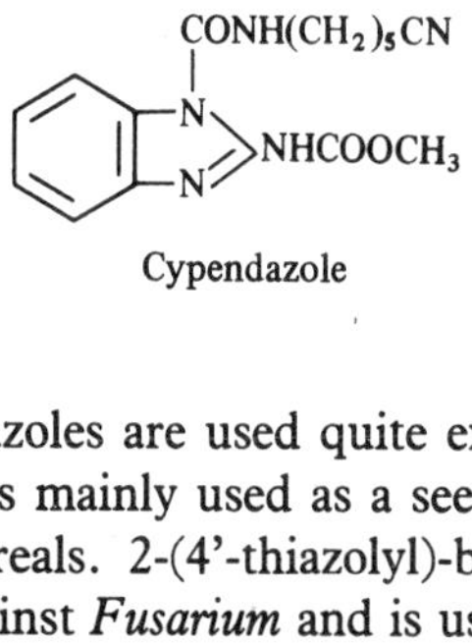   Cypendazole

Two heterocyclic substituted benzimidazoles are used quite extensively. 2-(2'-furyl)-benzimidazole (fuberidazole) is mainly used as a seed dressing to control soil-borne smut diseases in cereals. 2-(4'-thiazolyl)-benzimidazole (thiabendazole) is particularly active against *Fusarium* and is used on citrus, bananas, deciduous fruits, potatoes and soybeans. It is exclusively used to protect fruit, particularly citrus, from post-harvest decay and rot.

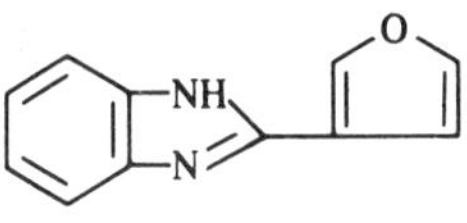

Fuberidazole 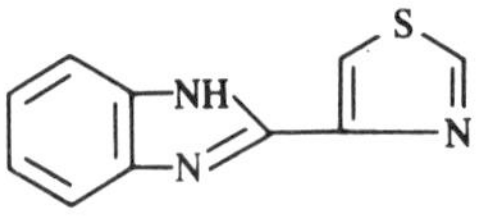   Thiabendazole

The benzimidazoles all inhibit mycelial growth rather than spore germination and probably act by interfering with synthesis of DNA. It appears that benomyl is metabolized to give carbendazim which is the active principle. This is the same compound that is produced metabolically from thiophanate (qv).

Benzisothiazole Derivatives

3-Allyloxy-1,2-benzoisothiazole-1,1-dioxide (probenazole) is effective against blast disease and bacterial leaf blight of rice. The compound is taken up by the roots and protects the plant against infection but is not curative.

Probenazole

General Comments

The presently available systemic fungicides are among the least toxic of pesticides and appear not to have any significant adverse environmental effects.

It is interesting to note that, whereas most protective fungicides act by interfering with energy production and transport processes in the fungus, all known systemic fungicides, with the exceptions of carboxin and oxycarboxin, act by interfering with biochemical processes of synthesis in the fungus. This is also true for systemic insecticides and for systemic antibacterials used in human medicine. This is probably because energy processes are basically similar for all forms of life and so it is not possible to achieve selective action in a systemic compound which interferes with energy processes.

The biochemical mode of action of systemic fungicides may be a factor in the biggest problem with regard to this type of pesticide, namely, development of resistant strains of the pathogen. If only one specific biosynthetic reaction is involved then only a small genetic mutation would be required to counteract the activity.

Although protective fungicides have been used for many years, very few examples of induced resistance have been reported and, where they have, resistance has always disappeared rapidly when use of the fungicide was discontinued. The resistance induced by systemic fungicides appears, on the other hand, to persist. There seems good reason, therefore, to use systemic fungicides judiciously, as with antibiotics in medicine, and not to use any single compound continuously for long periods but to "ring the changes" on various systemic fungicides and, possibly, alternate with protective fungi-cides. Apart from using systemic fungicides only where economically neces-sary, great attention should be paid to methods of application to confine the fungicide strictly to the crop plants and to avoid "drift".

Systemic fungicides, because of their biochemical action, tend to be highly specific to certain species of fungus. The compounds developed so far tend to be more effective against the surface fungi such as mildews than against deep-seated fungal diseases. However, the wide diversity of chemical structures which have been shown in the last decade to have systemic fungicidal activity makes it likely that specific cures for most fungal diseases will eventually be discovered.

Further Reading

Baker, K. F. and Snyder, W. C. *Ecology of Soil-borne Plant Pathogens*, John Murray, London, 1965.

Evans, E. *Plant Diseases and Their Chemical Control* Blackwell, Oxford 1968.

Green, M. B. and Spilker, D. A. (eds.) *Fungicide Chemistry: Advances and Practical Application*, American Chemical Society 1986.

Horst, R. K. *Westcott's Plant Disease Handbook*, van Nostrand, New York, 1979.

Langcake, P., Kuhn, P. J. and Wade, M. Mode of action of systemic fungicides, in Vol. 3 of *Progress in Pesticide Biochemistry*, eds. D. H. Hutton and T. R. Roberts, Wiley, 1983.

Large, E. C. *The Advance of the Fungi*, Jonathan Cape, London, 1958.

Marsh, R. W. (ed.) *Systemic Fungicides*, Longmans, London, 2nd ed. 1977.

Sharville, E. G. *Chemical Control of Plant Diseases*, University Publ, Texas 1969.

Thorn, G. D. and Ludwig, R. A. *The Dithiocarbamates and Related Compounds*, Elsevier, London 1962.

Torgeson, D. C. (ed.) *Fungicides*, Vols I and II, Academic Press, New York, 1967.

18

Chemicals for Weed Control: I

In this chapter we shall first be concerned with the history of application of chemicals for weed control and the development of "hormone" herbicides and selective control in the major cereal crops. These crops had more need of new methods of controlling weeds because their cultivation in extensive areas closely planted made hand or machine weeding after the seed was sown almost impossible, while in orchards and intensive vegetable cropping these methods were effective and economic.

For more than 100 years chemicals have been used for "total" weed control — the elimination of all vegetation on railway tracks, timber yards, unmetalled roads, etc. The earliest were crude products used in massive doses. They included crushed arsenical ores, oil wastes, thiocyanates from coal-gas washing and creosote. They met objections on grounds of toxicity, messiness and competitive demand within industry for the products which could be refined from them. Their place is now largely taken by more complex products of chemical synthesis, but chlorates, very rapid in action, and borates, very non-selective, are still used to some extent despite the fire-risk with the former. About 15,000 t/year of inorganic herbicides are manufactured in the U.S.A. but are mostly used in non-crop situations.

These uses for total plant destruction would be largely out of place in this book, but when carried out by chemicals leaving no persistent effect they are playing an increasingly important part in replacing energy-demanding mechanical preparation of land after one harvest to receive seed for the next, chemicals for which treatment are described in the next chapter. Moreover there is local use on many modern farms to keep machine-storage areas, access roads and fence-lines clear.

The earliest selective chemical treatments, at the beginning of the century, were made on cereals with sulphuric acid and with soluble copper salts. Sulphuric acid destroys the integrity of the plant tissue with which it comes in contact and opens the way to rapid advance of saprophytic (feeding on dead tissue) micro-organisms. Copper salts are toxic to all forms of plant life although copper at the trace level is an essential element. Both give rise to corrosion problems on exposed steel in machinery. Copper salts are no longer used. Sulphuric acid still finds limited use in the destruction of potato haulm at the end of the season to facilitate mechanical harvesting, and to a yet more limited extent for the control of weeds in onions. These essentially non-selective toxicants can be used selectively in cereals mainly by a physical mechanism. All the grasses, including cereals, have nearly vertical leaves, which are also difficult to wet. The base of the leaf is well designed to throw off water drops which descend the blade, and the growing point is well sheathed. Most broad-leaved weeds, on the other hand, have growing points exposed in the leaf axils where water drops tend to collect. The cereal therefore receives a much smaller dose than the weeds and what is received lies in a less vital site.

The modern period may be considered to begin with the use in France in 1933 of the sodium salt of 2-methyl-4,6-dinitrophenol (DNOC) as a selective herbicide in cereals. It was more efficient than acid or copper but suffered from two disadvantages. The dry salt is extremely inflammable and the compound is toxic and easily adsorbed through the skin. The first was overcome by changing to a suspension of the free acid, usually with added ammonium sulphate, which was found to be more effective as well as less inflammable. The second caused trouble. The safety record of spray operators in Britain has been on the whole very good, but DNOC has been responsible for most of the few fatalities.

DNOC is not, in fact, as toxic as many insecticides which have appeared since. Its bad record is due to its place in the history of pesticide use. It came in as a weedkiller, on a much larger scale than insecticides. It was used by operators much less accustomed to toxic sprays than were the orchardists who were the main users of insecticides. Its use spread widely during the war when safety was given least attention. It came before the growth of present government control measures, which it did much to bring about. Had it today been newly introduced, rather than nearly discarded, its record would be much better.

Some would give DNOC a third bad mark — its intense yellow colour, difficult to remove from wool and skin. This is not very logical. A strong colour is a good safeguard, since its enables contamination to be easily noticed and therefore avoided. It is, in fact, now established practice in most countries for agricultural products containing scheduled poisons to contain also a red or violet warning colour.

DNOC is hardly used at all nowadays as a herbicide but the related 2-sec. butyl-4,6-dinitrophenol (dinoseb) and 2-tert.butyl-4,6-dinitrophenol (dinoterb), and their acetates, are more toxic to most weeds and less toxic to mammals than DNOC and were used on a small scale in the U.K. as post-emergent selective herbicides in peas, and in the U.S.A. as pre- and post-emergent herbicides to control small annual broad-leaved weeds in a variety of crops. Dinoseb was also used on land deep-sown with cotton before emergence of the crop but this use is now mostly replaced. Dinoterb is more selective in cereals than dinoseb, less dependent on climatic conditions, particularly temperature, and has a longer period of use during the growing season. Dinoseb and dinoterb are manufactured by nitration of the appropriate alkyl-substituted phenols which are themselves made by vapour-phase reaction of phenol with an olefine over a suitable catalyst. About 4,000 t/year were manufactured in the U.S.A., but their use has been discontinued because of toxicity problems.

As mentioned above, physical differences were mainly responsible for the limited selectivity between crop and weeds achieved by copper or acid sprays and these differences also make a contribution to the better selectivity obtained with the dinitrophenols. This had created the persistent reference to "broad-leaved" weeds in cereals, a verbal usage now well entrenched but misleading. Wild onion and spurrey have leaves much narrower, relatively and absolutely, than maize and the reflection of spray drops from the broad leaves of the pea crop on to the small leaves of chickweed or the much divided leaves of mayweed is a major factor in the selective use of DNOC in this crop. Selectivity of later, improved herbicides is mainly due to biochemical differences and has little to do with leaf width or even with the implied, associated (but erroneous) difference between dicotyledons and monocotyledons. More generally significant is a distinction between grasses and other plants but important and useful differences of response to special chemicals have now appeared among grasses.

Phenoxyacid Herbicides

These were developed during World War II as products of war-directed research. They were the key compounds for the very rapid expansion of chemical weed control in the last 40 years. The phenoxy acids were undoubtedly suggested by the structure and activity of the then newly discovered endogenous plant hormone — or auxin — indolyl-3-acetic acid (IAA).

IAA   2, 4-D

This compound is produced in the growing shoot tips and controls cell elongation and root initiation. It was thought that synthetic imitations might interfere with these essential actions. Many ring-substituted acetic acids were made and tested. Outstanding was 2,4-dichlorophenoxyacetic (2,4-D) which seemed an unlikely mimic of indolylacetic acid in an activity so biochemically specific and delicate as hormonal control. Yet it was found that this compound had a growth-modifying activity even greater than that of the natural auxin. Unlike the natural auxin it was not subject to internal regulation of concentration, so that it produced lethally abnormal growth. In low concentration it could induce root growth from stem cuttings, but the margin of safety between induction of healthy root growth and the induction of excessive root thickening was far too small. It was the lethal effect of excessive growth in the wrong tissues which was exploitable, especially as this effect was far less in grasses than in most other species.

With hindsight, now that the biochemistry of the modes of action of both natural auxins and of phenoxyacetic acids are understood, it is apparent that substances of different chemical structures can have the same common mode of action provided they meet the geometrical requirements for the stereospecific interactions with cell protein which result in stimulation of RNA and DNA polymerase and other enzyme activities and consequent production of the characteristic auxin effects.

So, the "hormone" weedkillers were born. By one of those rare accidents a compound very simple for the industrial chemist to produce turned out to possess very good selective properties as a weedkiller in cereals, without any significant effect on animals and at a time when such properties were very much needed. Without their development at the right time, farmers would have been much slower to take up the new techniques. These compounds had four advantages which were vital at this stage. They were cheap to produce. They had so wide a margin of selectivity in favour of the cereal crop that little skill was needed in their use. They were virtually non-toxic to man and stock. They came forward at a time when maximum home production of food was essential and labour on farms very scarce.

The manufacture of 2,4-D and its close relation MCPA (4-chloro-2-methylphenoxyacetic acid) is very simple. Phenol is first directly dichlorinated or 2-methylphenol directly monochlorinated, in each case the desired positions of chlorination being those naturally favoured. The substituted phenol, as its sodium salt, is then reacted with sodium monochloroacetate, a Williamson ether synthesis of the most simple type. The reaction is carried out very efficiently, without the need for anhydrous conditions, by heating in concentrated solution in water. The sequence is simply, for MPCA:

MCPA

with a yield of 80% or more, there being some by-product 6-chloro-2-methylphenoxyacetate and 4,6-dichloro compounds.

In early production the by-products were not removed. Even the sodium chloride was retained in solution, limiting the concentration of the sodium 4-chloro-2-methylphenoxyacetate to about 10%, but with the advantage that the microflora of the vast areas of the farmers' fields disposed, without any cost, of the organic by-products. There can have been few chemical processes where the directly obtained products of reaction in solution could be sold direct to the user.

Economics of packing and transport later dictated the production of more concentrated products from which the sodium chloride must be removed. This is carried out by hot separation of the free phenoxyacetic acid after acidification, into an organic solvent from which it is extracted back into a more concentrated alkali solution. Other refinements have been made in the process. Good distribution of chlorine at the chlorination stage is essential to reduce loss in an unwanted mixture of unchlorinated and dichlorinated products. In manufacture of MCPA the Williamson condensation can be carried out before chlorination, with the advantage that the chlorination has even greater preference for the 4-position as opposed to 6 (the 6-chloro compound is virtually inactive). The chlorination of 2-methylphenoxyacetic acid is best carried out in 1,2-dichloropropane at 80°.

MCPA has an important advantage over 2,4-D in that the sodium salt is much more soluble. Most concentrates contain about 25% of the active acid in the saline form, some containing mixed sodium and potassium to decrease the temperature at which the salt may freeze out. The sodium salt of 2,4-D, on the other hand, is only about 2% soluble: the potassium not much more. In order to make an economically acceptable concentrate the acid must be neutralized with an amine, dimethylamine and mixed ethanolamines being most common.

From the beginning, 2,4-D was almost exclusively preferred to MCPA in the U.S.A. The reverse was, and still is, true in the U.K. Over the continent of Europe the two are more nearly equal in usage. The difference between British and American choice was dictated by two factors. 2-Methylphenol was relatively abundant in Britain as a product of coal-tar distillation. The American coal-fields were less rich in this product but, on the other hand, the production of synthetic phenol was much more advanced. The second factor was agronomic. Both products can do some damage to the cereal crops if over-dosing occurs or if sprayed too early or after the critical "jointing" stage. In this respect MCPA is the safer of the two. This was of less consequence in the U.S.A. since the agronomic practice was to keep weeds at a low competitive level rather than produce almost complete kill. Lower dosage was therefore acceptable. These compounds are not direct killers: rather they disorganize the weeds which then succumb to drought and competition. A better effect is therefore produced when the surface soil is too dry to enable plants with a deficient root system to survive. Even the lower dose is often lethal in the drier U.S.A.

2,4-D and MCPA have been described at some length because they were key compounds in the history of the subject. Without the fortunate combination of cheap production, safety to the operator and the need for no great skill, chemical weed control would not have become so quickly a very important tool in modern farming. Without these pioneers, many later compounds, requiring more skill and judgement in use, would probably have never become commercial. One must, however, be careful, in giving them an important place in history, not to emphasize the history to the exclusion of the compounds. They are still, in terms of world tonnage, the most important of all selective weed-killers. The U.S.A. manufactures about 20,000 t/year of 2,4-D.

The only other phenoxyacetic acid of importance is the 2,4,5-trichloro (2,4,5-T). It has advantages over the others, particularly in an ester formulation, against woody species. In this case, the biological preference is not for the 2,4,6-compound, obtained easily by direct chlorination. This is not active. Fortunately an easy alternative process is available. The 2,4,5-trichlorophenol is prepared by alkaline high-pressure hydrolysis of the symmetrical tetrachlorobenzene, just as phenol itself can be made from monochlorobenzene. Because 2,4,5-trichlorophenol is less reactive than 2,4-dichlorophenol the condensation with sodium monochloroacetate is usually carried out at about 150° in a higher-boiling organic solvent such as amyl alcohol, rather than in water. About 4,000 t/year of 2,4,5-T were manufactured in the U.S.A. and were mainly used for brush control in non-crop situations. Such great public objection to the use of 2,4,5-T has been aroused that its use is now discontinued in most countries. We believe manufacture and use are now confined to New Zealand and are under threat. The emotive objections were aroused by a combination of its use (or abuse) in the war in Vietnam and the discovery of an impurity of manufacture (symmetrical tetrachlorodibenzodioxin) of high and unexpected toxicity and teratogenicity Manufacturing processes have now been modified so that the dioxin content is well below the 0.5 ppm level which is regarded as safe.

Although some adverse effects have been reported in animals with doses of purified phenoxyacetic acids far beyond those likely to be encountered under normal conditions of use, there is no reason to believe that their agricultural use presents any danger to man or animals and, as they are rapidly broken down in vegetation or soil, they present no lasting hazard to the environment.

The earliest and most evident symptom in susceptible plants treated with the phenoxyacetic and related "hormone" herbicides is epinasty, or bending of the extending young stems and inward curling of leaves. This is a sensitive indication of contamination of susceptible crops by spray from a cereal area. If an ester rather than an alkali or amine salt is used, these symptoms may appear downwind of an area previously sprayed under still conditions. This growth distortion is not as important for weed killing as the damage to root function. In mild form it is often transient but can do economic damage to some crops. The grape vine is particularly sensitive. Roses and carnations for the cut flower trade lose their value when the stems are distorted.

Phenoxybutyrics

An extension of the phenoxyacetic herbicides is due to Wain in the U.K., following earlier observations of Zimmerman. The ω-phenoxy derivatives of fatty acids higher than acetic are not themselves active as herbicides. They can, however, be degraded biochemically by the β oxidation process to derivatives of the fatty acid with two fewer carbon atoms (similar to the process which occurs in the metabolism of the acids of true fats, which always occur in nature with an even number of C atoms).

$$RCH_2CH_2CH_2CO_2H \xrightarrow{O_2} RCH_2COCH_2CO_2H \xrightarrow{H_2O}$$
$$RCH_2CO_2H + CH_3CO_2H$$

When the 3-propionic derivative is degraded it probably goes through the unstable phenoxyformic acid to the phenol, but 4-(2,4-dichloro or 4-chloro-2-methylphenoxy)-butyric acid (2,4-DB or MCPB) gives the herbicidal derivative of acetic acid. The phenoxybutyrics are prepared by condensation of the substituted phenol with butyrolactone, preferably in a mixture of nonane and butanol at 160°.

Wain found that there are considerable differences between species in their ability to oxidize the higher acids. A new mechanism of selectivity is thereby introduced. It was discovered that leguminous species generally, but by no means invariably, are resistant to the phenoxybutyric acids. These compounds are therefore applied to cereals undersown with leguminous crops. While clover species and lucerne escape damage, "trefoil" (*Medicago lupulina*) is sensitive. The biochemistry is not as simple as at first supposed. In lucerne, 2,4-dichlorophenoxybutyric acid is decomposed rapidly but the phenoxyacetic acid is only a minor product. Sensitivity is probably mainly determined by the relative rates of β oxidation and attack on the benzene ring. There is also evidence that the phenoxybutyrics, partly because of their weaker acidity, are less freely translocated from a treated leaf.

MCPA and 2,4-D were effective against most of the weeds which were common in cereal fields 30 or 40 years ago. They are still widely used, although these weeds have become, in consequence, far less important. The phenoxybutyrics extended the range of tolerant crops rather than the range of susceptible weeds. Against certain weeds, one or other of these compounds proved superior, but against some none was effective. To the farmer these "hormone resistant" weeds took on greater importance. This was partly because, becoming more weed-conscious, he noticed them more, partly because changes in rotation and cultivation practice were giving them a better chance.

Phenoxypropionics

3-Phenoxypropionics do not show the characteristic "hormone" symptoms, but 3-phenyl-2-chloropropionic (chlorfenprop) is used as a wild oat killer by action more nearly related to that of 2,2-dichloropropionic (dalapon) than to that of the phenoxyacetics. 2-phenoxypropionics (i.e. 2-phenoxy-2-methyl-acetics) do have the hormone action. They have an asymmetric C atom and only one of the optical isomers is active, illustrating the importance of geometrical fit. Resolution of the isomers in the commerical product is not economic. The importance of the 2-phenoxypropionics is that they are active against some of the important weeds of cereals which are almost resistant to MCPA and 2,4-D. These weeds are chickweed (*Stellaria media*), mayweeds (*Matricaria* and *Anthemis* spp) cleavers (*Gallium aparine*) and some *Polygonum* spp. The analogues of 2,4-D and MCPA are active against all these but the first, dichlorprop, is preferred against polygonums and the second, mecoprop, against chickweed. The 2,4,5-trichloro compound, fenoprop, has advantage against woody plants. All are most frequently used as esters and in admixture with 2,4-D and MCPA to increase the weed spectrum of these less expensive chemicals.

Benzoic Acid Herbicides

2,3,5-Triiodobenzoic acid has long been known to have growth modifying activity chiefly in inducing fasciculation and abscission and has been much used in physiological studies. Its iodine content makes it too expensive for consideration in field weed control. A trichlorobenzoic acid of different configuration, the 2,3,6- was very active but appeared to have too little selectivity. It was found, however, to be very effective against cleavers and mayweeds at a dose so low that the crop was not damaged. In conjunction with MCPA it was effective against mayweeds and chickweed.

TBA is a difficult compound to make in high yield because the biologically desirable place for the chlorine substituents is not the place where they most naturally go by the obvious chemical process. The yield of the right isomer by direct chlorination of benzoic acid or benzoyl chloride is negligible. The successful route starts by monochlorination of toluene. The 2-chlorotoluene is separated from other isomers by distillation and then further chlorinated, yielding first mainly 2,5-dichloro and then a mixture of 2,5,6- (= 2,3,6-) and 2,4,5-trichloro. With careful choice of conditions, a mixture containing about 60% of the desired isomer can be obtained. This is then oxidized with nitric acid to the corresponding mixture of benzoic acids.

The scheme is oversimplified, since other isomers, in smaller quantity are produced, together with some di- and tetra-chloro compounds. The 4 substituted compounds are virtually inactive. The 2,6-di and 2,3,5,6-tetrachloro compounds have a similar activity to that of the 2,3,6 but are less powerful.

Most of the 2,4,5-trichloro acid can be removed from the final product by partial acidification and extraction, the 2,6-disubstituted acids being considerably stronger than those having a hydrogen atom remaining in the 2- or 6-position.

3,6-Dichloro-2-methoxybenzoic acid (dicamba) is used in combination with MCPA for selective weed control in cereals and is particularly effective against weeds of the genus *Polygonum* against which 2,4-D and MCPA are only moderately effective.

The crucial step in the synthesis is the Kolbe insertion of the carboxyl group which makes production of the desired 2,3,6 disposition more efficient than in the case of TBA.

Dicamba

TBA and dicamba, like the phenoxy aliphatic acids, are plant disorganizers rather than direct killers, but they produce very different symptoms. The phenoxy compounds produce contortions of the stems and leaf stalks and proliferation of stumpy roots, sometimes on the aerial parts. The benzoics produce very narrowed leaves and buds, but with much less twisting and without abnormal root growth. All hormones can produce gross swelling of the stems in some species and the benzoics particularly make the stem very brittle so that treated plants are often found in the field with the appearance of having them nipped off by rodents.

The analogue of dicamba with an extra chlorine atom, 3,5,6-trichloro-2-methoxy-benzoic acid (tricamba) has also found some commercial application.

The most commercially useful of the benzoic acids is 3-amino-2,5-dichloro-benzoic acid (chloramben). It is manufactured by chlorination of benzoic acid to 2,5-dichlorobenzoic acid, which is then ntirated and reduced.

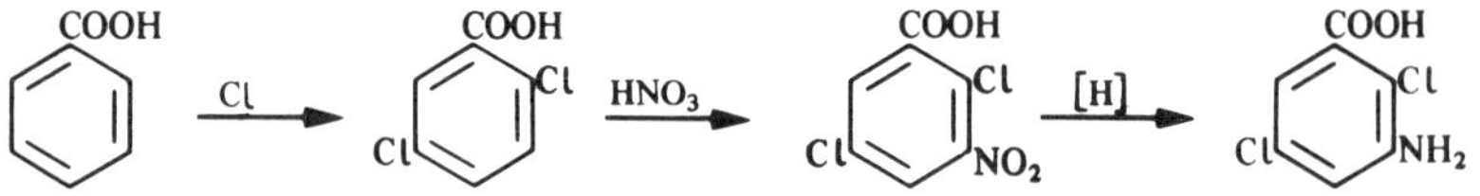

Chloramben

Chloramben is a selective pre-emergent herbicide which was widely used on soya beans, carrots and cucurbits but it has now gone out of fashion. It has a very low mammalian toxicity and is effective against both grassy and broad-leaved weeds. About 2,000 t/year are still manufactured in the U.S.A., whereas manufacture of TBA and dicamba together in the U.S.A. total only 500 t/year.

Pyridine Acid Herbicides

Of compounds analogous to the phenoxy acetic and benzoic acids in which the pyridine ring replaces benzene, the one which has achieved most commercial success is 4-amino-3,5,6-trichloropicolinic acid (picloram). It is manufactured by chlorination of 2-methylpyridine, reaction of the product with ammonia and then hydrolysis.

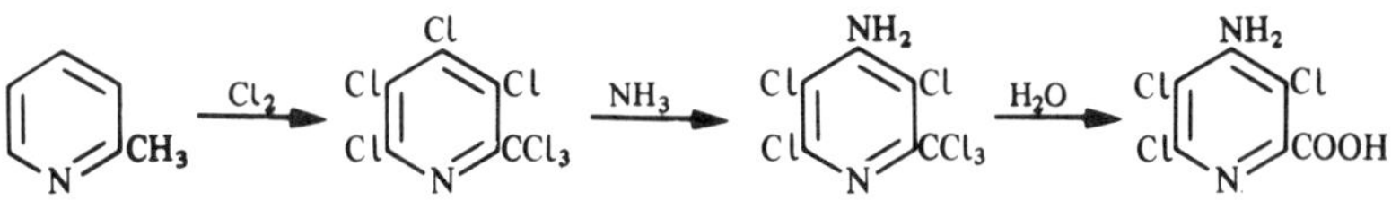

Picloram

It is a systemic herbicide which produces epinasty and leaf-curling, and is rapidly absorbed by leaves and roots and translocated to the growing shoots. Most broad-leaved weeds are sensitive to it, but most grasses are resistant. It is one of the most active herbicides known and has been used against annual weeds at rates as low as 15 g/ha, although perennials need higher dose rates.

It is also a very persistent compound in the soil so has fallen somewhat into disfavour.

A dichloropyridine acid (3,6-dichloropicolinic) is also in use, now called clopyralid. It is effective on many species of four important families and safe on onion, flax and beet as well as cereals. It has a shorter life in the soil than picloram. An analogue of the phenoxy acetics, (3,5,6-trichloro-2-pyridyl)-oxyacetic, triclopyr, is also very active on most broad-leaved weeds and finds use against some problems in tropical plantation crops.

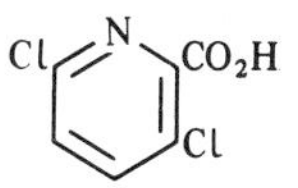

Clopyralid

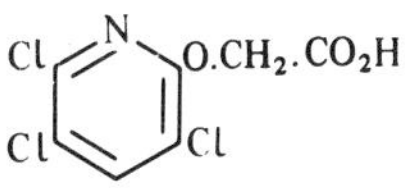

Triclopyr

Soil Activity and Persistence

2,4-D and MCPA applied to the soil will kill many weeds during or soon after germination but this effect is not reliable partly because the compounds are broken down by soil bacteria which can become adapted and so destroy a second application more rapidly than the first. Another factor is that since they destroy roots without translocation from roots to foliage the distribution in the soil must be very general to have other than a patchy effect. TBA, picloram and dicamba being taken up through the roots without local damage, have a more general and characteristic "hormone" effect. They are not used for soil application but they are, especially TBA and picloram, much more persistent in soil than the phenoxyacetics and can so give rise to problems in a subsequent crop. They are also retained in straw from a treated cereal crop and so can be concentrated in composted straw used for horticultural purposes. They are used in cereal crops only at low dosage in mixtures and the farmer warned not to pass on the straw to tomato growers. The main use of picloram is in mixtures for spot treatment of scrub weed in pasture.

2,3,6-trichlorophenylacetic acid (chlorfenac) is generally lethal to plants and very persistent in the soil. It has not found useful selective action at low dosage, as has TBA, but is used with other herbicides to keep industrial sites clear.

Dichlobenil

This is a herbicide used for safe clean-up of seedling weeds in orchards and berry fruit gardens. It inhibits actively growing meristems, is easily transmitted to emerging shoots by vapour diffusion and has no long-term residual action which could extend to well-established perennials. In some situations its rather high volatility makes it too transient and this limitation is extended by supplying a progenitor of the active compound formed by a reaction unique among herbicides.

Chlorthiamid   Dichlobenil

The progenitor, chlorthiamid, is much less volatile than dichlobenil and more water soluble so that it produces a more persistent effect by permitting more penetration of the soil from a surface application. Dichlobenil is manufactured from 2,6-dichlorotoluene via the aldehyde and oxime, chlorthiamid from it by reversal of the reaction shown.

One might expect that the nitrile group would be hydrolyzed to carboxyl under soil conditions, thus generating 2,6-dichlorobenzoic acid, which has activity similar to, but weaker than, TBA (the 2,3,6-trichloro acid). The action of dichlobenil on plants is quite different from that of TBA, which is also much more persistent. Under most conditions hydrolysis seems to stop at the benzamide stage and it is also probable that the 2,6 dichloro acid is much more vulnerable to ring-opening attack than the 2,3,6 and therefore decays as fast as formed.

Bromoxynil and Ioxynil

These are two other compounds used on standing cereal crops for killing broad-leaved weeds. They are directly toxic to the susceptible plants but can be used in some other crops than cereals, particularly onions, garlic and flax. They are usually referred to as hydroxybenzonitriles but their similarity in action to the earlier dinitrophenols makes the name cyanophenols more explanatory.

They are used in salt form or as emulsions of esters, usually octanoates. They are considerably less toxic to mammals than the dinitrophenols.

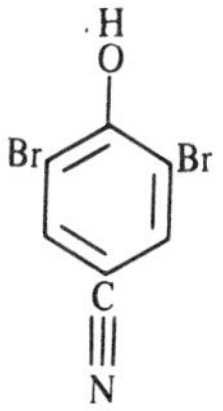

Bromoxynil 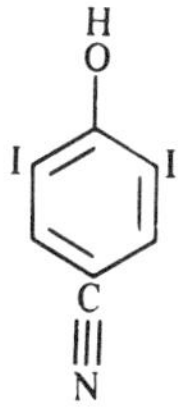   Ioxynil

Control of Wild Oat in Wheat and Barley

While the other chemicals mentioned above broadened the spectrum of control by the major hormone herbicides of weeds in dry-land cereals to include most of the problem broadleaved weeds, the most serious problem, that of wild oat, remained and indeed increased. The increase was due to chemical control encouraging a shift away from rotational cropping and periods of grazing: the hoe and the mouths of sheep and cattle no longer uprooted wild oat or consumed it before flowering. Its increase was particularly serious because it was more competitive than some more spectacular weeds, reducing the crop yield more than an equal population of charlock or poppy.

Its chemical control was severely challenging. Selection was needed between grass species, none of them very vulnerable to the first selective herbicides. Some progress was made by the discovery that trichloroacetate (TCA) had the reverse selectivity to that already established, killing most grasses in most other species but it was effective only via the soil and was needed at much higher rates than the hormones (but was of course much cheaper). An improvement was 2,2-dichloropropionic acid (dalapon) which was effective when sprayed on foliage. These compounds offered a solution by partial return to rotational cropping in that wild oat (and other grasses) could be dealt with in intervening crops of brassicas, sugar beet, potatoes or peas, provided cereals were not sown too soon after harvest while the chemicals were still active.

The first compound to show sufficient biochemical discrimination between wheat and barley (less vulnerable) and oat (more vulnerable) was a carbamate, chloromethylpropargyl N-3-chlorophenyl carbamate, barban. Sprayed as an emulsion on most varieties of spring wheat and some varieties

Cl —◯— $NH.CO.O.CH_2.C{\equiv}C.CH_2Cl$

Barban

of spring barley while the wild oat is in the appropriate juvenile stage (between 1 and 2.5 leaves unfolded) it gave satisfactory control. Its safe use demanded much more knowledge and judgement on the part of the user than did the use of "hormones" on "broad-leaved" weeds. Other highly selective compounds giving control by spraying on the young growing crop followed, some demanding not quite such fine judgement. Benzoylprop-ethyl is shown below.

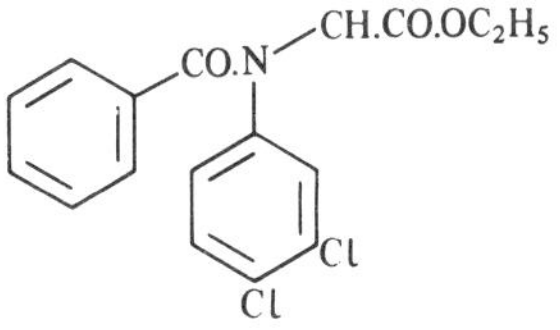

Benzoylprop–ethyl

Flamprop-isopropyl has the Cl substituent at position 4 replaced by F, as well as the change of alcohol moiety. These owed their selective action to more rapid enzymic ester hydrolysis in oats while detoxification by sugar condensation proceeded at the same rate. They are used in spring or winter wheat. The methyl ester is advised for barley. They can be used over a wider range of growth stage than barban but are not effective against another important grass weed, blackgrass (*Alopecurus myosuroides*). A wholly different compound, difenzoquat, is also used for wild oat control by spraying in water solution on the growing crop.

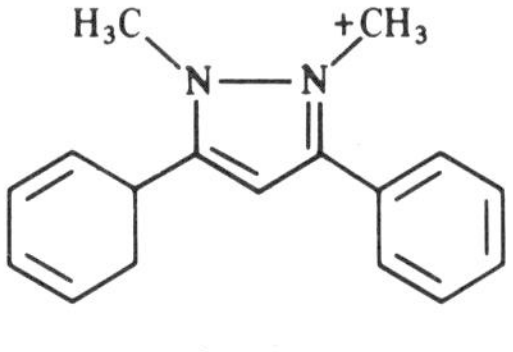

Difenzoquat

Other developments in this highly selective chemical usage involve action in the soil and, with some in the rice crop, in water. They are dealt with in the next chapter.

Selective Grass Killers

It will be convenient to deal here with recent new selective herbicides in which the selectivity is reversed, more clearly and more actively than with dalapon and which are effective by foliage application. The distinction can no longer be made between cereals (narrow-leaved) and broad-leaved plants nor between monocotyledons and dicotyledons, because the compounds are active against weed grasses in onions and other members of the lily family and of iridaceae. Also the narrow-leaved Dianthus species are resistant.

Remarkably, one important group is based on the phenoxyacetic structure, all previous examples of which were selective in favour of grasses against broad leaved weeds. The difference depends on an extension of the ring structure. 2,4-D is the classic example of the herbicide for use in a grasss crop. 2,4-dichlorophenoxyphenoxyacetic acid shows the reverse selectivity! It has not been developed because the same substitution in the propionic acid was more effective and selective and is further improved by application in ester formulation as diclofop-methyl. Other ring extensions have led to other successful products. Three of current importance are formulated below.

The breakthrough originated with diclofop and fenoxaprop but these have encountered some problems with mammalian toxicity. Fenthiaprop, with S in place of O in the heterocyclic ring was introduced but withdrawn. The most widely-used and safest product is fluazifop-butyl. Haloxyfop, with an additional chlorine substituent in the 3-position in the pyridine ring is also used. Clobenprop is also active showing that the rings do not necessarily have to be bridged through oxygen.

The outstanding commercial importance of these compounds is that they can be used to control grassy weeds in broad-leaved crops while the crop is actually growing. The margin of safety is very wide. Virtually all grasses are controlled while soybean, sugar beet, cotton, oilseed rape, potatoes, vines, vegetables, ground nuts, soft fruit and tree fruit, bananas, pines are completely unaffected. The compounds move in both xylem and phloem to all parts of the plant. Active growth of grasses ceases after 2 days and, after 7 days, the growing points turn brown and kill is complete in 3 to 4 weeks. The mode of action is interference with production of ATP.

Two compounds with main structure in common but quite unrelated to the extended phenoxyacids were developed in Japan with formulae given below. Alloxydim is marketed as the water soluble sodium salt but sethoxydim as an emulsifiable concentrate.

These developments have stimulated research into grasskilling action and new compounds are likely to appear.

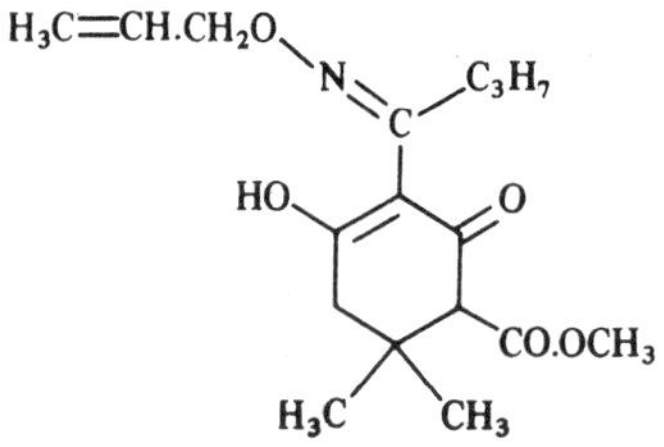

Alloxydim

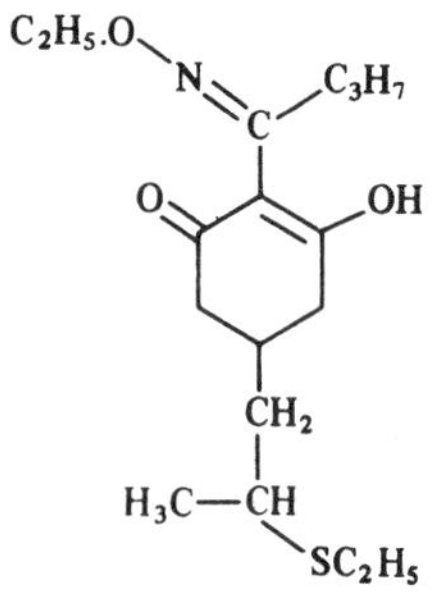

Sethoxydim

This chapter began, as did the whole subject of selective herbicides, with what came to be thought of as the easy problem of controlling broad-leaved weeds in cereals. It ends with the prospect that control of grass weeds in non-grass crops may soon become the most successful.

Further Reading

See p. 245.

19

Chemicals for Weed Control: II

We now move on to some chemicals in great variety and of varying importance which rely rather more on physical factors to achieve selectivity useful in agriculture. Many are usefully active only via the soil and we must first explain the ways in which action or inactivity in the soil can contribute to selectivity.

A compound may be inactivated by the soil or be unable to enter the plant through the roots. It can then avoid damaging the crop if it is applied before the crop seeds germinate or the shoot emerges. If the seed is sown after the bed has been prepared, preferably several weeks after, the herbicide can be used to eliminate emerged weed seedlings.

A compound may remain active for several weeks in the soil but be only slowly leached downwards and root uptake may be necessary for lethal action. If a large seeded crop is deep-sown before treatment of the soil surface with such a compound, its active roots can escape while small-seeded weeds, mainly germinating only nearer the surface, are killed.

The leaf cuticle is not adapted to transmit molecules other than those of oxygen, carbon dioxide and water — in a state of nature it is not normally required to do so. The root hairs on the other hand have to accept important mineral nutrients and keep out a much greater variety of chemicals dissolved in soil water than are present in air. The area and spread of accepting root surface is relatively enormous. This difference of function affects herbicidal selectivity in two ways. A compound has to be much more soluble to enter significantly via the leaf. The root, intimately contacting a much greater volume of water than can be supplied by spray or retained on the leaf, has the possibility of taking up much more of a low-soluble herbicide. The root however is much more likely to be selective in its acceptance or transmission of foreign molecules.

The greater solubility required for effective leaf uptake is not necessarily in water. An oily ester or one dissolved in an oil may penetrate more easily through the hydrophobic cuticle than a water soluble salt and then be hydrolyzed and become transportable in the water-filled transport vessels. Frequently this useful sequence of oil solubility as applied, followed by water solubility after penetration, is achieved by oxidation.

The solubility necessary for leaf penetration may be solubility in air, i.e. volatility. Certainly plants can be adversely affected by nitric oxide, ozone and sulphur dioxide, and volatile herbicides can cause drift damage to neighbouring crops. In the normal working of herbicides, vapour transfer is mainly important in the air-space of the soil. The ascending shoot from a germinating seed is adapted to avoid contact with water. Its surface is usually hydrophobic and its upward extension pushes soil crumbs apart. The radical, on the other hand, is water-seeking and its hairs penetrate narrow water-filled spaces between soil crumbs. Most of the herbicides which affect the shoot directly are sufficiently volatile to supply it with a lethal dose through diffusion in the soil air spaces.

The emerging shoot of a seedling is usually unique. If it is severed below the cotyledons it cannot be replaced whereas the radicle is adapted to send out adventitious rootlets from a very early stage. If a herbicide kills a portion of the root without entering the transport system, growth may be delayed only. The shoot, therefore, though having much less access to a soil-applied herbicide, is intrinsically more vulnerable. This difference can be more local and extreme in some plants. In the grasses the first or coleoptile node in the shoot is very vulnerable and very vital. In the case of wheat, extension below does not occur and it remains at seed level. In the case of oats, the extension continues and the node is pushed up to the soil surface. A herbicide applied to the soil surface and able to leach downwards only slowly because of adsorption on the soil particles can destroy the oat seedling but leave wheat, if the seed lies at adequate depth, unharmed.

There are, of course, biochemical factors operating in selectivity and these are more important and reliable where they can be exploited, but in many applications of the herbicides now to be described, the physical factors are determining. They are necessarily modified by climatic and soil conditions and methods of cultivation so that, as with most other operations in farming, knowledge and experience of local conditions are important. This book is concerned with the chemicals themselves and, in general terms only, with the factors affecting choice of chemical and method of use. Local advice of manufacturers and government experts must be sought.

Bipyridylium Herbicides

Diquat cation   Paraquat cation

The salts of the quaternized bipyridylium cations, diquat and paraquat, are freely water-soluble and kill top growth very quickly when applied to foliage. They are both general herbicides but are much better translocated than the old-fashioned contact herbicide DNOC. Both, particularly paraquat, are effective against grasses. There are differences in susceptibility of species, e.g. wireweed, *Polygonum aviculare*, is rather resistant, and, with care, at low dosage, in some districts, they have been used to increase clover at the expense of grasses in pasture. Generally however their selective use depends on aiming of the spray or brush application. This is practicable on an agricultural scale in orchards, woodland plantations and ornamental shrubberies, where a perennial crop stands up on a clean stem with well developed bark. With greater care, hand spraying between well-spaced lines of annual crops can replace hand hoeing with the advantage that non-disturbance of the soil does not bring dormant weed seeds nearer to the surface where their germination is more probable.

Both paraquat and diquat are immediately absorbed very strongly onto the clay minerals which are present in every soil. They are so strongly bound to these minerals that they can be removed only by completely breaking down the structure of the soil, e.g. by heating with concentrated sulphuric acid. In practice, although physically present in the bound form, they are completely inert biologically.

This fixation in the soil is essential for the safety of directed spraying since it ensures that there is no effect on plants not hit by the spray or hit only on well-matured bark. It also makes possible the major use of these compounds in agriculture, to clean up the weed and stubble aftermath of harvest but leave the ground at once safe for another crop. They thus offer the possibility of a chemical alternative to ploughing. Naturally this revolutionary use took some time to become accepted and there are doubtless situations where mechanical soil disturbance will still remain desirable. A problem of "chemical ploughing", particularly when applied to old grassland, was the mechanical problem of sowing the seed in the dense mat of fibre, but new and simple agricultural machinery has been developed for this purpose. This is an example of chemical usage not simply contributing an alternative procedure, but initiating a whole new strategy in farming which has been very widely adopted.

The bipyridyls inhibit the normal and essential process of photosynthesis in green plants. They do so at later steps in the complex sequence which are common to the basic processes of respiration, but the energy to drive them is obtained, via chlorophyll, from light rather than from oxidation of carbohydrate fuel. The reduction of pyridine nucleotide (the TPN $\rightarrow$ TPNH reaction) and the phosphorylation of adenosine diphosphate (ADP $\rightarrow$ ATP) are light-driven reactions in the chloroplasts and carry out important further reduction processes. These processes are inhibited by the bipyridilium herbicides which are reduced in the presence of light to free radicals and give rise to peroxides during the subsequent dark reoxidation to the quaternary ions. The presence of these compounds causes the reductive power of the whole photosynthetic process to be wasted in useless side reactions.

2,2'-Bipyridyl, the parent intermediate for diquat, is made by oxidative coupling of pyridine over heated Raney nickel

Direct coupling of pyridine in the 4,4' positions is not possible and all earlier methods gave mixtures of 2,2', 2,4' and 4,4'-bipyridyl. In the present process pyridine is reacted with sodium in liquid ammonia to give the transient pyridyl radical anion which immediately dimerizes to 4,4'-tetrahydro-bipyridyl which is then oxidized by air to 4,4'-bipyridyl. This process gives only the required 4,4'-isomer and is an interesting example of application of a free radical reaction on an industrial scale. Paraquat can also be manufactured directly be reaction of N-methylpyridinium chloride with sodium cyanide in aqueous sodium hydroxide, ethylenediamine or liquid ammonia, followed by reaction with chlorine.

Interference with a basic respiratory process makes these compounds toxic to most forms of life. Their toxicity to mammals is not very high but the result of an overdose, which could not be taken in during normal use of the compounds, is irreversible. Paraquat is the only herbicide since DNOC which has caused human fatalities but they have resulted from swallowing concentrate transferred, carelessly or maliciously, to a wrongly labelled container, or from being taken with suicidal intent (see Chapter 25).

The bipyridyls have no herbicidally useful analogues. Cyperquat has a formula resemblance but, of course, lacks the conjugation function and free-radical versatility of paraquat. Its action is quite different. It has some use against the serious problem weed, nutsedge, but is now withdrawn in favour of competitors.

Another compound having slight structural resemblance is norflurazon which inhibits photosynthesis by reduction of carotenoid production. It is effective on many grasses and some other weeds but cotton and many orchard species show biochemical tolerance probably by N-demethylation.

Cyperquat   Norflurazon

Glyphosate

Another very important compound occupying a similar place to paraquat in agronomy is glyphosate. It is an organophosphorus compound but unrelated in structure or action to the numerous insecticides and it has very low mammalian toxicity. It is N-phosphonomethylglycine. It is manufactured from phosphorus trichloride, formaldehyde and glycine, and is generally used as the isopropylamine salt.

$$PCl_3 + CH_2O \longrightarrow Cl_2POCH_2Cl \xrightarrow{H_2O} (HO)_2POCH_2Cl$$

$$(HO)_2POCH_2Cl + NH_2CH_2COOH \longrightarrow (HO)_2POCH_2NHCH_2COOH$$

Glyphosate

Glyphosate exerts its general, powerful but slow action on plants following application to foliage, green stem or cut stumps. It is adsorbed in soils, in competition with phosphate, by reaction with heavy metal, particularly iron, ions, but, although the adsorption is never so complete as that of paraquat on clays, glyphosate also has negligible action via the root. While the root-inaction of paraquat is due to the strong adsorption, that of glyphosate must be mainly due to some impedance of root uptake. Glyphosate is not biochemically selective although some species, e.g. white clover, are less susceptible than most. Being also root-inactive it can be used, like paraquat, for weed control in orchards and other plantations, but even greater care must be taken to avoid contamination of leaves and green stems. Although not effectively translocated *from* the root environment it is very effectively translocated *to* roots from foliar application and is thus more useful than paraquat against established perennials. With some species, e.g. blackberry, however, regrowth may occur as much as 12 months after apparent complete kill. This starts in a very abnormal form — as a multiplicity of very small shoots, but a few of these may later mature. This behaviour illustrates well the persistence of this compound in plant tissues.

Glyphosate is unusual among herbicides in being almost exclusively hydrophilic. It has a small molecule with three potential anionic and one potential cationic function, normally existing, both in the concentrate and in plant tissue, as an anion-zwitterion $(- + -)$. It has been suggested that it acts by suppressing biosynthesis of phenylalanine by inhibiting chrorismate mutase or prephenate dehydratase.

Like the bipyridyls, glyphosate is extensively used to kill residual vegetation after harvest in preparation for "direct drilling". The chief differences between glyphosate and the bipyridyls, from the agronomic aspect, are that the bipyridyls are very much more rapid in top kill but more limited in eventual kill of established perennials. These behaviours are rather inevitably associated. A rapid killer, applied to the accessible top growth only, has little chance of deep root penetration because it destroys the mechanism of transport.

Glyphosate not only kills slowly but is exceptionally well translocated into root tissue. It can kill some tall weeds when applied to the tops only and this property has been turned to advantage in dealing economically with weeds which stand well above the crop or pasture (see Chapter 21).

The activity of glyphosate, like that of the bipyridyls, seems unique. Glyphosine, which has two phosphonomethyl substituents on the N atom of the glycine, is not used much as a herbicide but it hastens the ripening of sugarcane, retarding growth but increasing the sugar content.

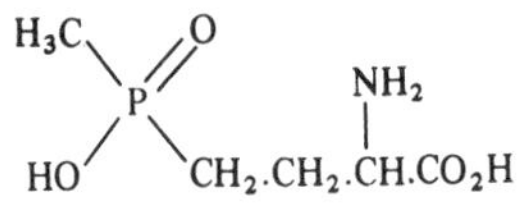

Glufosinate

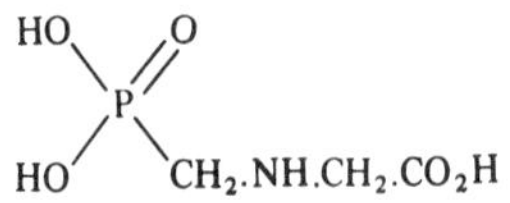

Glyphosate

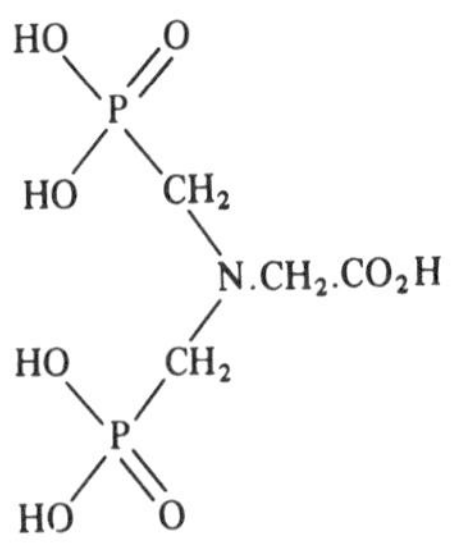

Glyphosine

Glufosinate also combines phosphate and amino-acid, but the NH_2 group is unsubstituted. It is DL-homoalanin-4-yl(methyl)-phosphinic acid, supplied as the water soluble ammonium salt. Unlike glyphosate it is not extensively translocated and kills by inhibiting photosynthesis.

Other Phosphorus Herbicides

Several organophosphorus compounds of the chemical type used as insecticides have been found to have herbicidal action. It seems that higher alcohols are necessary in the ester positions for this action compared with the ethyl, and, more frequent, methyl substituents in insecticides. Two are in minor use, bensulide for pre-emergent use in some vegetable crops and butamiphos for similar use against annual grasses. Tributyl phosphorotrithioate is used as a defoliant in the cotton crop.

$$\langle\!\!\!\bigcirc\!\!\!\rangle\!-\!\!\overset{\displaystyle O}{\underset{\displaystyle O}{\overset{\|}{\underset{\|}{S}}}}\!\!.NH.CH_2.CH_2.S.\overset{\displaystyle O.CH.(CH_3)_2}{\underset{\displaystyle O.CH(CH_3)_2}{\overset{\diagup}{\underset{\diagdown}{P}}}}\!\!=\!\!S$$

Bensulide

Ureas and Triazines

Two families of chemicals are so widely used that they are always referred to by manufacturers and farmers by these very abbreviated class names. Mainly they are applied to soil and have persistent action in suppressing vegetation in industrial sites, railway tracks and unsealed roads but, at lower dosage, can have valuable selective action. The general formulae are given below and the compounds in commercial production at the time are tabulated. A great number of other substitutions have been tried and almost any suggested member would be active. Both series are almost embarrassingly rich in active compounds. Many of these show some potentially exploitable selectivity. Owing to the confusion which could arise among farmers and the heavy cost of securing government safety approval, it is not practical to produce commercially all the variants which could have some specific advantage for minor crops.

TABLE 19.1 *Ureas of general formula*

Phenylureas

R	X	Y	Z	Name
H	H	CH_3	CH_3	Fenuron
4Cl	H	CH_3	CH_3	Monuron
3,4 di Cl	H	CH_3	CH_3	Diuron
3 Cl, 4 CH_3	H	CH_3	CH_3	Chlortoluron
3 CF_3	H	CH_3	CH_3	Fluometuron
3 Cl, 4 OCH_3	H	CH_3	CH_3	Metoxuron
4 H_3CO—⟨⟩—O—	H	CH_3	CH_3	Difenoxuron
4 Cl—⟨⟩—O—	H	CH_3	CH_3	Chloroxuron
4 $(CH_3)_2CH$	H	CH_3	CH_3	Isoproturon
4 Cl	H	OCH_3	CH_3	Monolinuron
3,4 di Cl	H	OCH_3	CH_3	Linuron
4 Br	H	OCH_3	CH_3	Metobromuron
3 Cl, 4 Br	H	OCH_3	CH_3	Chlorbromuron
3 $(H_3C)_3C.NH.CO.O$	H	CH_3	CH_3	Karbutylate
3,4 di Cl	H	C_4H_9	CH_3	Neburon
4 Cl	H	$CH(CH_3)C{=}CH$	CH_3	Buturon
H	H	⟨cyclohexyl, H_3C⟩	H	Siduron
H-Note 1	H	CH_3	H	Benzthiazuron
H-Note 1	CH_3	CH_3	H	Methabenzthiazuron
$C_2H_5.SO_2$-Note 2	CH_3	CH_3	H	Ethidimuron
F_3C-Note 2	CH_3	CH_3	H	Thiazafluron
$(H_3C)_3C$- Note 2	CH_3	CH_3	H	Tebuthiuron

Note 1 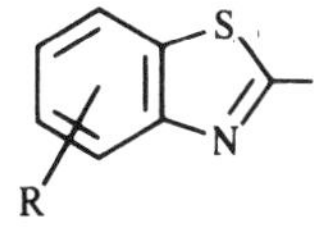 in place of

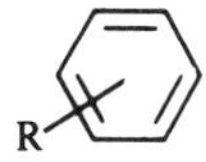

Note 2 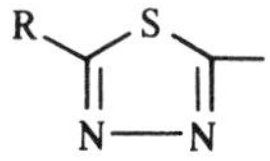 in place of

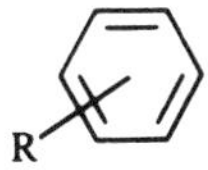

TABLE 19.2 *Triazines of general formula*

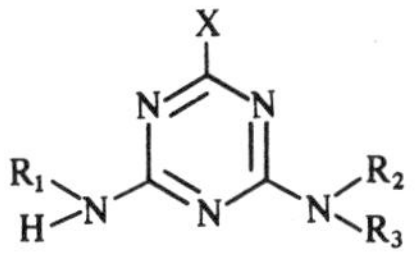

Diamino-s-triazines

X	R_1	R_2	R_3	Name
Cl	C_2H_5	H	C_2H_5	Simazine
Cl	C_2H_5	H	$CH(CH_3)_2$	Atrazine
Cl	$CH(CH_3)_2$	H	$CH(CH_3)_2$	Propazine
Cl	C_2H_5	H	$C(CH_3)_3$	Terbuthylazine
Cl	C_2H_5	H	$C(CN)(CH_3)_2$	Cyanazine
Cl	C_2H_5	C_2H_5	C_2H_5	Trietazine
Cl	C_2H_5	H	CH_2CO_2H	Eglinazine
Cl	$CH(CH_3)_2$	H	$CH_2CO.OC_2H_5$	Proglinazine ethyl
OCH_3	C_2H_5	H	$CH(CH_3)C_2H_5$	Secbumeton
OCH_3	C_2H_5	H	$C(CH_3)_3$	Terbumeton
OCH_3	$CH(CH_3)_2$	H	$CH(CH_3)_2$	Prometon
SCH_3	CH_3	H	$CH(CH_3)_2$	Desmetryne
SCH_3	C_2H_5	H	C_2H_5	Simetryne
SCH_3	C_2H_5	H	$CH(CH_3)_2$	Ametryne
SCH_3	C_2H_5	H	$C(CH_3)_3$	Terbutryne
SCH_3	$CH(CH_3)_2$	H	$CH(CH_3)_2$	Prometryne
SCH_3	$CH(CH_3)_2$	H	$C_3H_6.OCH_3$	Methoprotyne

SCH$_3$	C$_2$H$_5$	H	CH(CH$_3$)CH(CH$_3$)$_2$	Dimethametryne
SCH$_3$	CH(CH$_3$)$_2$	N*	N*	Aziprotryne
SC$_2$H$_5$	CH(CH$_3$)$_2$	H	CH(CH$_3$)$_2$	Dipropetryne

*NR$_1$R$_2$=azido

Compounds of both series are taken up by roots without local damage and then inhibit photosynthesis. Emergence of seedlings is not usually affected but they die off as the nutrient supply in the seed is exhausted. Most of them have too low solubility to be effective by foliage application, but this can be enhanced by adding emulsified non-phytotoxic oils to the spray. Exceptionally soluble members, usually containing methoxy groups, e.g. linuron and methoprotryne, are used post-emergence in some crops. Desmetryne is useful post-emergence against some weeds in some brassica crops.

Atrazine has a commanding position for weed control in the maize crop, although simazine is preferred in wet districts. The tolerance of maize to atrazine and simazine is an outstanding example of biochemical selectivity. It has been established that the maize plant contains a hydroxamic acid which is able to remove the Cl substituent very easily, probably by first adding oxygen to one of the adjacent ring N atoms. This reaction can take place *in vitro* in expressed maize sap.

Practice in Hungary provides an interesting example of adaptation of crop rotation to exploit fully the properties of available chemicals. Four or more successive maize crops are taken on suitable land, the first receiving a heavy dose of atrazine at sowing time. This gives an extremely clean crop. A rather lower dose is applied in the second year and none, or only a small "maintenance" dose, in the third year. By this method, there is time for the rather persistent herbicide to decompose in the soil before a sensitive crop is taken. Probably the later maize crops themselves contribute largely to the elimination of the herbicide by taking it up and decomposing it.

Some fruit crops, particularly raspberries and blackcurrants, and asparagus are rather tolerant of these herbicides. Top fruit orchards can be kept moderately clean with simazine, but are damaged by a dosage which will eliminate all weeds.

The partial resistance of many tree and bush species to these herbicides is probably helped by their greater size as compared with the annual weeds which are mainly controlled at the seedling stage. On a milligram-kilogram basis a mature tree requires a much larger dose and it has a greater proportion of its root system in lower levels of the soil than has a young seedling. Owing to adsorption of the herbicide on the colloidal components of the soil, chiefly the organic matter, the leaching of these herbicides downwards proceeds much more slowly than the movement of water itself, just as does an adsorbed solute in a chromatographic column. Since these herbicides were the first of the almost water-insoluble type to be widely used, their slow leaching is often put down to their low solubility, but this is of negligible importance compared with adsorption, except for compounds less soluble than simazine (5 ppm).

Where these compounds have been used alone for many years, especially atrazine in maize, some problem grasses have increased to yield-suppressing levels. The use of additional or alternative herbicides has increased. This is in fact a general tendency in the use of herbicides in agriculture.

By far the most commercially useful ureas are diuron, of which about 3000 t/year are manufactured in the U.S.A., fluometuron (2,000 t/year) and linuron (4,000 t/year). The total amount of all other ureas manufactured in the U.S.A. is only 200 t/year.

Of the triazines, by far the most important is atrazine, which at its peak was the largest tonnage herbicide of all, about 45,000 t/year being manufactured in the U.S.A. Manufacture of all other triazines in the U.S.A. amounts to about 5,000 t/year.

The substituted ureas are made by a process analogous to the formation of carbamates, differing only in that both partners to the reaction with phosgene are amines. The substituted triazines are made from the trichlorotriazine (cyanuric chloride), itself made by trimerization of cyanogen chloride. Reaction of cyanuric chloride with excess amine readily replaces the chlorine atoms. As the successive chlorine atoms are replaced, the reactivity of those remaining decreases, a fact which greatly facilitates the production of compounds with different substituents. Replacement of the first chlorine

Desmetryne

atom occurs rapidly at below room temperature; replacement of the second requires moderate, and of the third, strong heating. Replacement of the third by methoxy or methylmercapto is more facile than by amino. The sequence is shown for the case of desmetryne.

Uracil Herbicides

A useful group of herbicides is derived from the pyrimidine compound, uracil. The most commercially important compounds are bromacil and terbacil.

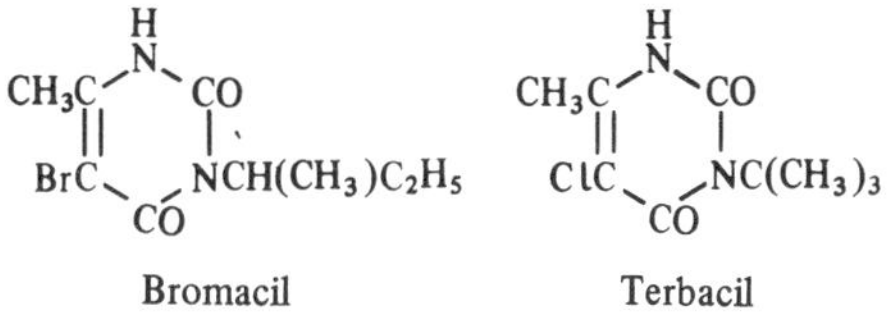

Bromacil   Terbacil

These are powerful total herbicides which can be used for general weed control in non-crop situations. They are particularly effective against perennial grasses. Bromacil is also used selectivity in citrus and sisal, and terbacil is used selectivity in sugar cane, apples and peaches. These compounds appear to be general inhibitors of photosynthesis and their selectivity arises from positional and physiological factors which prevent transport of the compound to an active biochemical site.

They are manufactured by reaction of ethyl acetoacetate with an N-substituted urea (prepared from phosgene and the appropriate amine) to give the uracil which is then halogenated, either with bromine or chlorine.

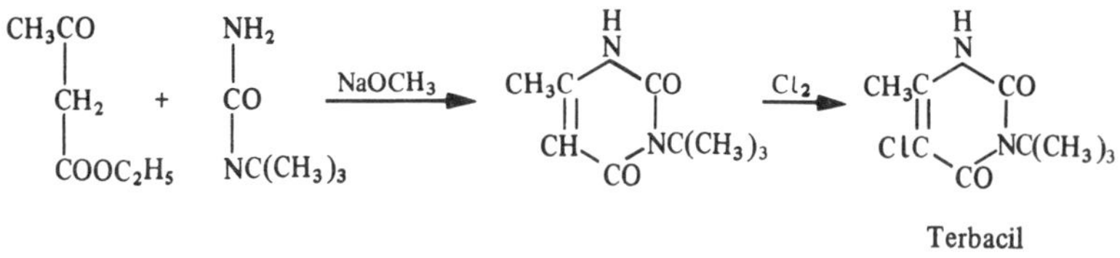

Terbacil

Dinitroanilines

The herbicidal activity of the dinitrophenols encouraged chemists to explore the dinitroanilines because these have long been commercially available as dyestuffs intermediates. The initial observation that 2,6-dinitroaniline had significant general herbicidal activity, whereas 2,3- and 2,4-dinitroanilines did not, focused attention on this isomer and stimulated attempts to achieve selectivity by introducing substituents into the benzene ring and onto the amino group. This led to one of the most commercially successful herbicides of the sixties, trifluralin. Toluene is chlorinated to give 1-chloro-4-trichloromethylbenzene which is reacted with hydrogen fluoride in the vapour phase over a catalyst to give 1-chloro-4-trifluoromethylbenzene which is then dinitrated and the product reacted with dipropylamine to give trifluralin.

Trifluralin

About 25,000 t/year of trifluralin are manufactured in the U.S.A. where it is mainly used by pre-sowing incorporation into soil for weed control in many important crops, particularly soya beans and cotton. It is effective against many of the most troublesome grassy weeds as well as against broad-leaved weeds. It kills germinating seedlings by inhibiting both root and shoot growth and development. The mode of action is not certain but it is probable that inhibition of mitosis may be the main lethal effect since effects on cell division in the roots of germinating seedlings have been observed, but there are also indications of interference with photosynthesis and respiration. There is evidence that the lipid contents of various plants may influence the selectivity of trifluralin. Also, it is clear that, in established plants, little trifluralin is translocated from roots to aerial portions.

Changes in substituents in the 3- and 4-positions of the benzene ring and on the amino group do not essentially change the type of herbicidal activity, provided that the 2,6-dinitroaniline structure is retained, but do produce variations in patterns of selectivity and degrees of activity. A wide range of molecular structure is therefore possible and a number of products which have advantages in certain situations have been introduced commercially. Thus dipropalin has more foliar contact activity than trifluralin, isopropalin controls grasses and broad-leaved weeds in tomatoes and tobacco crops, oryzalin is a selective, surface-applied herbicide for soya beans. The most widely-used compound after trifluralin is nitralin, of which about 4,000 t/year are manufactured in the U.S.A.

2,6-Dinitroanilines

TABLE 19.3

X	Y	R_1	R_2	Name
CF_3	H	C_3H_7	C_3H_7	trifluralin
CF_3	H	C_2H_5	C_4H_9	benfluralin
CH_3SO_2	H	C_3H_7	C_3H_7	nitralin
CH_3	H	C_3H_7	C_3H_7	dipropaline
$(CH_3)_2CH$	H	C_3H_7	C_3H_7	isopropalin
NH_2SO_2	H	C_3H_7	C_3H_7	oryzalin
CF_3	H	C_3H_7	$CH_2CH(CH_3)_2$	profluralin
$(CH_3)_2CH$	H	H	$C_2H_5CHCH_3$	butralin
CH_3	CH_3	H	$(C_2H_5)_2CH$	pendimethalin
CF_3	H	C_2H_5	$CH_2=C(CH_3)CH_2$	ethalfluralin
CF_3	NH_2	C_2H_5	C_2H_5	dinitramine
CF_3	H	C_3H_7	CH_2CH_2Cl	fluchloralin

All these products are manufactured by methods similar to that used for trifluralin. An aromatic compound with a substituent in the 4-position and a chlorine group in the 1-position is dinitrated, which directs the nitration into the 2,6-positions and the nitro groups thus introduced then activate the chloro group sufficiently for it to be reacted with an amine.

Diphenylethers

A number of nitrophenyl ethers have been developed as herbicides, the most commercially important of which are nitrofen and fluorodifen.

Nitrofen   Fluorodifen

They are manufactured by reacting the sodium salt of the appropriate phenol with 1-chloro-4-nitrobenzene. The aromatic chlorine is made reactive by the electron-withdrawing effect of the nitro group. Nitrofen is a pre-emergence herbicide, toxic to various broad-leaved and grassy weeds when left as a thin layer on the soil surface but it rapidly loses its activity if incorporated into the soil. It is used for weed control in cereals and various vegetables. Fluorodifen is used mainly on soya beans but, like nitrofen, loses its activity if incorporated into soil. About 600 t/year are used by U.S.A. farmers.

Several other compounds have been tried differing in ring substituents. Three which are currently in production are chlomethoxyfen and bifenox, which are nitrofen with methoxy and carboxy groups respectively added ortho to the NO_2, the carboxy as methyl ester, and acifluorfen which is nitrofen with the 4Cl replaced by CF_3 and with carboxy (free) ortho to the NO_2. They have similar contact action and are particularly useful in transplanted rice.

Amide Herbicides

Herbicidal activity was discovered in the chloroanilides. The most commercially successful compound has been 3',4'-dichloropropionanilide (propanil) which is a contact herbicide of particular value for post-emergent control of grass weeds in rice, especially of barnyard grass, which is one of the most troublesome weeds of this crop. It has no pre-emergent activity. About 3,000 t/year are manufactured in the U.S.A. by reaction of 3,4-dichloroaniline with propionic acid in the presence of thionyl chloride.

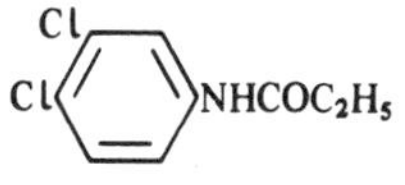

Propanil

Other successful anilides are pentanochlor, where the acid moiety is n-pentane-2-carboxylic and the 4'Cl is replaced by CH_3, and monalide, where 2,2-dimethylpentanoic acid is condensed with 4-chloroaniline. Pentanochlor is used against most weeds in tomatoes and monalide in umbelliferous crops.

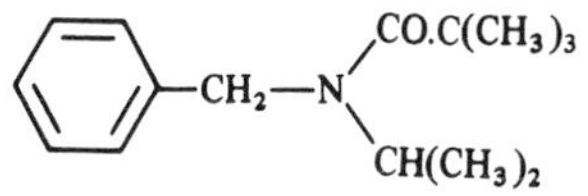

Butam

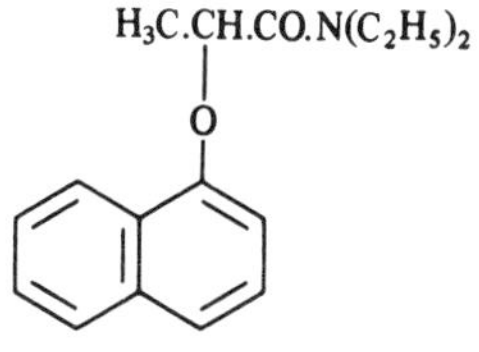

Napropamide

Two very different amide herbicides with aromatic rings are butam, in which N-isopropylbenzylamine is condensed with pivalic (trimethylacetic) acid, and napropamide which is N,N-diethyl-2-(1-naphthyloxy) propion-amide. Butam is effective pre-emergence on two troublesome weeds, *Amaranthus* and *Chenopodium* spp, in several crops and napropamide is effective against annual grasses. Unrelated amides are N-1-naphthyl-phthalamic acid, naptalam, made by condensation of one molecule of phthalic anhydride and one of naphthylamine and propyzamide made by condensation of 3,5-dichlorobenzoic acid and 1,1-dimethylpropynylamine. Both are used pre-emergence, mainly in perennial and deep-sown annual crops.

It has long been known that some chloroacetamides are herbicidal and a systematic study of their phytotoxic properties led to the most commercially successful compound, N,N-diallylchloroacetamide (allidochlor), which is made by reaction of diallylamine with chloroacetyl chloride. It is a selective pre-emergent herbicide which is active against certain grasses, and has a wider range of activity than TCA or dalapon. It is of interest that the dialkylamides of the herbicidal TCA have negligible activity.

$$ClCH_2.CO.N(CH_2CH{=}CH_2)_2$$

Allidochlor

The herbicidal activity of chloroacetamides on the one hand and of chloroanilides on the other, led to investigation of N-aryl substituted chloroacetamides. This study yielded a number of herbicides of very great commercial utility.

Writing the general formula as:

the compounds at present in use are:

Propachlor,	R = H	X = CH(CH_3)_2
Alachlor,	R = 2,6−diC_2H_5	X = CH_2OCH_3
Butachlor,	R = 2,6−diC_2H_5	X = CH_2O(CH_2)_3CH_3
Diethatyl ethyl	R = 2,6−diC_2H_5	X = CH_2COOC_2H_5
Metolachlor	R = 2CH_3, 6C_2H_5	X = CH(CH_3)CH_2OCH_3

Propachlor is a pre-emergent herbicide which was widely-used against annual grasses and certain broad-leaved weeds in maize, cotton, soya beans, sorghum, sugar cane and peanuts. It is one of the few herbicides which retain their effectiveness in peat and muck soils. In general, best weed control is obtained when rain falls within ten days of application, but the product is still effective even in dry conditions. About 12,000 t/year were manufactured in the U.S.A. in 1971 by reaction of chloroacetyl chloride with N-iso-propylaniline in an inert solvent, but it has now been largely superceded by metolachlor of which about 18,000 t/year were used in the U.S.A. in 1983.

Alachlor is used for much the same applications as propachlor but it requires more moisture for activation than does propachlor. It is particularly safe for use on soya beans. It is now (1986) the most widely used herbicide in the U.S.A. About 50,000 t/year of alachlor are manufactured in the U.S.A. by reacting 2,6-diethylaniline with formaldehyde to give the N-methylene derivative, adding chloroacetyl chloride to this and reacting the product with methanol.

Alachlor

It appears that crop species which are resistant to these herbicides can rapidly detoxify them either by reaction of the aliphatic chlorine atom with exogenous substrates or by cleavage of the amide linkage. Their mode of action is not completely known. It is possible that they interfere with protein synthesis but that they react by a variety of mechanisms at a number of different sites.

Another chloroacetamide, quinonamid, has 2-amino-3-chloro naphtho (1,4) quinone as the amine moiety. It is very selective against algae and mosses.

Benzoylprop and flamprop are two amide herbicides which have already been mentioned as wild oat killers in Chapter 18.

Carbamate Herbicides

Another war-time product, at first thought to be highly selective against grasses, was isopropyl phenylcarbamate (propham). It was most effective via the soil to which it was applied as a fine suspension of the crystalline solid (soluble only to about 70 ppm in water). Although effective at lower doses than TCA or dalapon, its selectivity is not so clear. It is now largely replaced by the 3-chloro compound (chlorpropham) in limited use in some vegetable crops and sugar beet, and by the methyl 3,4-dichlorophenyl carbamate (swep) which is used for control in rice.

Chlorpropham   Swep

It will be noted that the aromatic ring is attached to the N atom in these compounds, the ester moiety being aliphatic, whereas in the more numerous simple insecticidal compounds these roles are reversed. This difference however is not general. Two compounds developed as herbicides but no longer in production were aromatic esters of N-methyl carbamic acid. In one of these, terbucarb, the alcohol partner was 2,6-di-*tert*butyl-4-methylphenol while the corresponding 3-methyl-5-isopropyl compound, promecarb, is still in use as an insecticide on some fruit crops. The other herbicide was dichlormate, in which the alcohol was 4-chlorobenzyl. It may be noted also that carbaryl (1-naphthyl methylcarbamate) the first, and still very important, carbamate insecticide is also used for one plant growth modifying purpose, namely chemical thinning of the apple crop. It is also generally recognized as inviting plant damage to use insecticidal carbamates with oils.

Simple carbamates have not made much progress as herbicides. In more active or selective examples some other active group is present. Barban, mentioned as a wild oat killer in Chapter 18, has a chloroacetylenic alcohol partner. Karbutylate is 3-(3-hydroxyphenyl)-2,2-dimethyl urea esterified with N-methyl carbamic acid. Phenmedipham is a double carbamate having both sequences. The isomeric desmedipham is without the methyl on the left

Phenmedipham

and has ethyl in place of methyl on the right. Phenisopham has the right hand alkyl increased to isopropyl and carries an ethyl in the central N atom. All three, usually in admixtures, are important in weed control in sugar beet.

Another herbicide, very but slowly effective against two important weeds of pasture and forestry, dock and bracken, is asulam which is the methyl ester of carbamic acid carrying the 4-aminobenzene sulphonyl group on the N atom. It is manufactured from 4-aminobenzene sulphonamide and dimethyl carbonate.

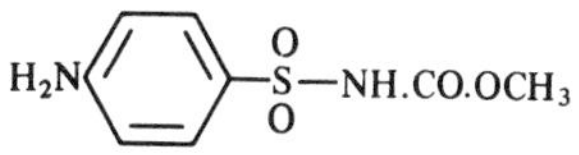

$$H_2N\text{—}C_6H_4\text{—}\overset{\displaystyle O}{\underset{\displaystyle O}{S}}\text{—}NH.CO.OCH_3$$

Asulam

Thiocarbamate Herbicides

These form a more consistent series. The general formula is $R_1S.CO.NR_2R_3$ and the compounds currently in use are tabulated below.

TABLE 19.4

R_1	R_2	R_3	Name
C_2H_5	nC_3H_7	nC_3H_7	EPTC
C_2H_5	$isoC_4H_9$	$isoC_4H_9$	butylate
C_2H_5	C_2H_5	$cycloC_6H_{11}$	cycloate
nC_3H_7	C_2H_5	nC_3H_7	pebulate
nC_3H_7	nC_3H_7	nC_3H_7	vernolate
$CHCl=CCl-CH_2$	$isoC_3H_7$	$isoC_3H_7$	diallate
$CCl_2=CCl-CH_2$	$isoC_3H_7$	$isoC_3H_7$	triallate
benzyl	$secC_4H_9$	$secC_4H_9$	tiocarbazil

These compounds are among the most volatile and least water favourable of herbicides and have lethal effect on the shoot of germinating seeds, access to which is mainly via vapour diffusion in soil air space. They are preferably incorporated in the top few centimetres of soil by light cultivation to prevent too rapid loss, but they are rather strongly adsorbed on dry soil and can then persist apparently inactive until the soil is wetted. They are active against annual grasses and many small-seeded dicotyledons and are the most successful compounds against a serious problem weed, nutsedge (*Cyperus rotundus*). Tiocarbazil is used mainly in rice and diallate and triallate against wild oat in sugar beet, flax, maize and barley (triallate also in wheat).

Butylate is now (1986) the third widely used herbicide in the U.S.A. (25,000 t/year) mainly on maize. EPTC is used in potatoes and beans.

Various Heterocyclic Herbicides

A large number of heterocyclic compounds, apparently quite unrelated to one another, have been reported to have herbicidal activity. It is impossible to make any logical classification of them. Few have achieved any substantial commercial success. The following are important in special situations.

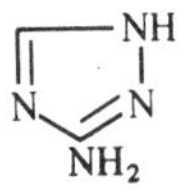

Aminotriazole 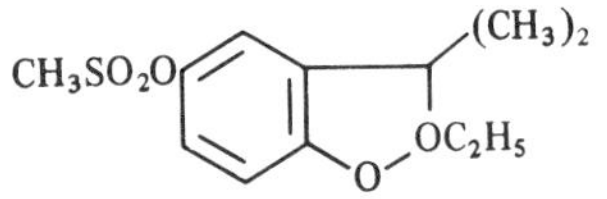   Ethofumesate 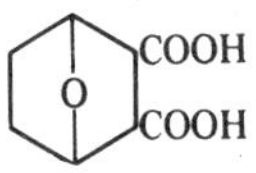   Endothal

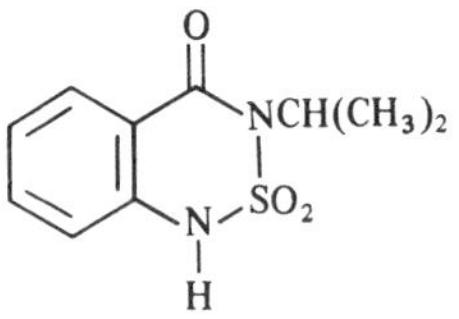

Bentazone 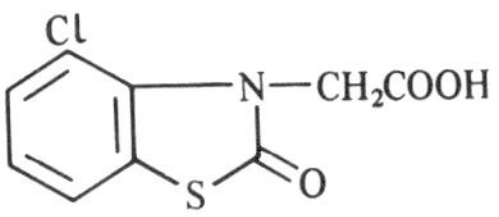   Benazoline

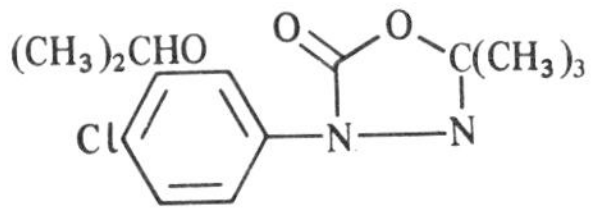

Oxadiazon 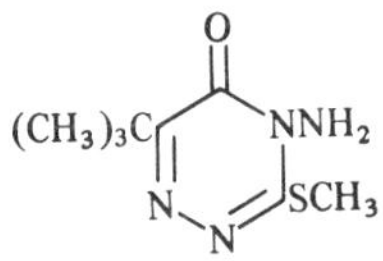   Metribuzin

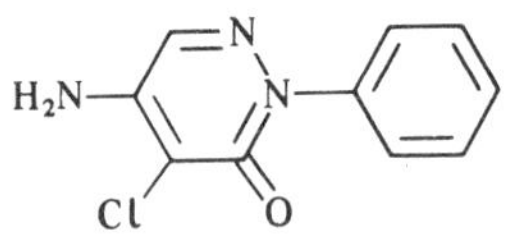

Chloridazon 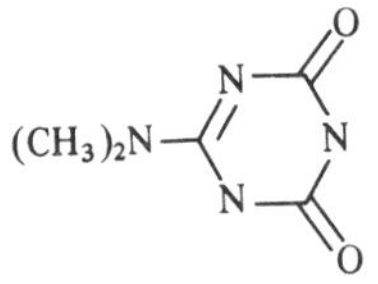   Hexazinone

Aminotriazole is very water soluble and rapidly halts further growth of plants by elimination of chlorophyll. It is very well translocated and, applied at the season of declining top growth, can penetrate to underground stems and rhizomes and so kill difficult weeds like couch-grass and horsetail. Addition of ammonium thiocyanate to the spray has a clear synergistic effect.

Ethofumesate is selective in favour of beet and the spectrum of weeds controlled in this crop is complementary with that of phenmedipham so that these compounds form an effective mixture. Ethofumesate is highly selective among grasses, arresting the growth of most species completely.

Endothal is used for pre- and post-emergent weed control in sugar beet.

Bentazone is a contact herbicide which provides useful post-emergent control of some troublesome weeds in cereals.

Benazolin is a very highly specific post-emergent herbicide effective against cleavers and chickweed in cereals and in oil-seed rape.

Oxadiazon is used as a post-emergent herbicide in rice.

Metribuzin is useful in potatoes, pre- and post-emergent, and also in some situations in tomatoes, soya beans, asparagus and lucerne.

Chloridazon is one of the several herbicides found effective on many weeds in the beet crop. Other substitutions in the same ring structure have been found active but are no longer in commercial production.

Hexazinone controls seedling weeds in many perennial crops and is especially useful in conifer plantations.

Herbicide Antidotes

There would be great advantage in protecting sown crops against the action of herbicides applied to the soil. Selectivity could then be at the choice of the farmer and he could kill *Solanum nigrum* while saving the closely related tomato or even wild oat in an oat crop. Several attempts have been made to use adsorptive charcoal for this purpose, but roots rapidly grow away from the necessarily small volume containing the adsorbent and are then vulnerable. Seed coating with charcoal is therefore useful only if the germinating seed is specially sensitive or if the crop seed is naturally nearly resistant to the herbicide and the treatment can improve a nearly sufficient safety.

Mobile chemicals having an antagonistic effect to that of the herbicide offer more chance of success. Some chemicals are now known which act as antidotes to the action of the thiocarbamate herbicides and one is in extensive use. When N,N'-diallyl-2,2-dichloroacetamide is incorporated into soil along with butylate, maize becomes more fully resistant to this herbicide while most weeds are still vulnerable. Some other experimental compounds show promise and the subject is being actively researched. The full potential of the method indicated in the opening sentence of this section will not, however, be realized until the antidote can be safely applied to the seed before sowing.

Sulphonyl Urea Herbicides

Most new pesticides have been discovered by screening of a very large number of speculative compounds. One recurrent theme in the choice of lines of synthesis is to try to marry known active groupings. The progeny are often quite useless. Sometimes they have interesting activity but not of the expected kind. Occasionally they are very successful. For example, chlorsulfuron appears to be a union of the urea and triazine herbicides but the general class title above suggests, to continue the analogy, an act of adultery by the benzene sulphonamides. Whatever the intellectual origin, the practical outcome has been a whole order of magnitude increase in phytotoxicity.

Chlorsulfuron has the formula:

Chlorsulfuron

Its selectivity is mainly on the early pattern of control of "broad leaves" in cereals but it is active at less than 10 g a.i./ha! Inhibition of cell division is induced in growing roots and shoots after foliage uptake. The safety of resistant species seems to depend on biochemical degradation. In sulfometuron the Cl substitution is replaced by CO_2H and one methoxy by methyl and the triazine ring becomes pyrimidine, the N between the methyls being CH. This compound deals with some perennial grasses, particularly *Sorghum halapense*.

A third member, DPX-T6376, under extensive trials, retains the carboxyl of sulfometuron but as methyl ester, and returns to the triazine ring of chlorsulfuron. There will doubtless be further developments.

Modes of Action of Herbicides

Much less is known about the biochemical action of herbicides than about that of organophosphorus insecticides. Many different types of action must be involved. The "hormone" herbicides, as has been mentioned, are essentially disorganizers of plant growth rather than direct killers and clearly interfere with, or compete with, the action of natural hormones. By contrast, the carbamates appear to be more truly toxic. They inhibit the development of juvenile tissue in shoot or root.

Some of the important compounds act mainly by drastic interference with the photosynthetic process. This is probably true of the anilide herbicides and certainly of the phenylureas and aminotriazines. These inhibit an early reaction in the photosynthetic chain in which water is oxidized with liberation of elementary oxygen. Some at least of the steps of *in vivo* photosynthesis can take place in a suspension of chloroplasts (the sub-cell units which contain the chlorophyll) in suitable solution containing a reducible model substance — usually ferricyanide ion. This is reduced, with liberation of oxygen, when the suspension is illuminated. The phenylureas and aminotriazines, at very low concentrations, inhibit this reaction.

We have already mentioned that the bipyridyls inhibit some later light-driven process. This cannot, however, be the complete explanation of the action of diquat and paraquat, because although their action is much faster in the light than the dark, it is also, in the light, faster than death by starvation in the dark. Also the lethal effect of keeping plants in the dark is accelerated by their treatment with these compounds. The action of the phenylureas and triazines, however, seems to be fully linked with the effect of light. Seeds germinate normally in treated soil, but the seedlings die off when photosynthetic processes should be taking over. It is consistent with their interference with the early, unique, steps in photosynthesis, that the phenylureas and aminotriazines have very low toxicity to animals, in which photosynthesis plays no role.

The dinitrophenols and probably bromoxynil and ioxynil, act as respiratory accelerators by inhibition of oxidative phosphorylation. In the absence of this mechanism, the energy of sugar-oxidizing processes is largely diverted to useless side reactions.

Amitrole also acts on the photosynthetic process but in a third way. Chlorophyll is an inherently unstable substance in the presence of light but is normally returned to its initial state during the transfer of its light-derived extra energy to other reactions. New growth in plants treated with amitrole contains no chlorophyll. Either its synthesis, or its continued reformation, is inhibited.

Further Reading

Ashton, F. M. and Crafts, A. S. *Mode of Action of Herbicides*, Wiley — Interscience, London and New York, 1973.

Audus, L. J. (ed.) *Physiology and Biochemistry of Herbicides*, Academic Press, London and New York, 1964. Now 2 Vols, 1976.

Corbett, J. R. *The Biochemical Mode of Action of Pesticides*, Academic Press, London and New York, 1974.

Fletcher, W. W. and Kirkwood, R. C. *Herbicides and Plant Growth Regulators*, Granada, London, 1982.

Grossbard, E. and Atkinson, D. (eds) *The Herbicide Glyphosate*, Butterworths, London, 1985.

Kearney, P. C. and Kaufman, D. D. *Herbicides*, Vols. I and II, Marcell Dekker, New York, 1975.

Pallas, F. M. and Casida, J. E. *Chemistry and Action of Herbicide Antidotes*, Academic Press, New York, 1978.

Plimmer, J. R. (ed.) *Pesticide Chemistry in the 20th Century*, American Chemical Society, Washington, D.C., 1977.

Street, J. C. (ed.) *Pesticide Selectivity*, Marcel Dekker, New York, 1975.
Summers, L. A. *The Bipyridilium Herbicides*, Academic Press, 1982,
Urenovitch, J. V. and Dixon, D. D. *Synthesis of Commercial Herbicides*, Vols. I and II, David Chemical, Pennsylvania, 1971.
Weed Science Society of America, FAO International Conference on Weed Control, Illinois, 1970.

20

Plant Growth Modification

Man not only wants to populate his arable land with the species of plants best suited to his needs but he is also never fully satisfied with their natural manner of growth. He would, for example, prefer wheat to have shorter straw and cotton to shed its leaves as soon as the seed hairs have developed in the bolls. The possibility of using chemicals to produce such desirable modifications has long been considered and a number of noteworthy discoveries have been made in the past 40 years. Plant growth regulators (PGR), as they are generally called, are thought to have a great future potential in agriculture. Pesticide chemists have, up to now, concentrated mainly on discovering and developing chemicals which kill plants but which desirably are selective in their toxic effects so that weeds can be destroyed with minimal damage to crops. The more subtle targets of making plants grow the way we should like them to grow and of diverting the energy which they obtain by photosynthesis into those types of plant growth which are most desirable for the farmer, have only recently become the subjects of intensive research.

In primary herbicide screening the effect of the candidate chemical, applied to the soil or by overall spraying, is examined in an all-the-year-round artificial environment on a range of crop and weed seedlings. If kill of all or some species results from a reasonable dosage, further trials on a wider range of species and under different conditions are indicated. If some abnormality of growth is observed which is considered to merit further tests, these at once become more elaborate and expensive for the basic reason that death is definite and terminal while modified growth may develop in various ways for varying periods and be more dependent on environmental factors. Intensive work by experienced plant physiologists is necessary and greater demands are made on many resources than in field testing of a clearly indicated herbicidal effect. Moreover, in further testing of a "spin-off" from herbicide screening, the commercial objective is less well defined. An effect may be looking for an application.

If, from the beginning, screening for a chosen desired objective is undertaken, more expensive procedure is necessary. Fruit, for example cannot be grown all-the-year-round on small seedlings. Flowering cannot be known to be affected until the test plants have been observed for a long period. Moreover, the chance of success of randomly selected candidate chemicals is much less. The arrow is no more aimable, the range longer and the target smaller. It is noteworthy that, even in laboratory work in plant physiology, growth-modifying chemicals are often selected from commercially available herbicides.

A further brake on growth modification research is that many of the useful modifications are needed on perennial crops where long-term testing is, of course, essential. "Dwarfing" compounds are already used with advantage on many annual crops but the effect on a tree species grown for fruit, shelter, timber or ornament could well be only transient; retardation one year could be followed by a surge of growth the next or a desired effect later become undesirable deformity. Reliable performance can only be assured by testing, necessarily to some extent in public, over a substantial fraction of the life of a valid patent. Such testing is not attractive for the chemical industry which must fund its research from profits.

Another problem is that the market for a plant growth regulator is generally much less than that for a herbicide in a major crop but the costs of research and development and of obtaining the toxicological and environmental data for registration tend to be independent of the size of the ultimate market and may be even greater for a PGR than for a herbicide, for the reasons stated. In the U.S.A. in 1982 farmers used only 2,700 tonnes of PGRs compared with 205,000 tonnes of herbicides.

Breeding and Propagation

For many centuries before Mendel or Darwin, the cultivators of crops were selecting seed from their best individuals. The main grain cereals are now producing heavier yields of larger grains than their wild ancestors. As breeding became more scientific, selection became more successful and more directable to improvement in particular qualities. Recent advances in genetic engineering are increasing both the speed and scope of improvements by breeding. The most important plant growth modifications have been, and will continue to be, the products of plant breeding, no less unnatural, one should note, than the use of chemicals.

Improvements of most perennial crops can only be perpetuated by vegetative propagation. For more than 100 years the main vineyards of Europe have been planted with stems of selected American wild stock grafted with the selected European classical variety and rooted while the graft union occurs. Sometimes an intermediate stem, double grafted, is used because of unreliable compatibility of the chosen scion and stock. In this operation, carried out by big nurseries in a manner more resembling a motor car assembly line than a traditional farm, chemicals are being increasingly used.

This is an example, and there are many others, where the plant breeder, already perhaps assisted by chemicals at the genetic manipulation stage, is further helped to get his new developments reliably propagated on a commercial scale. Chemicals assisting root development in stems are therefore the first to be described in this chapter.

First is the natural auxin, indol-3-ylacetic acid (IAA), which is generated in growing shoot tips and stimulates callus formation and root initiation at the site of injury. The related "hormone herbicides" were, of course, examined for this property but found to have too small a margin of safety. 2-Naphthylacetic acid is much safer but the preferred compound for most species is the butyric analogue of the natural auxin-4-indol-3-yl-butyric acid (IBA). In some species, application of the same compound can hasten the graft union.

Drying-out of tissues is, of course, inimical to the striking of cuttings or grafts and is prevented by continuous fine spraying or other means of maintaining high humidity. This increases the risk of fungal damage and necessitates the use of sterile equipment and rooting medium in difficult cases and/or the application of fungicide.

There is increasing use of vegetative propagation starting from very small growing points or even single cells. This has the double advantage over conventional rooting of cuttings that transmission of virus from the mother plant can be avoided and that a very large number of individuals can be generated in a small space from one mother. The technique has been made possible by years of laboratory work in plant physiology which revealed that cells from many plant organs have genetic totipotency, i.e. they can, in a suitable environment, divide and differentiate into complete plants. The cells are suspended in an aqueous sterile medium with controlled light, carbon dioxide and oxygen supply, essential nutrients and certain organic compounds in hormone quantities controlling cell division and expansion. Natural auxin or synthetic mimics, including 2,4-D, are essential, but the final key to success lay in stimulants of cell division, the cytokinins. For long these had to be supplied from coconut milk but compounds were eventually isolated and synthesized.

The first identified cytokinin from coconut milk was kinetin, being adenine with a furfuryl substituent on the side nitrogen, but this active compound was later considered an artefact of the separation process. Zeatin, extracted, as the name implies, from immature maize grains, is more active as is a benzylaminopurine carrying a cyclohexyl substituent. These compounds are formulated overleaf.

It was later found that symmetrical diphenyl ureas exhibit the cytokinin behaviour to varying extent according to substitution in one or both benzene rings. Very high activity results when one or both benzene rings is replaced by pyridine. Further research is likely to provide an almost embarrassing selection of active promotors of cell division to add to other growth controlling compounds in the tissue culture media.

Kinetin X = H R = —CH₂—(furfuryl group)

Zeatin X = H R = —CH₂—CH=C(CH₃)(CH₂OH)

Very active X = (cyclohexyl) R = —CH₂—(phenyl)

The profits to the chemical industry from compounds for tissue culture are at present trivial but the contribution of research in this field to the advancement of agriculture may become quite disproportionate. We make further comment in our final chapter.

Another use of chemicals, very minor for the manufacturer but very important for the breeder, is in assisting pollination when cross-fertilizing doubtfully compatible strains or species. The failure is usually in the initiation of growth of the pollen tube and this can sometimes be overcome by application of natural auxin or a synthetic mimic, even 2,4-D, to the stigma.

Retardation of Vegetative Growth

In developed countries with intensive agriculture, such as those in Europe, yields per hectare of cereals have been steadily pushed up by applying greater amounts of nitrogenous fertilizers. In some weather and soil conditions this has caused harvesting difficulties and losses consequent on increased lodging. A compound which is extensively used, particularly in Holland and Germany, to reduce the length of the wheat straw and the risk of lodging is 2-chloroethyltrimethylammonium chloride (chlormequat chloride). It is manufactured by reaction of ethylene dichloride with trimethylamine. Apart from acting as a growth retardant and producing compact plants with shortened internodes and petioles it may also affect the response of the plant to pests and pathogens, thus, it has been reported to decrease the susceptibility of tomatoes to verticillium wilt and of cabbages to aphid attack.

Runner type peanuts are difficult to harvest because of their spreading lateral shoots. A retardant spray which is widely used in the U.S.A. is N-dimethylaminosuccinamic acid (daminozide), which is manufactured by reaction of succinic anhydride with 1,1-dimethylhydrazine. Apart from its use on peanuts, it is also used to control the vegetative growth of fruit trees and to modify the stem length and shape of ornamental plants. Like chlormequat, it reduces internodal distances and is said to increase heat, drought and frost resistance.

Retardation of growth of grass, as an alternative to regular mowing, has long been a desirable target particularly for golf courses, cemeteries, airfields,

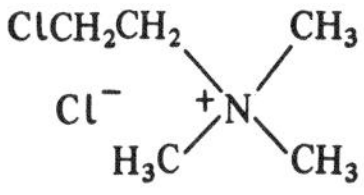

Chlormequat chloride

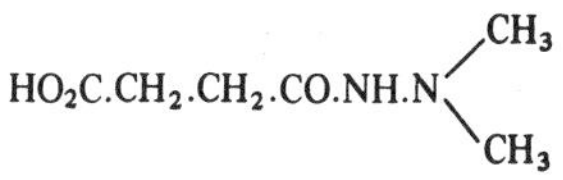

Daminozide

roadside verges and amenity areas. A disadvantage for home lawns or regularly used grass areas is that grass rapidly becomes dirty and trampled, and mowing has the advantage that it continually presents a fresh, clean, upstanding grass surface. Nevertheless, there is a commercial market for such products and two of the most successful have been 6-hydroxy-3-(2H)-pyridazinone (maleic hydrazide) and 2-chloro-9-hydroxyfluorene-9-carboxylic acid methyl ester (chlorflurecol-methyl).

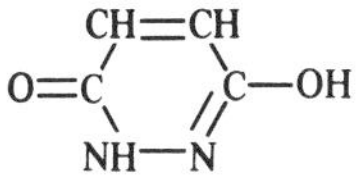

Maleic hydrazide

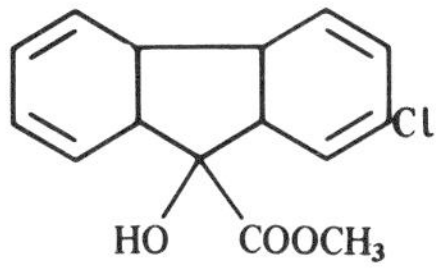

Chlorflurecol-methyl

Tobacco plants, when topped to remove the flower buds, develop lateral shoots from the leaf axils. Maleic hydrazide is widely used to supress these shoots, but a cheap and effective material is a mixture of the methyl esters of C_8 to C_{12} acids $(C_8–C_{12})$. $COOCH_3$. Dimethyldodecylammonium acetate has also been used for this purpose.

Two recent compounds which appear to be particularly effective for reducing the growth of woody plants are ethyl hydrogen 1-propylphosphate and 1-propyl-phosphonic acid.

The search for growth retarders has recently been active in several industrial laboratories and several new compounds are under trial but not yet commercially available. Compounds of the formulae below all have useful activity but are by no means equivalent. The effect of none of them is simply confined to decrease of internode length. The effects wanted in different crops are also different. The suppression of side shoots after de-topping tobacco is most clearly achieved by topical application of flumetralin. It may act by restoring the effect of apical dominance. The fatty acid esters act by direct killing of the axillary buds and are sometimes called "chemical assassins". Chlorphonium inhibits internode extension but encourages lateral branching. Ancymidol activity is more nearly confined to inhibition of extension.

An effect which may reasonably be included under suppression of vegetative growth is the prevention of sprouting in stored potatoes, and a compound which has been widely used for this purpose is 1,2,4,5-tetrachloro-3-nitrobenzene (tecnazene), which is made by nitration of tetrachlorobenzene. Use has also been made of isopropyl 3-chlorophenyl-carbamate (chlorpropham). Another quaternary ammonium salt is now finding increasing use on ornamentals, particularly all-year-round chrysanthemums to promote sturdier, darker growth. It is piproctanyl, which is mepiquat with one CH_3 replaced by allyl and the other by 3,7-dimethyloctyl.

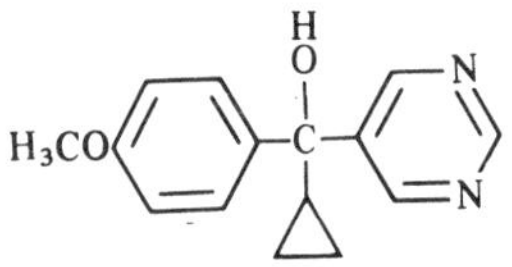

Ancymidol

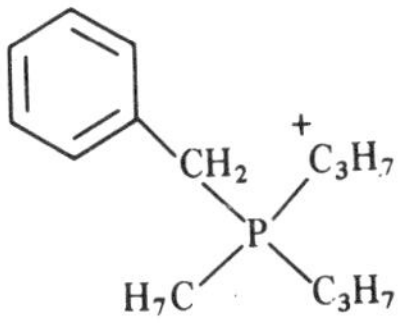

Chlorphonium ion

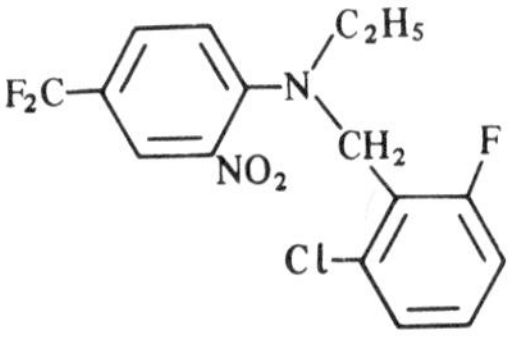

Flumetralin

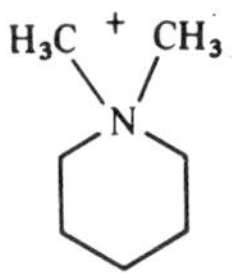

Mepiquat

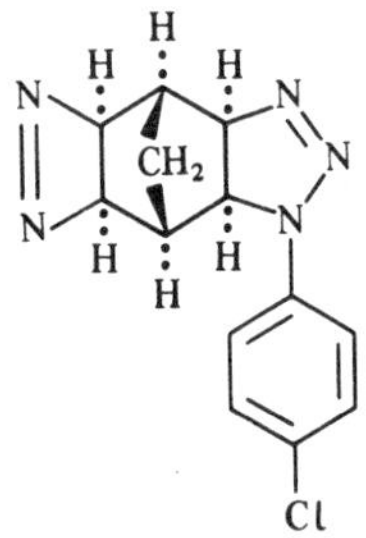

Tetcyclasis

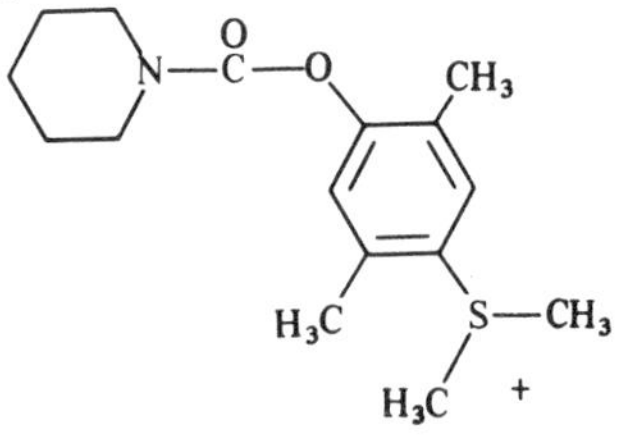

Dimethyl (4 – piperidinocarboxyloxy–
-2,5xylyl) sulphonium ion

Control of Fruit

In most fruits the edible portion is not the true seed but some fleshy covering or receptacle, the function of which is to assist dispersal of the seed by providing a tempting food for mobile animals. In most cases, the plant breeder has selected strains which give very much bigger fruits, and has even succeeded in suppressing the true seed. Seedless raisins are well-known and a banana containing fertile seed is a rarity.

Although the fleshy fruit will not usually develop unless the flower is fertilized and viable seed is set, some fruit can be produced parthenocarpically by spraying the flowers with 1-naphthylacetic acid or with 4-chlorophenoxyacetic acid. This technique is particularly widely used on tomatoes.

Many types of fruit trees thin out naturally by dropping a proportion of the first-formed fruit, but there are some — for example, peaches — where it is necessary to thin in order to obtain reasonably sized fruits. Chemical thinning is more economical than hand thinning. Compounds which have been used for this purpose on apples are the insecticide 1-naphthylmethyl carbamate (carbaryl), 1-naphthylacetamide and 1-naphthylphthalamic acid (naptalam), and also the naturally occurring plant growth regulator, abscisic acid, which controls the normal autumnal fall of leaves.

Abscisic acid

On peaches, the main compounds used are 2-(3-chlorophenoxy)-propionic acid and 2-(3-chlorophenoxy)-propionamide. Other compounds finding increasing use are 2-chloroethyl-tris-(2-methoxyethoxy)-silane (etacelasil), used to cause abscission of olives and 2-chloroethyl-methyl-bis-benzyloxy silane.

1-Naphthylacetic acid is also used to prevent developed apples from dropping before they are really ripe, which a number of varieties are very prone to do. That this compound, though more often the amide, is used at an earlier stage to cause small fruits to drop, is a good example of the complexity of hormone response. Considerable judgement and knowledge of local conditions and varieties is required. Ethepon, chloroethyl phosphonic acid, a producer of the versatile hormone ethylene *in vitro*, has both a thinning effect in juvenile fruitlets and a ripening effect in mature fruits.

A number of compounds have been developed to prevent post-harvest "scald" of apples, which is a physiological effect. These include 1,2-dihydro-6-ethoxy-2,2,4-trimethylquinoline (ethoxyquinol) and diphenylamine.

Fresh oranges have to be harvested by hand because of the need to maintain a high standard of appearance. At present, pickers snip the stem of each orange, but if the fruit could be loosened sufficiently to allow pickers to twist it off the stem, then two-handed picking would be possible with consequent increase in harvesting speed and reduction in costs. Oranges which are used to make juice do not have to be treated so gently but they are generally harvested by tree shakers and catch nets, so loosening agents would be of utility here also to ensure total harvest.

Defoliation and Desiccation

The falling of leaves of deciduous plants, although assisted by rough weather, is mainly a seasonally induced positive act of plant growth. A layer of corky tissue develops at the base of the leafstalk which induces weakness and seals off the wound. Abscisic acid is responsible for this development. Where only the seed or, in the case of cotton, the hairs attached thereto, are required, it would be an advantage to cause the leaves to fall prior to harvest. Leaves which dry up but remain attached are a nuisance in processing. If the cut crop needs drying, the prior abscission of leaves would speed the process. Whether harvest is by hand or by machine, the process is simplified or accelerated if the required plant organ is left outstanding on otherwise naked stems.

Two compounds which have been effectively used to produce the desired clean defoliant action on cotton are calcium cyanamide, $CaNCN$, and tributyl-phosphorotrithiolate. $(C_4H_9S)_3P$. The former compound is dusted on and the latter is sprayed as an emulsion. Extracted natural absciscic acid is also being used.

Destruction of vegetative tissue in a mature crop can facilitate harvesting of roots or seeds. The action needed in this case, is, of course, directly herbicidal. There should be no systemic transfer to the organs which are required for storage and food, unless the herbicide were to improve storage while introducing no toxic hazard.

Reduction of the leaf and stem to a dry skeleton can facilitate the drying of remaining seed pods which may remain into wet autumn weather without assistance and suffer fungal attack. Paraquat has been used for this purpose on clover seed crops but a specific defoliant would be more effective.

Potato-haulm is killed off by contact herbicides prior to harvest (i) to facilitate this mechanical operation, (ii) to kill late-germinating weeds before they set seed and (iii) to destroy blight fungus before exposure of the tubers. It is universally agreed that sulphuric acid produces the most satisfactory effect, having an advantage over most other compounds in hastening the decay of the tough fibres of the stem. Its application, however, requires special clothing and machinery. DNOC in oil and, more recently, diquat, are now more often used. Arsenites were at one time favoured but their use has been discontinued, owing to toxic risk to workers in the harvest.

Treatment of the harvested crop before or during storage is an important market for some fungicides and insecticides. Many crops, including the main cereal grains, hay and some fruits have to be dried before they can be safely stored and, although this is mainly an engineering problem, some use of chemicals is involved. Several oily products help to break down the water resistance of cuticles and so accelerate the drying of cut leaves and stems; and a very ancient practice of dipping in a slurry of plant ash and olive oil accelerates the drying of grapes. Spraying an emulsion of oils in potassium carbonate solution on to seedless grapes in drying trays is used extensively in Australia to accelerate production of sultanas, and it has been found that similar treatment of lucerne (alfalfa) while cutting can, in favourable conditions, shorten the haymaking period from 3–5 days to 1–2. The mechanism is uncertain but the potash in both cases is as important as the oils.

Improvement in Photosynthesis Efficiency

Photosynthesis is a very inefficient process from an energy conversion viewpoint. On average, less than 1% of the solar energy falling on a leaf is converted to chemical energy by photosynthesis. Yields per hectare of most crops can be increased by supplying adequate water and sufficient synthetic fertilizers but there is a limit to the yield improvements which can be achieved in this way. Given enough water and fertilizer, the limiting factor to photosynthesis in the field is concentration of carbon dioxide in the air and the ability of the plant to fix it. Glasshouse growers often increase the concentration of carbon dioxide in their houses.

It has been shown unequivocally in laboratory experiments that plants do respond to increased carbon dioxide concentrations, although to differing extents according to species, and that the normal level of carbon dioxide in air (0.030–0.035%) is well below the photosynthetic optimum for leaves illuminated with even moderate sunlight. It is thought that this may be a reflection of a much higher atmospheric carbon dioxide concentration on earth at the time plants evolved. However, too great a concentration of carbon dioxide is deleterious, and the optimum concentration is probably 0.05–0.10% for most plant species.

We should temper our exasperation at the inefficiency of photosynthesis with the reminder that the resources of modern chemical engineering can as yet not do so well. Stored chemical energy to fuel our extravagant civilization is not economically obtainable from current production of wood. We use the limited accumulation of coal and oil laid down from past products of photosynthesis. As Milton put it, but not in this context, we "rifle the bowels of our mother earth for treasures better hid".

If we could — and fortunately we cannot — raise the CO_2 level of the whole atmosphere, the climatic consequences would be disastrous. A brief glance at the carbon cycle balance sheet is of interest. The atmosphere contains about 0.03% by volume of CO_2, not very variable with latitude or altitude. This amounts to about 45 tonnes in the whole column of air over 1 hectare. Putting all other figures in tonnes per hectare units, good agricultural production fixes about 20 per season, eventually returnable through other forms of life. A mature forest holds the reduced product from 2,000. A limestone layer only

1 mm thick holds 11,000. Complete combustion of the remaining world forests might increase the atmosphere content to near 0.05%.

Only exceptionally will significant local depletion of atmospheric CO_2 occur, because the solar radiation inevitably produces vertical stirring of the major mass of the atmosphere. Under average summer conditions the atmosphere must accept as vapour from a crop about 100 times as much water as it supplies CO_2 but its capacity to hold water is only around 30 times as much. Most agricultural crops would suffer from excess humidity before deficiency of CO_2. In dense rain forest the CO_2 content can be limiting.

The improved efficiency we need is within the leaf and improvement by chemical treatment is a worthwhile objective as, of course, is that by plant breeding. So far, no progress by chemical treatment can be reported. An approach to the problem might be to discover chemicals which will inhibit the process of photorespiration. This is the process by which a certain proportion of the carbohydrates which are formed by photosynthesis are converted back to carbon dioxide. It is not, at the moment clear what purpose photorespiration serves in the life of the plant and whether its inhibition would have any damaging effects.

Some compounds sprayed on leaves have the effect of closing stomata. 1-hydroxy sulphonic acids generally have this property and the most active known is 2-pyridyl-hydroxymethyl sulphonic acid. In investigating the mechanism of this effect, Zelitch found that this chemical inhibited glycolate oxidase, which is one expression of photorespiration. This results in accumulation of glycolate. Dark respiration is not affected. Water loss is of course reduced and stomata-closing compounds have been used to make mesophytes more tolerant of arid conditions. Growth continues, so CO_2 fixation is not, surprisingly, much retarded. Stomatal closure has also been used to reduce damage to leaves by atmospheric contaminants.

Improvement of Crop Yields

Assuming that a crop can carry out only a specific amount of photosynthesis during a growing season, the problem of yield improvement is essentially one of trying to divert as much as possible of this photosynthetic energy to production of those parts of the plant which are of most value to the grower. For vegetables this may mean prevention of flowering and of formation of side-shoots, and some examples of the use of plant growth regulators to produce these effects have already been given. For root crops it means diversion of the photosynthetic energy away from vegetative growth towards the laying down of energy resources as chemicals such as starch stored in roots and tubers. For crops grown for seeds or fruit — and this includes all the vitally important cereals — the aim is to make the stage of vegetative growth as short as possible consistent with the health of the plant and to proceed as rapidly as possible to the reproductive stage. For plants grown for ornaments the aim may be to induce more profuse and prolonged flowering.

Not many chemicals have yet been discovered which produce these effects, and this is certainly the area in which plant growth regulators have the greatest potential in the future.

An interesting compound is gibberellic acid, which was first isolated from a fungus (gibberellus), which attacks rice and produces abnormal elongation of the stem between nodes. The compound occurs to some extent normally in most plants but has now been made synthetically. The effect it produces is the opposite of that produced by the growth retarding plant growth regulators.

Gibberellic acid

Its most important commercial use is in production of table grapes. As a result of elongation of the fruit stalks, more open bunches with larger and more shapely fruits and less susceptibility to fungal attack, are produced. The compound is also used as a seed treatment to hasten emergence of beans, peas, cotton and cereals; to produce bigger, firmer, better-coloured cherries, to hasten their maturity and to prolong their harvesting period, and to counteract the effects of yellowing viruses; to delay ripening of lemons and thus to produce a greater percentage of larger fruits with improved storage lives; to increase the yields and aid the harvesting of hops; to hasten maturing of artichokes and to extend their picking season; to produce longer-stemmed celery and rhubarb; to apply to barley to increase the enzymatic content of malt so that distillers can use less malt in production of grain spirits; to break dormancy of seed potatoes and to stimulate sprouting thus allowing immediate planting of red varieties which normally require two to six months' storage to break their dormancy. It is also used to produce various effects on ornamental plants such as earlier blooming, more profuse flowering and longer flower stalks.

Gibberellic acid is a very safe and extremely non-toxic chemical. It affects only those parts of the plant which are above the soil surface but its effects are transient so that repeated applications are necessary.

Some compounds which have already been mentioned have been used to increase yields. Thus, daminozide (p. 251) can increase yields of tomatoes, and claims have been made that ethyl hydrogen 1-propylphosphate and 1-propylphosphonic acid both may increase yields of potatoes and sugar beets and similar root crops. A compound recently introduced for the same purpose is glyphosine (p. 228). Chlormequat chloride (p. 251) is used to increase tillering and reduce lodging in cereals.

A particular area in which use of chemicals has been successful is in increasing the amounts of specific useful products which can be extracted from plants, in particular, sugar and rubber. A number of compounds have been suggested to increase the amount of sugar in sugar-cane, of which the most successful is methyl 3,6-dichloro-2-methoxybenzoate (disugran) which is applied with a non-ionic surfactant two to four weeks before harvest.

It has long been known that ethylene will stimulate the production of latex by rubber trees. Ethylene is a natural growth regulator given off by a number of fruits during ripening. It is used commercially in fruit storage rooms to hasten ripening of bananas, citrus, melons, pears and pineapples, and also to induce flowering of pineapple plants. Application of ethylene gas to rubber trees is not very convenient so a number of "ethylene generators" have been developed. These are chemicals which can be applied to cuts in the bark and which break down within the tree to give ethylene which stimulates the production of latex. The most successful of these compounds is (2-chloroethyl) phosphonic acid, $ClCH_2CH_2PO(OH)_2$, (ethephon).

An interesting recent observation is that application of the bipyridylium herbicide paraquat dichloride to pine trees greatly increases the formation of oleoresins. It appears that the tree normally maintains a specific pressure of these resins within the cells and that application of the paraquat dichloride increases the permeability of the cells and allows the resin to leak out so the tree produces more to try to maintain the pressure.

An important step in reducing the waste of photosynthesis in making products which we do not want could be to exploit more water culture, as advocated early in this century by the German scientist Nernst. He caused his country estate to be lavishly provided with fish ponds, not for aesthetic or sporting reasons but because he saw no sense in photosynthesis having to be wasted in maintaining animals above ambient temperature with skeletons sufficiently strong to support them in air. Unicellular algae have a minimum of non-photoactive substance and fish live in water of nearly the same temperature and density as themselves. It is now of course well accepted that a well-run fish pond is a much more efficient producer of high quality protein than a dairy and beef farm, but it has a very high capital cost and, if extended to the sea, there is a high cost of restraining and protecting desirable live stock. Farming algae and extracting protein without animal aid could be more efficient, but at present algal protein is not a satisfactory diet. We should, however, encourage our plant breeders to give more attention to non-traditional crops. High technology has produced enormous changes in our lives in the last half century but we still concentrate on the food sources which our ancestors have lived on for thousands of years (p. 342).

Prevention of Flowering

It would be desirable to prevent crops which are grown for their vegetative parts from flowering as this diverts photosynthetic energy. Disbudding is commonly done by hand but with the object of reducing excessive flower numbers in ornamentals with a view to increasing the value of the remainder. Chrysanthemums and carnations for the cut flower trade are treated this way and chemical treatment has partly replaced this labour-costly job; but to stop vegetables like lettuce, beet and carrots from "bolting" requires a different approach. Once floral initials have formed such flowering cannot be stopped, only altered. Formation of the initials is controlled genetically and by photoperiodic response and the cure must lie with the plant breeder and cultivator. Some grass strains, for example, habituated to long day length of sub-arctic summers will not flower if transplanted to regions of longer nights. Manipulation of night length is much used by growers of all-year-round chrysanthemums. Hope for chemical treatment must be sought in interference mechanisms mediated by phytochrome.

A chemically induced complete arrest of flowering would be doubly valuable in the cultivation of crops for roots and or leaves because it would not only avoid waste of photosynthetic energy but would prevent annual weeds from seeding. Achievement of this goal seems very unlikely. A very fundamental response of plants — indeed of all life — to individual injury is to divert the remaining capacity for growth to reproduction. It is very easy to initiate premature flowering and no herbicide has yet, after application in normal amount, inhibited the germination of seed. Assistance to specific weed control might be more probable if a particular feature of growth, characteristic of the species, could be attacked. As an example, some weeds of cereals have an adverse effect on harvesting disproportionate to their total volume, because they climb, and so entangle the straw, by means of twining of stems or coiling of tendrils. A particular form of growth is involved and if it could be eliminated by a chemical treatment the weed could not cause its present problem and would probably, unable to lift itself to light, die on the crop floor. Forestry has similar problems on a larger scale. The introduced *Clematis vitalba* is causing great damage in native forest in New Zealand by smothering and breaking down its supporting hosts. If robbed of the coiling response of its petioles it would remain on the forest floor.

Many other examples could be quoted where interference with some particular growth feature could have a profound ecological effect, good or bad, but we must conclude with repeating an argument of our introduction. The search for such particular responses among randomly chosen chemicals would be prohibitively expensive in a chemical industry which has to pay for its research out of profits. Such developments must await guidance from physiologists and biochemists.

Some special effects, perhaps useful, will become known of course incidentally to research towards more likely profitable directions. It has been claimed that several of the "dwarfing" compounds make some plants more resistant to drought and cold, and dinonylsuccinic acid is used on apples, peaches and pears to protect the flowers against frost.

Further Reading

Audus, L. J. *Plant Growth Substances*, Hill, London, 1972.

Fletchui, W. W. and Kirkwood, R. C. *Herbicides and Plant Growth Regulators*, Granada, London, 1982).

Hanson, L. P. *Plant Growth Regulators*, Noyes Data, London and New Jersey, 1973.

McLaren, J. S. (ed.) *Chemical Manipulation of Crop Growth and Development*, Butterworths, London, 1982.

Plimmer, J. R. (ed.) *Pesticide Chemistry in the 20th Century*, American Chemical Society, Washington, D.C., 1977.

Society of Chemical Industry, *Plant Growth Regulators*, SCI Monograph, No. 31, London, 1968.

Steward, F. C. and Krikorion, A. D. *Plant Chemicals and Growth*, Academic Press, New York, 1971.

Weaver, R. J. *Plant Growth Substances in Agriculture*, W. H. Freeman, San Francisco, 1972.

Wellensiek, S. J., (ed.) *Symposium on Growth Regulators in Fruit Production*, International Society for Agricultural Science, The Hague, 1973.

21

Application of Pesticides

Most modern pesticides are powerful and expensive. Distribution of excessive dosage might lead to undesirable biological side effects and is always economically wasteful. Maldistribution or application at the wrong time may cause crop damage or result in failure to control the pest. It is the business of the field biologist, in the light of his knowledge of the pest and according to the results of many replicated trials, to define the best time and manner of application. In this he must take into consideration the performance of available machinery and the physical properties of the pesticide.

With regard to the latter he must be advised by the formulator whose business is to put the pesticide into a form suitable for application. The formulator must consider not only the requirements as defined by the biologist but also problems of packaging and mixing of the product and its stability in transport and storage. Both biologist and formulator must keep in mind the probability of the product being mixed with others in the spray tank so that compatibility — chemical, physical and biological — must be examined. It is evident that some compromises must be made between very different, but often conflicting, requirements.

This book is about pesticide chemicals and cannot go into details of machinery design and operation. In this chapter only the broad principles of distribution and deposition are discussed. They are influenced by the properties of the pesticide and formulation, which in most cases is diluted before it is applied. In the next chapter, the formulations themselves, i.e. the concentrates as packaged and supplied, will be discussed, together with some devices which are supplied with the means of application "built in".

Some pesticides are used very locally. Seed-borne fungi are often well controlled by dressing the seed with a liquid or dust formulation of a suitable fungicide. A rat-poison is usually put down as a bait in places frequented by rats and not accessible to domestic animals. Houseflies are often successfully controlled by setting out pads attractive to this species and contaminated with insecticide. Materials of construction such as wool cloth, roof timbers or telegraph poles are often treated by a factory dipping or impregnation process to protect them from insect or fungus attack.

With increasing governmental control of the use of pesticides, aimed at reducing unwanted side-effects, localized application is likely to increase in importance. Increasing knowledge and skill can be expected to extend its usefulness. At present, however, by far the major proportion of pesticides produced is distributed more or less uniformly over much larger areas. Growing crops, harvested products and constructed buildings are treated by dusting or spraying. The necessary selectivity on growing crops is partly dependent on physiological and biochemical differences between species and partly on time of application in relation to pest attack and stage of growth. The use of a very general poison in which safety depends entirely on timing is illustrated in Chapter 23.

Most pesticides are sprayed or dusted as dispersions in an inert carrier. In the case of spraying, this is necessarily a liquid and, on grounds of inertness, safety and an enormous advantage in cost, this liquid is almost always water. In the case of dusts, the inert carrier is usually a ground mineral material, with obvious preference, on grounds of transport cost, for a locally available one. Dust bases are therefore very variable.

Dust, a fine-droplet air-blast or aircraft spray can give very good cover of an extensive crop, but cannot be closely localized. It is inadvisable to use these methods for distribution of a selective herbicide in small-field agriculture as there is far too much risk of drift damage to neighbouring sensitive crops. They are suitable only for large areas or where drift would not be environmentally damaging, although it might be wasteful.

In applying soil-acting herbicides to soil before the emergence of crops, such as sugar beet and cotton, grown in widely spaced rows, band-spraying of the seed rows can be practised, leaving the inter-row weeds to the hoe. In a standing crop, such as sugar cane, the spray can be directed to avoid the crop leaves and cover the emerging weed seedlings. It is obvious that only a coarse spray can be so directed.

A liquid flowing under gravity from the finest of hollow needles never falls in drops less than 1 or 2 mm diameter. That natural rain often contains much smaller drops is due to these being condensed from vapour (see section "Smokes" later in this chapter). Drops of size useful in agricultural sprays (less than 500 μ or 0.5 mm diameter) can be obtained mechanically only by calling on forces greater than gravity. Most commonly the liquid is forced out at high velocity from nozzles designed to spread it out in sheet form. As the sheet expands under its own momentum and therefore becomes thinner, contraction due to surface tension becomes more important and the unstable film breaks up into filaments and then into drops. These are of a rather wide size range but with mean size, and to some extent size range, controllable by nozzle design and pressure.

The commonest type of nozzle has a specially shaped slit orifice causing the liquid to issue in a divergent fan form. This is the "fan jet". Impingement of a high velocity cylindrical jet obliquely on a smooth plate, called the "anvil" nozzle, produces a similar divergent fan best suited to high volume discharge of rather coarse drops. A third form of nozzle, the first to be used extensively, directs liquid, obliquely to the jet axis, into a small cavity from which it emerges, through a circular hole, rapidly rotating and therefore expanding to a hollow cone. This is the "swirl chamber" nozzle.

None of these devices can produce, economically on an agricultural scale, drops much below 100 μ diameter (but see "Aerosol and other Automatic Dispensers" in Chapter 22).

Increased force for liquid disruption can be centrifugal, frictional or from sudden jerking movement. The last is exemplified by the "flicking brush". It is not now used except in special form as a laboratory device but was in fact the first type of sprayer used in vineyards. Centrifugal force is used in various spinning dish devices and is capable of dispersing liquids in droplets as small as 20 μ diameter. Very small drops are also produced when a high velocity air stream flows past a liquid emerging from an orifice — the traditional "scent spray" mechanism. This mechanism is sometimes combined with centrifugal or liquid pressure dispersal.

Apparatus for throwing off small drops centrifugally takes three forms: (1) A rapidly rotating cylinder of stiff wire mesh is fed through a perforated tubular axle. Coarse jets from the tube spread out momentarily on the wire mesh and, if the feed rate is not excessive, are rejected from the varicose envelopes around the wires; (2) A cylindrical brush, the bristles of which project from a perforated tubular axle; (3) A circular flat disc rotating rapidly and fed near the centre with an oil. These devices cast off drops in all directions and the first two are used in aircraft spraying, mounted with axles vertical below the wings.

The third device has long been used to obtain, independent of feed rate if this is not excessive, drops of very uniform size, except that some very much smaller droplets are also produced. These are usually called satellites and, if the liquid has normal viscosity, they are produced in equal numbers with the main drops and are formed by the extending thin neck behind each separating main drop breaking in two places.

In addition to the property of producing uniform-sized drops, the spinning disc has another potential advantage as a field tool in that the liquid can be fed on to it through a wide tube at low pressure and it is therefore less subject to blockage or need of good filtration: any foreign particles are thrown off the disc. Several practical problems however had to be solved to make the device reliable and economic. Water solutions tend to run over the disc in discrete streams leading to irregular performance. This problem was solved by Edward Bals who pioneered in U.K. the production of field-worthy spinning devices and their use in Africa and South East Asia. He used a shallow dish in place of the flat disc so that there was always a component of the centrifugal force pressing liquid on to the concave surface. He found also that a toothed edge to the dish gave a better performance. This design was made possible by advances in injection moulding and tough thermoplastic materials. Another problem was to achieve sufficient speed in a lightweight device, solved by the development for many other purposes of small oil-free electric motors that could be powered by dry batteries, conveniently housed in the hollow handle in the right number for the speed desired.

Many units giving droplets of insecticidal liquids of around 50 μm diameter are in use by diligent peasant farmers able to get good insect control over several rows of cotton, sorghum and other wide-spaced crops, making use of natural cross-wind. Similar units, adapted to distribute larger drops from dishes held nearer to the ground rotating about a vertical axle, give good herbicide distribution, with no drift problem.

In collaboration with the Weed Research Organisation and the National Institute of Agricultural Engineering in the U.K. machines have been designed to extend the advantages of Controlled Droplet Application (CDA) to wide booms. It was necessary to restrict the full-circle distribution to enable outputs from separated units to combine to give a uniform rate across the swath and to avoid contamination of the tractor. This was done by using the liquid collected in the shield of each member of a tier of rotating dishes to feed the next below. The chief advantage of the CDA principle is, as the name implies, that the drop size can be much more precisely controlled and kept within much closer limits than when hydraulic nozzles are used. The drop size is also nearly independent of volume output rate if this is kept below a reasonable limit. The more uniform drop size enables a lower mean size to be used without excessive drift and so permits effective cover at a lower output. Also, it reduces weight to be carried or increases area sprayed per load. Since a more concentrated pesticide solution or suspension is permissible the CDA machines are adapted well to ultra low volume (ULV) spraying. However, there is a tendency to confuse these two developments to the detriment of the best use of either.

Another important advance in droplet production and application is the use of high voltage at the nozzle to create dispersion. Droplets created by the high electric potential are repelled from one another by their like charges and attracted to earthed surfaces. The mechansim offers the desirable combination of dispersal followed by attraction to the target. It also offers advantage in energy consumption. Energy inescapably necessary to divide one litre of water in bulk into 100 μm diameter droplets is the product of the increase of surface area by the surface tension. When the latter is reduced to 30 mN/m by wetting agent, this energy comes to about 0.2 joules. If the water were forced at a pressure of 25 kPa through a spray nozzle, energy of 250 joules must be wastefully expended and complete shatter into 100 μm droplets would be nowhere near attained. When drops are given an electric charge the mutual repulsion of the surface charges directly lowers the surface tension. An isolated 100 μm diameter drop raised to a voltage of 830 would have surface tension reduced to zero: it could not lose volume by evaporation without spontaneously dividing, behaviour which can be clearly demonstrated. The electrical energy necessary to balance the surface energy in 1 litre of 100 μm drops comes to about 0.35 joules.

Electrical dispersion and deposition have been used for a long time in factory-based processes, e.g. spray painting and writing and transfer of short fibres to a glued surface to make velvet-type packing material and decorated wallpaper. To make a device suitable for field use required considerable further research and the development in the electronics industry of voltage multipliers to generate high voltage from small portable batteries. The "Electrodyn", produced by I.C.I. in the U.K., applies a few thousand volts to liquid issuing from an annular slit causing spontaneous dispersion into very small droplets with electrical energy expenditure not greatly in excess of the theoretical minimum. The cloud of droplets is attracted to earth but bellies out owing to mutual repulsion. It can therefore conveniently embrace an upstanding plant, reaching all sides. If formulation problems can be solved, the Electrodyn may well become an important contribution as a cheaper and lighter device for production of very small drops. At present special formulations are supplied in expendable combined nozzles and bottles (called "bozzles").

The effective attraction to the target crop also causes the droplets to be filtered out in the periphery. A device produced in the U.S.A. forms the drops with the assistance of an air blast, charging them to lower potential by a rather different electrical system, thus making a compromise in favour of better penetration of a canopy. The advantage of lower energy consumption in electrical dispersion has to be sacrificed. Not only is hydrodynamic dispersion very inefficient but wind creation by any means is more energy demanding than dispersion. If the 1 litre is dispersed in 10m^3 of air (a very dense spray cloud) and the air blown at 3 m/s the energy demand is 50 joules.

A recent application development has novelty not in jet generation but in its collection. A narrow jet is projected horizontally across the line of travel into a collecting funnel from which it is returned to source. A plant growing to a height above the jet intercepts it. The method is selective against tall undesirable weeds in pasture or such problems as Johnson grass in soybeans. Killing tall weeds by application to the tops has been made possible by the remarkable translocation of glyphosate.

Rope wick applicators have the same objective. A long transverse tank contains the liquid herbicide and a thick multi-fibre rope is looped along its front, making contact with the liquid at intervals where it passes tightly through ports. The exposed part of the rope wick is held just above liquid level so that there is no drip from it at rest. When a tall weed presses against the wick liquid is squeezed out on to the weed. In neither of these devices can the dosage be well controlled but, since the target is a fairly sparse population, its overdosing can still be economic. In both cases is there some unwanted scatter on to non-target crop or pasture. The wick application of glyphosate is very effective on rushes in pasture.

Dosage and Cover

Most modern pesticides are used in agriculture at rates of 1 kg or less per hectare. If density is 1 kg/l the thickness, if uniformly spread over 1 flat hectare, would be 0.1 μm. A well grown crop has a leaf area 10–20 times the ground area it stands on. The leaf surface is often very wrinkled — when looked at on micron scale, so the thickness at uniform spread on the crop would be less than 0.01 μ m. Even 50 μm particles would have to be several millimetres apart.

A 50 μm diameter particle in still air falls at only about 8 cm/s. It takes only 0.03 sec time of fall through 2 mm to reach this speed relative to the air. It is therefore at the mercy of the slightest wind. It cannot be aimed except in a controlled air stream. The possibility of spontaneous spread of much larger drops of liquid, carrying much smaller particles, is considered under "Form of Deposits" below.

The Carrier Function

With a well-translocated herbicide or systemic insecticide or fungicide it may only be necessary to obtain a grossly uniform cover — a few drops on most leaves. Many pesticides, however, require a fine pattern of particles over the leaf surface to be effective. This could be obtained with undiluted pesticide only by using particles so small that they could not be *aimed* at a small target, but find their way, by wind and gravity, to a large area. Natural wind can be exploited, in "drift-spraying", to carry fine particles into a porous target, e.g. insecticide into orchard or herbicide into scrub.

Momentum for aiming the spray can be supplied by air rather than water. This directing force is obtained by high-powered fans which blow the air towards the target, the spray being introduced near the outlet. This method is frequently applied to tree-spraying from the ground when a spray produced by water pressure only would not carry far enough, unless an uneconomic amount of water (which must be carried) is used. The aiming of such "air-blast" spray differs from that of a water-pressure spray, generally used for ground crops, in that the particles in the former are usually much smaller and are carried by the blast towards the target only in a gross way. Some collide with leaves but many drift into the interior of trees or forest and settle under gravity. When a dust is used, it is also distributed in an air blast, or a series of blasts from separate openings on a boom. The main function of the inert dust used as a diluent is to provide visibility. A 50% active dust at

2 kg/ha could do as good a job as a 2% active dust at 50 kg/ha, but it would not be easily visible in the air and hardly visible at all on the crop. Visibility is also another function of the diluent water used in spraying. It is necessary not only to arrange that the pesticide can be dispersed and distributed but to be able to check that the intended operation is in fact being carried out. The blockage or wrong setting of a nozzle must make itself at once apparent. Hydraulic nozzles must be backed by good filters. Conducting tubes in aircraft equipment should have in-line flow sensors.

It will be evident that the more reliable the machine, the more skilled the operator and the greater his faith in his machine, the less important is visibility of the carrier. Good results have been obtained by spraying undiluted malathion and very concentrated non-aqueous solutions of other insecticides. When these operations are carried out by aircraft, the wide swath obtained with very fine droplets enables the job to be done with only few dispersing units, usually rotating discs or cages.

The use of ULV spraying has increased in recent years not only for application from aircraft but also for ground spraying. It is less demanding on increasingly expensive fuels because less inert material has to be carried and returns to base for reloading are greatly reduced in number. It has been made possible by the great improvements in the design and technology of spraying equipment already described.

Form of Deposits

Differences in the small-scale pattern of deposits left on leaf or wall surfaces by air-borne dust or very fine spray on the one hand and by a relatively coarse water-pressure spray on the other may be important. The fine particles, having very little momentum independently of the air in which they are carried, tend to follow the air movement around obstacles. The smaller the obstacle, the less the flow of air is deviated and impact of the particle is more probable. In an air stream, therefore, thin stems, hairs and leaf edges collect a disproportionate deposit of fine particles by "dynamic impaction". Relatively little deposit is collected in this way on the central areas of large, smooth leaves. When the air movement slows down as the blast from the machine is dispersed or when the crop or forest canopy has been penetrated, deposition is mainly from slow fall under gravity. Upper leaf surfaces are thus more heavily contaminated than lower ones.

Coarse droplets are deposited very quickly after their release from the nozzle. They tend not to be collected on fine hairs. A spider's thread passes cleanly through a moderate sized rain drop without collecting any liquid and with very little disturbance. Since the spray transfers momentum to the air, a directed spray-jet disturbs the crop leaves and they may be hit by droplets while in an abnormal posture. Particularly if jets from a boom are set at different angles, a coarse pressure-spray can give better underleaf cover than a fine spray or dust, but the initial cover is still far from complete.

A third function of liquid carrier is to enable the spray drops to spread out when they hit the target. Two hundred litres of water sprayed in drops of mean diameter 300 μ supplies only as many particles as would 1 kg of pesticide alone in 50 μ particles. To obtain uniform cover (which is not always desirable) it is therefore necessary that the drops themselves should spread. Water drops in the 200–500 μ diameter range are totally reflected from many leaf surfaces without leaving any deposit, a property that can make a contribution to herbicide selectivity if the crop (e.g. peas or brassicas) is very reflective and the weeds receptive. Oil drops are always accepted and water drops can be made acceptable by reducing the size below about 100 μ or by adding sufficient wetting agent. Water drops may spread to an extent limited by a finite contact angle but, even if zero contact angle could be expected on a similar, but smooth and homogeneous surface, spreading of an aqueous solution on a leaf surface becomes very slow and eventually ceases. The actual mechanism of spread is complex and is nearly always arrested by evaporation. Suspended solid particles will be stranded on the leaf surface, unable to reach as far as the liquid. Even oils, in the absence of water, spread very slowly once the film has thinned down to a few microns and spread is limited by evaporation, penetration into the lipophilic cutin and deposition of dissolved waxes.

There are three stages of discontinuity in the final deposit from a suspension of powder: (a) coarse pattern determined by the discrete deposit of drops in low-volume spraying or, after initial complete wetting by high-volume spray, by the structure and posture of the surface — on leaves, for example, the deposit is much denser in the zone in which the liquid collects before dropping off and, on the rest of the surface, there is usually more deposit in the channels above the main veins in the upper surface; (b) A finer pattern of aggregated particles within this; (c) a yet finer structure within the aggregates which have been built up by flocculation of the "ultimate" particles produced during formulation in the grinding or precipitation process.

The fine structure within the particle aggregates is probably rarely of biological significance. Any water within the pores of the aggregate is fully saturated with the active compound and an insect walking over a dry deposit will detach aggregates *in toto* if at all rather than pick up single ultimate particles. If a powder is fine enough to be serviceable for spraying, it will be finer than necessary for maximum biological effect. It is more likely that the size of ultimate particle giving maximum kill of walking insects will be too coarse for satisfactory suspension in the spray tank.

If the active compound is dissolved in the spray water, or in an oil emulsified in the water, it arrives in a form which has the potentiality of much more complete spreading. It does not, however, necessarily follow that the final deposit, after evaporation of the solvents, is more evenly spread or more active than that left by a suspension of powder. The oil globules in the emulsion may not spread on a surface already wetted by water, or the oil may evaporate before the water, according to the volatility. The active compound may remain in a super-cooled state for a long time, depending on many factors. Almost always the final pattern of crystals will be much coarser than that left by a suspension of pre-existing crystals.

In the application of pesticides to crops, particularly in temperate climates, resistance to removal by rain-washing is often an important property which may be improved by special additives to the formulation, or may influence the basic choice. An emulsified oil will usually leave a more resistant deposit than a simple wettable powder, because the oil globules, if they coalesce before evaporating, dissolve some resinous constituents of the leaf cuticle which act as adhesives. If an emulsion breaks on exposure, rain-resistance is improved. In the case of wettable powders, an adhesive substance, such as starch, is sometimes added. Dusts give good initial cover but poor weather resistance.

Addition of adhesives to the formulation may reduce the contact action of an insecticide deposit, because the adhesive is more effective in sticking the insecticide to the leaf or wall surface during drying than in helping the individual particles to stick to the insect's legs. Adhesives make little or no difference to the toxicity of the deposit to a leaf-eating insect and may therefore contribute to selectivity in favour of predators.

Evaporation of deposited pesticides is much more important than is generally realized. The compound is distributed in very thin layers or small dots over a very extensive area exposed to wind and sunlight. Attempts have sometimes been made to cut down evaporation by the incorporation of resinous substances. Penetration into leaf or insect is, however, also retarded. Significant transfer from deposit to pest often occurs in the vapour phase acting selectively against small insects keeping close to the leaf surface and also against fungus spores.

Choice of Type of Residual Deposit

Such conflict of requirements is very frequent in the study of the biological effects of formulation changes. A fungicide deposit provides another example. It is desirable that the deposit should not be washed off by the first shower of rain, but, in order that the active chemical should reach all alighting spores, it is desirable that there should be some redistribution by light rain or dew.

It has already been noted that the deposit of a crystalline substance from solution has a coarser pattern than that left by a suspension of an insoluble powder. The emulsion deposit is, however, generally more rain-fast. More penetration into leaf tissue may have occurred before crystallization. This may make a herbicide more active but also less selective: it may make an insecticide or fungicide more phytotoxic.

Occasionally there is a clear choice on grounds of biological activity. If an active residual deposit of insecticide is to be left on a porous wall surface, a crystalline compound is preferable to a liquid one. A suspension of wettable powder, which is filtered out on the wall surface, is preferable to an emulsion or straight oil solution, which penetrates into the capillary spaces where much of the compound remains uselessly hidden.

The occlusion of a deposit on a micro-wrinkled or hairy leaf becomes a possibility in the use of extremely active insecticides which are applied at very low dosage, particularly if remaining liquid. This may account for insecticidal action decreasing more rapidly than chemically determined residues. Even human feet would pick up less dirt from a pile carpet than from a hard floor if these had the same "dose" of dirt. It may therefore be desirable in some situations to "bulk out" very active pesticides.

Some compromise must nearly always be made and the best formulation will vary with the crop or fabric to be protected and the prevailing climatic factors. The interplay of factors is too complex to resolve in any other way than by numerous replicated trials under realistic conditions. The physical chemist can best contribute by helping the biologist in the design of these experiments.

Biological preference for one formulation or another is therefore much less easy to establish than preferences based on stability, storage, packaging or economic grounds dealt with in the next chapter. These production and commercial factors at present tend to dominate the choice. With increasing interest, particularly in the high living standard countries, in more selective use of pesticides, it is to be expected that increasing attention will be paid to the part that refinements of formulation can play. Until there is a greater appreciation of the possibilities by the user, the formulator cannot play his full part.

Granule Application

Pesticides are sometimes applied in granular form to a crop, sometimes to water and, much more frequently, to soil. There is a technical advantage when a herbicide is intended for action through the soil but is applied in the presence of a standing crop. The dry granules have much less tendency to lodge in the crop. A higher proportion of the pesticide gets to the right place and there is much less risk of damage to the crop leaves. For the same reason, insecticides for control of mosquito larvae in overgrown pools or streams are frequently applied as granules, which are more effective than spray in penetrating the canopy.

There is, however, at least one crop-pest combination where the argument is reversed. The maize leaf clasps the stem, forming a funnel in which granules collect. It is just in this region that the destructive stem-borer makes its entry and this treatment is therefore very efficient. The funnel is not water-tight and a spray is not so effectively collected.

Another situation where granules have a technical advantage is for localized treatment of widely spaced plants subject to root attack by insect larvae. The female often lays her eggs close to the base of the stem and a deposit of granules on the soil around the stem gives very efficient protection. The root-fly which attacks members of the cabbage tribe provides a good example.

Very often, however, granules are used, not for a technical advantage in performance, but purely for convenience. This argument appeals particularly strongly to the small domestic user. A sprinkler tin of dry granules can be ready to hand for treatment of small areas and there is no messiness or need for tedious washing of equipment. Granular herbicides are available in this form for total weed prevention in gravel paths, along wall bottoms, etc., and also (often the same herbicide but used at much lower dosage) for selective weed control in beds of roses, soft fruit or asparagus. In this selective use, the technical advantage of avoiding leaf contamination is also gained.

Insecticide and herbicide granules are made of much smaller size than is customary for fertilizer granules. Fertilizer granules are usually in a diameter range of 1–2 mm whereas pesticide granules are usually in a diameter range of 0.4–0.7 mm. Recent development of "micro-granules" (see "Granules" in Chapter 22) has reduced the lower limit to about 0.2 mm.

One reason for this difference is that pesticides are applied at a much smaller rate per hectare. Most of the weight is inert granule base and is, for economy, kept to a minimum consistent with adequately uniform coverage and no excessive scatter by the wind. Fertilizers are applied at higher rates and, as far as possible, their whole weight is made directly useful. They are formed largely of soluble salts so that they disintegrate rapidly in moist soil but need special formulation to avoid stickiness. It is therefore less necessary to produce satisfactory small granules and at the same time more difficult to do so.

An important difference between fertilizers and herbicides, having significance for choice of granule size, is that plant foods are actively sought by the root system. Some herbicides are destructive to root tissue and none is conducive to root growth. Systemic insecticides suitable for application to the soil are taken up passively by the root, and insecticides having direct action on soil-dwelling pests must have maximum opportunity of contact. Generally speaking, therefore, uniform distribution is more necessary for pesticides than for fertilizers. Average pesticidal granules number about 5 million to the killogram. If 20 kg could be distributed with perfect uniformity on a hectare, they would lie about 1 cm apart. If they were of the size commonly used for fertilizers they would lie about 5 cm apart.

Insecticides are often introduced into the seed furrow to protect the roots of the seedlings from insect attack. If the insecticide is systemic, some protection of the aerial portion of the seedling, particularly against aphids, can also be achieved. Granules are preferred for this use since the same type of distributor is used for granules and seed and since there is risk with liquid application of upsetting the function of the seed-drill.

Fertilizer is often required in the same situation, relative to the seed, as is insecticide and it would clearly be an economic advantage to combine the two, i.e. to have the insecticide impregnated on to the fertilizer granules. Few insecticides however are stable enough in contact with the strongly saline and frequently acid fertilizer. Aldrin and dieldrin were at one time used for this purpose but adverse environmental impact has brought their use into disfavour. Since this adverse impact is primarily due to the extreme stability of these compounds, new compounds of great stability are not now developed and combined fertilizer-insecticide products will become obsolete, unless one component is formulated as granules with an adequately protective coating.

Smokes

A much finer dispersion of stable, low volatile substances can be achieved by condensation of hot vapour than by any process of mechanical shatter of liquid. The vapour must be diluted with air before condensing in order to give a fine-particle smoke and the process must be carried out very quickly to keep down chemical decomposition to an acceptable level. Initially the particles in a condensation "smoke" are less than 0.1 μ diameter but they grow rapidly in a concentrated smoke by collision and distillation. For a given concentration, the light-scattering effect or "obscuring power" of the smoke is at a maximum when the particles are about 1 μ diameter. As little as 25 mg of dispersed material per cubic metre gives a very dense fog.

Dispersion as a smoke can confer on some nearly involatile substances something of the penetrating power of true vapours. Penetration of a smoke into crevices, however, is much more dependent on air circulation than is that of a true vapour, since the thermal diffusion process is very slow. Pick-up by impact is much less rapid from a smoke than from a coarser fog or even a falling spray, because the small particles have too little inertia or momentum. The smoke, however, is more persistent.

Effective smokes of stable substances of not too low volatility can be made by improvized methods such as leading an oil solution into the exhaust pipe of a tractor or aircraft. The substance is evaporated by the hot gases in the pipe and then condensed as soon as these mix with the air. Special oil-burners are made for more efficient smoke generation in apparatus which can be carried by hand and used in closed spaces, especially against glasshouse pests. Entirely self-contained smoke generators are available. These are described in Chapter 22. Insecticidal smokes are most used for treatment of pests in glasshouses. Some organic fungicides can also be used in this way, but the copper products are too involatile and elementary sulphur too flammable. Sulphur has of course been used in glasshouses as a fungicide, by transfer in vapour form at very low concentration from suspensions painted on hot pipes.

Drift

It will be appreciated that prevention of drift is one of the most significant problems to be solved in future application of pesticides. To place pesticide on the leaves of a crop some form of dispersion is necessary, particularly if uniform cover of the leaf surface is desired. The dispersed material cannot be aimed perfectly: some drifts away on the wind, often assisted by local draught created by the machine.

Direct economic loss because not all the chemical gets to the right gross target is rarely serious. Most pesticide molecules are wasted because they suffer some other fate than that incurred in initiating lethal biochemical damage in the target pest. The economic desirability, for the target crop, is to reduce this wastage to a minimum. At one extreme, pesticide dumped as a massive solid in the middle of the field would all stay there but it would do no useful job against the pest. At the other extreme, aerial spraying of very fine droplets would give the most uniform cover within the gross target (the field) but most of it would fall elsewhere. For most efficient kill of the real target within the gross target there must be an optimum degree of dispersal. Its position will depend on the pesticide (systemics need less dispersal than superficial pesticides) and on the pest (whitefly must be attacked with smaller droplets than tobacco hornworm). Methods of application and formulation also influence the position of this optimum.

Drift may also cause damage outside the target area: this is of two kinds which must be kept distinct in planning its reduction. A high area density deposited just outside the target area may cause evident crop damage, a risk, obviously greatest with herbicides, which has led to the owner of the target crop being liable for compensation. Insecticides also can cause off-target damage as when mulberry (the food of the silkworm) is downwind of a cotton crop. Even sprayed motor cars have caused complaint.

Remote damage and general environmental contamination are much more complex and difficult to assess. Causatively they differ from near crop damage in important respects. Drops in the 50–100 microns range, if they escape from the delivered spray curtain, drift far enough on a light wind in inversion and high humidity to carry damaging amounts of pesticide on to an adjacent crop. Droplets in the 20–50 microns range, particularly if water-based and therefore rapidly decreasing in size in low humidity, will carry so far in turbulent wind (associated with low humidity) and impact so inefficiently that they contribute little to local damage but may contaminate a vast area at extremely low density. Much of their content will be lost by evaporation: much will suffer photochemical decomposition.

There used to be a rather general official recommendation, based only on unsound theory, to spray potentially damaging chemicals only at the evening and early morning inversion. It is now recognized that, while reducing the general effect (if there is one), this invites local damage. Accepted recommendations to reduce drift are to avoid *unnecessarily* fine spray, to deliver spray as closely as possible above the crop and to avoid strong crosswind (because it releases more spray from the curtain). The most important improvement will come from cutting down the proportion of small droplets in the spray without unduly increasing mean dropsize. If, for a particular direct insecticide operation, 200 micron droplets are optimal, 500 micron droplets will be largely wasted (they each carry 15 times as much and have much less chance of scoring a hit). Most hydraulic nozzles currently in use were developed twenty or more years ago and produce drops in a wide size range. To have only a small proportion of droplets below 100 microns the mean size would have to be much above 200 microns. If a much closer range could be obtained a lower rate of application and less drift could be achieved together. For most spray applications a range of 100–150 microns droplet size is optimal. This is becoming possible now that practical commerical spinning-disc machines are being developed. These will make ultra-low volume spraying (ULV) a much more generally practicable technique.

Adjuvants which increase viscosity or retard evaporation can decrease the drift potential of hydrodynamic nozzles. Granules in the normal size range of 500–2000 μ, if they are free from dust, can eliminate drift, but they are useful only for application to soil or water. Recent development of "micro-granules" in the 50–300 μ range makes possible their use for foliar application. They provide the solid equivalent of the CDA made possible by the spinning disc. The physics of adhesion becomes of major importance. A flattened shape and some slow development of stickiness are desirable. By contrast, the spherical micro-granules left by evaporation in flight of droplets of a wettable powder suspension, are extremely non-adhesive and this property can help in decreasing the risk of damage from such spray to adjacent crops. Devices to impart a high electrostatic charge to dispersed particles have been developed with the object of increasing attraction to the primary target (see p. 265).

Micro-granules are potentially the safest formulation in relation to drift if specification of freedom from active dust can be closely met, but machines to distribute them from a wide boom usually employ forced airflow to transport the material along wide horizontal tubes to the outlet ports. This rather violent treatment can create dust and distribute it. There is need for development of alternatives. If the granules are made very non-spherical so as to increase retention on foliage they are, en masse, less easy flowing, which makes distribution more difficult. If they are to become sticky on exposure, the use of air-flow to carry them is not possible. There is a considerable problem here for the engineer.

A problem not usually considered under "drift" but very directly related is the safety of the operator. He is for long periods close to the source of drift and, in a following wind, can be heavily contaminated, making protective clothing essential. In this respect, granules, including micro-granules, if free from dust, are safer than spray. It is, incidentally, necessary that micro-granules be free from dust in order to keep them free-flowing. Not only the operator, but also the machine, can become contaminated with spray liquid and, where a combination with seeder or fertilizer drill is used, this can cause mechanical trouble.

Avoidance of drift has usually been considered a problem for the engineer. This is not really fair. True, useful improvements have been made, as mentioned, above, to design and physical performance, but, to a considerable extent, the requirements for good local control and no drift damage are conflicting. The engineer has been able to get more liquid in useful- (not necessarily, for control purposes optimal-) sized drops while decreasing the amount in potentially damaging size, but not much attention has yet been given to decreasing the effect of unavoidable drift, in which there may be scope for the chemist and formulator.

One such possibility has just been mentioned. An inert powder in the spray liquid can reduce the collection of evaporated drops by a crop over which the drops, becoming hard spheres, escape. Electrically charged sprays may also help pull the whole drift-cloud down to earth although effect on individual particles is small. Other possibilities seem not to have been explored. The pesticide in small drifting droplets receives much more light and has freer access to oxygen than that in larger drops travelling a short distance to the target. There may be possibility of exploiting photochemical destruction to reduce the effect of drift, particularly the problematically remote pollution by very small drops. This probably does happen quite incidentally with many pesticides and there is now much more interest at research level in photochemical decay. Introduction of photoactive catalysts is a possibility.

Since there is a tendency among the more vocal environmentalists to regard the chemist as guilty until he can be proved completely innocent (a philosophical impossibility) it is desirable to point out that drift damage is not a new problem. The bad farmer, the good wilderness manager, even unaided nature, have been causing or permitting damage to neighbouring crop production by wind-blown weed seeds, fungus spores and insect pests for a very long time. Protective legislation does exist but cases of chemical drift damage are more often successful in court than are cases of avoidable weed drift.

Further Reading

See p. 298.

22
Formulation

The formulator aims to bring the pesticide into a form convenient to apply, either directly, as in the case of granules or special self-dispensing packs, or after dilution, usually with water. Not only must the product be convenient to use when freshly prepared but also after packaging, transport and storage. In addition to the biological problems discussed in Chapter 21, chemical stability, corrosion of containers, sedimentation of suspensions and packing together of powders must also be studied. A few frequently occurring problems of this kind will be mentioned but the experienced formulator has long since learned that the next problem, particularly in the case of a solid product, will often be a new and unexpected one.

Formulation for Spray Application

In the spray as applied in the field the active ingredient may be: (a) dissolved in the water; (b) dissolved in an oil emulsified in the water; or (c) suspended as fine solid particles. The possibilities of (a) and (b) may be restricted by the solubility; (c) is not, of course, directly possible if the active ingredient is liquid. In these respects the properties of the active ingredient may dictate the method of formulation.

If the active ingredient is freely soluble in water, it will be sprayed in form (a) no matter whether supplied as a concentrated solution in water, or in a better solvent, or as a solid. If it is soluble in oil but not in water it can be supplied as a thick concentrated "stock" emulsion ("mayonnaise" type, as it used to be called) or as "self-emulsifying (sometimes called "miscible") oil. If the final form is (c), the concentrate supplied must be either a concentrated paste or a wettable powder.

It is usually necessary for the spray drops, after dilution of the formulation with water, not to be reflected from leaf surfaces. Spontaneous spread of the accepted drops and penetration of a porous hairy or waxy layer is often required. The concentrate must therefore contain some "wetting agent". The main effect of the wetting agent is to reduce the surface tension of the very self-attracting water, making it more willing to spread on waxy surfaces. These agents often have other effects which may be desirable but may also be better performed by other compounds. A formulation suitable for spraying on one crop may need more wetting agent for spraying on another, and suitable auxiliary material may be advised for addition in the spray tank.

Wetting Agents and Additives

A wetting agent is a compound with one or two paraffin chains totalling 8–20 C atoms, attached to a hydrophilic group, which may be anionic, cationic or neutral. To be sufficiently strongly hydrophilic the neutral group must be an amine or phosphine oxide or, much more usual, contain several –OH units or even more ether (–CH$_2$–O–CH$_2$–) units as provided, e.g. by sugars or polyethylene oxide chains.

The paraffin chains provide the most extreme contrast to water in physical behaviour and, as they are covalently linked to a hydrophilic group, the compounds form bridges between water and air or any oily liquid or surface. They are often called "amphiphiles" (having both loves) and the two tendencies must be as extreme as possible, spatially distinct, but inseparable. Since the development of industrial fluorocarbon chemistry it has been possible to replace the paraffin chains by the even more hydrophobic fully F-substituted ones. These form molecules even more surface-active but their cost restricts their use to special industrial applications.

Some compounds in which two or more short paraffin tails are attached to one hydrophilic head have superior wetting action to equivalent compounds having the same paraffin content in one long tail. The long tails more easily form micelles in which they are less available for adsorption on an existing surface. The extreme form would be a fully methylated short chain — e.g. C$_4$(CH$_3$)$_9$– — and would have the added advantage of presenting only methyl groups, known to be more hydrophobic than methylene. If attached to an ethylene oxide hydrophile, the head–tail geometry would be reversed.

Compounds in which a poly-dimethyl-silicone chain replaces the paraffinic one have become available. These are so much more effective in promoting spread of water on waxy surfaces, i.e. effective at much lower concentration, that they are being considered as practical alternatives in agricultural sprays. They can reduce the surface tension of water to 20 mN/m — appreciably below that of a liquid paraffin. This remarkable property has been considered to be due to the rotation of the Si–O bond which enables the chain to lie on the surface exposing only methyl groups.

$$CH_3CH_3CH_3CH_3CH_3CH_3CH_3CH_3$$

Neutral and ionic hydrophiles may be linked together and many chemical tricks are available to link either or both, covalently, to the paraffinic groups. A substituted benzene ring is often involved. It is evident that an enormous number, even of commercially feasible, surfactants can be made and an extensive industry has arisen. It is inherent in the action of these compounds to have an auxiliary, though essential, function and the surfactant industry supplies compounds for a wide diversity of industrial uses as well as the large domestic detergent market. Few, if any, surfactants are specifically designed for pesticide formulation, but this is an important use, particularly of the ethylene oxide type which is preferred where suitable because of general compatibility with the active ingredients and insensitivity to the saline impurities of dilution water.

All surfactants lower the tension of water at the interface with oils and at the air-water surface, but the rate of spreading on hydrophobic solid surfaces is not determined solely by this property and more research could well be directed to the selection or design of compounds for increased rate of spreading which must compete, in spraying operations, with evaporation.

Wetting agents, particularly, of the ethylene oxide type, leave a viscous liquid residue after evaporation of water. This is a good general solvent and may help a systemic pesticide to penetrate the leaf cuticle. In this function a non surface-active additive such as diethylene glycol or hexanediol could be more effective. Whether retention of a non-penetrating insecticide in viscous liquid form is desirable depends on the anatomy and behaviour of the pest and its enemies. The silicone wetting agents, needed in lower concentration, will have reduced residual solvent action and could have advantage in some applications.

Only when the concentrate is an aqueous solution is the formulator free to use surfactants for the sole purpose of assisting spreading and penetration. Wettable powders and self-emulsifying oils need surfactants to make them serviceable for quick dilution and dispersion before spraying and their presence necessarily modifies behaviour after spraying.

Wettable Powders

Preparation of Free-flowing Powders

The grinding of coarse solids is carried out in many types of mill, ranging from those used in the grinding of grain, which depend on shearing between solid surfaces, to high-speed hammer mills and "fluids energy" mills. In the latter, the pre-mixed, roughly ground material is passed through a quite small chamber in which air is circulated at very high velocity in turbulent flow. The particles are shattered by sudden accelerations and centrifugal forces. This process, generally called "micronizing", is capable of reducing most materials to a very fine powder and is now the most widely used. The micronizing chamber is very compact but high power is necessary to drive the air-stream and, after collection of the powder in a "cyclone", extensive air filters or further cyclones are necessary to avoid contamination. The air can be circulated, if necessary, without exchange with the outside air and, in this closed circuit, it can be replaced by nitrogen or carbon dioxide in processing compounds that are easily oxidized or perhaps form explosive mixtures in air.

Few, if any, organic compounds can be, by themselves, ground to a satisfactory fine powder which does not "cake" on storage. The stickiness of the powder is often aggravated by impurities of manufacture which it may not be possible to remove at a cost acceptable to the consumer. Heat generated in grinding, which can be locally intense, can also fuse together particles of quite high-melting compounds. The wetting and dispersing agents which it is necessary to add tend to increase the problem of stickiness. It is therefore the universal practice to mix in some inert infusible mineral diluent. The function of the mineral diluent is to buffer the organic particles apart. Sometimes a fine clay will suffice but a more absorbent material with an internal "spongy" structure may be necessary. The specially absorbent Attapulgus clays and diatomaceous earths are much used. Some fibrous minerals, e.g. meerschaum, are specially adsorbent, consisting of microscopic tubes.

In some powder formulations, the active ingredient may be one which dissolves completely at spray dilution. The object of fine grinding, which necessitates the admixture of an insoluble filler, is to get the active ingredient into a rapidly soluble form. Dimethoate, 2.5% soluble in water, is an example. At the dosage and volume rate usual in ground-spraying, the compound is wholly soluble. A coarsely crystalline preparation, even if it did not cake in storage, would, however, dissolve too slowly for convenience. Uneven dosing of the crop would result.

If the active compound is itself a mineral substance of low solubility or a rather insoluble organic salt, a filler may not be required, since there is no tendency to stickiness. Single-pack copper fungicides are an example. Copper oxychloride or basic sulphate or cuprous oxide is obtained in very fine-particle form by precipitation reactions and is milled only to break down the aggregates formed on drying. A small percentage of wetting and suspending agents makes up the rest of the "formulation". Wettable sulphur and the zinc and manganese dithiocarbamates can also be formulated in very high concentration, but these compounds introduce a different problem. Both can form explosive mixtures with air. They must be milled in an inert gas or agents must be added to inhibit the build-up of the static electricity which initiates the explosion.

Even a liquid active compound can be successfully put into the wettable powder form if a very absorbent mineral filler is used and care taken not to overload its capacity. Usually, on dispersion in water, the water displaces the organic compound from the hydrophilic mineral and the final spray liquor is really an emulsion in which the mineral powder may contribute to the stabilization.

Generally more troublesome to the formulator than an active ingredient which is always liquid is one with a melting point within the normal temperature range, because this means that change from solid to liquid frequently occurs in storage and the growing crystals can bind the powder together. It is not unknown for storage troubles to arise in wettable powders due to change of crystalline form of the organic compound even when this has a high melting point. The compound may come out of the manufacturing process in a metastable modification and slowly change over to the stable form on storage. New nuclei may be formed which are fed by diffusion in the vapour state so that large particles, often needle-shaped, may grow slowly in an initially satisfactory powder and make it quite unserviceable.

Chemical Stability

Although most compounds are more stable in the solid than the liquid state, because their molecules are held fast in the crystal lattice, the powder contains continuous air channels in which diffusion is far more rapid than in liquid. Consequently, unless the outer package is impervious, a compound sensitive to oxidation may be less stable in the wettable powder formulation. Rates of the heterogeneous reactions have a more complex dependence on time and temperature than those of reactions in solution.

Chemical stability must always be proved by storage of the wettable powder, even when the evidence for stability of the pure substance is satisfactory. Some clays contain strongly acid centres which may catalyse a decomposition reaction. Some compounds may be intolerant of an acidic and others of an alkaline diluent. One compound, e.g. diazinon, may be satisfactorily formulated with chalk as a filler: for another, e.g. dimethoate, chalk may be a highly undesirable constituent. Obviously knowledge of the reactions of the active compound, particularly of acid or base catalysed hydrolysis, can be a useful preliminary guide to the choice of mineral filler.

Physical Stability

Physical stability must always be proved by storage trials. These should include subjection of the sample to vibration and compression. Temperature fluctuation, since it gives rise to local diffusive distillation within the sample and also to partial solution and recrystallization, is particularly prone to produce caking. The tests should therefore include taking the sample from one extreme of the probable range of storage temperature to the other, as frequently as the thermal capacity and conductivity permit.

A powder settles into a container with a large proportion of included air. The actual solid itself occupies generally between about 40% and 60% of the total volume, though extremely "fluffy" solids such as light magnesium oxide may occupy as little as 20%. The "bulk density" of the wettable powder is therefore subject to variation with slight changes in composition and in handling and packing operations. The powder will frequently settle down on storage. The formulator must keep these variations as small as possible.

Technically, the variations may appear to matter little, if the powder is measured out by weight or packed in suitable units, but variation of bulk density can be an important commercial disadvantage. The customer does not like to receive a half-full container and the packaging department does not like to find that a new formulation cannot be got into a stock of labelled containers.

Performance

It is easier to make a wettable powder which can give a good suspension only by "creaming" before dilution than one which disperses rapidly and easily when scattered on a water surface or rinsed through a filter-basket. By "creaming" is here meant the process of stirring the powder to a stiff, smooth paste with a little water before adding the bulk of dilution water. Pockets of dry powder shear more easily than the stiff paste between and are therefore reduced in size and eventually eliminated. With the very wide range of wetting agents now available, however, it is nearly always possible to make the powder dispersible quickly and completely in the full bulk of water, and this should always be the aim of the formulator. A good wettable powder should disperse without agitation in a few seconds when scattered on the surface of water in a large beaker and very little should fall to the bottom without dispersing.

An insoluble powder must remain suspended for an adequate time. Obviously it cannot remain in suspension indefinitely since the filler at least, and usually the active compound, is heavier than water. Suspensibility is usually tested by a W.H.O. (World Health Organization) standard method. The suspension is held at rest in a 250 cm^3 measuring cylinder for half an hour and the upper 90% of the liquid drawn off and analysed. The ratio of active compound found to that which would be present in 90% of the volume initially is defined as the suspensibility and should exceed 80%. This is not a very severe test. If the top 90% has an average concentration of 80% of the initial, the bottom 10% has a concentration 2.8 times the initial. This variation may be acceptable for an insecticide or fungicide, but, with a herbicide, overdosing with the first offtake from a spray load could lead to crop damage. For the operator, time as well as chemical, costs money and he has therefore a good reason to spray out his load quickly, but he should advisedly have some means of agitating the contents of his tank on long runs.

The powder may settle too quickly for one or both of two reasons. The "ultimate" particles may not be small enough. More often, they may loosely aggregate together — "flocculate" — after dispersion. The first fault, unless the particles have grown during storage, can be cured by finer grinding. The second requires alteration of the amount or composition of the suspending agents included in the formulation. The agents included to make the powder rapidly wettable are not usually adequate to protect the suspension. Suspending agents are usually of much higher molecular weight than the wetting agents. They include lignin sulphonates from waste-liquors of wood-pulp refining, sulphonated naphthalene formaldehyde condensation products proteins and gums. Selection of the best compound can be made only by trial.

Although prolonged storage of the diluted suspension is not usually necessary, it may sometimes be unavoidable if spraying is interrupted by adverse weather or mechanical faults. It is therefore desirable that the settled powder should be easily resuspended by agitation. To meet this requirement some compromise may be necessary because the cake, which eventually forms at the bottom of a tank on long standing of a very good — not flocculated — suspension, is usually much more difficult to disperse than a more quickly settled flocculated precipitate.

Packaging

For many uses, wettable powder formulations are preferred at the merchanting and user level because they are considered less subject to loss during transport and handling, and can be packed in cheaper containers. The industrial chemist, experienced in the manipulation of liquids, regards the liquid state as by far the most convenient for measuring, piping and mixing. The preference for powder formulations may seem illogical to him but it has to be accepted as the purchaser's choice.

An advantage often claimed for the powder is that it can be packed in cheaper containers, from which it is not all lost if these are broken in transit; but it must be remembered that a poorly packed powder may be vulnerable to oxygen and water vapour permeating this container inwards and to evaporative loss occurring through it outwards. Perhaps the commonest of all mistakes made in this subject is to believe that a solid is involatile. Compare a little naphthalene wrapped in paper, lubricating oil in an open dish and some ether in a well-stoppered bottle. What the solid does do is to stop the contained air from moving. Evaporation from the interior of the powder must take place by diffusion. Consequently a large package of powder loses its active ingredient much more slowly than a small one.

Emulsifiable Oils

Composition
Many water-insoluble pesticides are supplied to the user in the form of an emulsifiable concentrate. This is a solution of the pesticide, together with oil-soluble emulsifiers, in a solvent which is mainly a hydrocarbon oil. The formulation should disperse as a fine emulsion when simply poured into water, but gentle agitation is, of course, necessary to ensure that the emulsion

CIPM-J*

is uniformly distributed throughout the contents of the spray tank. The formulation of emulsifiable oils has been greatly facilitated by the commercial development over the last 20 years of non-ionic emulsifying agents in which the hydrophilic portion of the molecule consists of a polyethylene oxide chain. A typical example is

$$CH_3 \left\langle \bigcirc \right\rangle - O-CH_2-CH_2-(O-CH_2-CH_2-)_nOH$$

where n is distributed rather widely about a mean value which, for emulsification of oil in water, is around 12. An advantage of these compounds over the ionic types in their much greater oil solubility. To get an effective concentration of soap or sodium high alcohol sulphonate into the oil, it is usually necessary to include a more polar solvent and perhaps even a little water. Chemical instability may result.

Another advantage of the ethylene oxide type emulsifiers is that their behaviour is little influenced by saline impurities which vary in amount and composition in water from different sources. The hydrophilic property is the combined effect of a large number of moderately hydrophilic ether groups which form hydrogen bonds with the water. The hydrophilic property of the ionic agents is usually concentrated in a single ionized group which is much influenced by other ions, particularly multivalent ions of opposite charge.

There is now available a very wide range of non-ionic emulsifiers having various bridging groups between the paraffinic and hydrophilic groups. Some have both an ethylene oxide chain and an ionic group in the same molecule. In the example illustrated, a branched nonyl alcohol of petroleum origin is condensed with phenol, substituting the ring mainly in the 4 position, and ethylene oxide is then condensed with the phenolic OH group. Ethylene oxide can also be condensed, with rather more difficulty in control of the reaction, with the OH groups of a primary fatty alcohol or of a polyhydric alcohol already partly esterified with a fatty acid. It may also be condensed with a carboxylic acid, an amide or an amine. Compounds in which a carboxylic ester group forms the bridge are rather sensitive to alkaline hydrolysis.

Bearing in mind that the number of ethylene oxide molecules condensed in the chain can be increased almost indefinitely, it is evident that there are very numerous possible chemical structures. Also very important are the "block" co-polymers of ethylene and propylene oxides, in which considerable lengths of the chain consist of one kind of unit only. The extra methyl groups in the portions of the chain made up of propylene oxide make these regions predominantly hydrophobic.

No example, seems to be known where the use of only a single, pure emulsifying agent can give a satisfactory self-emulsifying oil. A mixture of rather different emulsifiers seems to be necessary. Even a mixture of similar non-ionic compounds, but with two widely different mean numbers of ethylene oxide molecules in the chain, can be successful when neither alone would be. More commonly a mixture of non-ionic and anionic emulsifiers is used, around, say 4% of the former and 1% of the latter, choosing for the anionic constituent one with a branched hydrophobic chain, which generally forms more soluble salts.

Generally speaking, the more hydrophobic the emulsifying agent, the greater its tendency to produce water-in-oil rather than oil-in-water emulsions. The best system for producing a self-emulsifying oil is usually found to be near the limit for good oil-in-water emulsifiability. Some authorities consider that a water-in-oil emulsion is first produced when the two liquids meet and is then inverted on further dilution. Frequently, the larger globules in a dilute emulsion prepared by pouring a self-emulsifying oil into water are found to be multiple, i.e. finer globules of water inside a larger globule of oil.

Performance

The detailed mechanism by which an emulsifiable oil breaks up into globules in the 1–10 μm range on simply pouring into water is by no means clear but it is certain that the process is not strictly spontaneous. If water and an emulsifiable oil are carefully layered, the lighter over the heavier, and left at rest for a long time, there will be found only a narrow zone of emulsion and the rest will not now emulsify on gentle shaking. It seems therefore that the agitation caused by pouring the oil into the water is necessary for the process. Deliberate extra agitation, however, short of the high velocity agitation of an emulsifying machine, makes little difference to the degree of dispersion.

The fat globules in milk rise to form a cream layer but, in this layer, the fat is still dispersed and can be stirred back into the skim milk. This "creaming" is very different from the "breaking" of an emulsion, when the globules coalesce to give a coherent separate phase, but breaking is accelerated by creaming since the globules are forced into contact by gravity. The larger the globules and the more their density differs from that of water, the more rapidly will the emulsion "cream". In many pesticide emulsions the oil phase is heavier than the water and the "cream" concentrates downwards. Since the active compound is usually heavier than water and the solvent lighter, it is sometimes possible, but may not be economic, to adjust the density of the solution to that of water. Otherwise creaming can be prevented only by agitation, but, in the dilute emulsion formed by a good emulsifiable oil, the globules are usually fine enough to remain well suspended for an adequate time.

There is sometimes a good case, on biological performance grounds, for the emulsion to be an unstable one that breaks easily, since the oil layer is then held preferentially by the plant surface. There is no point in using an over-coarse density-adjusted oil phase for this purpose, since the spray nozzle itself breaks up the oil phase further. Instability in the spray tank is undesirable since the separated oil phase of a broken emulsion cannot, like the cream, be easily resuspended. If instability is required, it should develop after the spray has been exposed to air. Instability is achieved in old-type tar oil winter washes for fruit trees by using alkaline soap as the emulsifier. The soap is reduced in effectiveness by uptake of atmospheric carbon dioxide after exposure. Replacement of mineral alkali by a volatile amine can accelerate breaking on exposure.

Dilute emulsions, formed easily from a self-emulsifying oil, are not of very high stability. They do not remain dispersed as long as do emulsions produced in an emulsifying machine with careful selection of the stabilizers, particularly when these include macromolecular agents such as casein. Generally, in fact, good emulsion *stabilizers* are not facile *emulsifiers*. A stable emulsion can often be made unstable by adding a good emulsifier. An emulsifiable oil which gives satisfactory emulsion at, say, 1 in 100 dilution will often be much less stable at much lower dilution, say 1 in 10. The self-emulsifying oil can, however, give emulsions of adequate stability for spraying purposes where it is not necessary to keep the diluted liquor for long periods.

Solubility Limitations

The emulsifiable oil is much more restricted than the wettable powder in the number of compounds for which it is suitable. Many pesticides are of too low a solubility to be supplied economically in this form. Not only is the cost for solvent, packaging and transport too high, but the excessive oil often gives rise to crop damage when used in agriculture. The choice of oil is necessarily restricted because it must have a very low water solubility; otherwise the oil itself will be dissolved on dilution and the pesticide, usually less soluble in water and now with no separate phase to dissolve it, becomes supersaturated and crystallizes out in an uncontrolled manner. It is unwise to risk the use of a supersaturated spray liquor. It may give rise to no trouble in two or three successive spray loads but further loads can crystallize quickly once nuclei have been formed. Under-dosing, poor control and nozzle blockage can result.

The limitation of choice to oils of very low water solubility is more restricting than is often realized. Many modern pesticides have moderately polar molecules for which rather polar solvents are optimal. Ketones are usually much better solvents than hydrocarbons, but acetone is completely miscible with water. Methyl ethyl ketone and cyclohexanone are around 10% soluble in water. Chloroform is often an exceptionally good solvent and is only about 0.5% soluble in water but it is expensive and frowned upon by medical authorities. The choice is, in fact, limited to crude aromatic hydrocarbon mixtures from coal-tar or petroleum sources. Methyl naphthalenes in the 230–250°C b.p. range are much used in formulations of the organochlorine insecticides.

It may be permissible to boost the solubility to some extent by the addition of more polar, and therefore more water-soluble, solvents without incurring risk of crystallization in the spray tank. Some relaxation is general and arises from the fact that the marketed concentrate must remain a solution at the lowest temperature likely. Spraying, on the other hand, is usually carried out well above this temperature. It may therefore be permissible to add a proportion of ketone to an aromatic solvent to keep the active compound in solution at −5°C, provided it would remain in solution at 10°C if the ketone were removed. Further relaxation is permissible where the active compound is soluble in water at the spray dilution. An example is provided by a dimethoate concentrate in cyclohexanone. For the recommended dilution, emulsification need only be transient, to hasten the process of solution, all constituents being dissolved in the water when this dilution is reached.

Stock Emulsions

Emulsions are sometimes marketed as such — in concentrated cream form — to be diluted in the field. A cheaper product can be made this way because less emulsifier is needed. With the rapid advance in recent years in the availability of good emulsifiers for the oil concentrate, the stock emulsion has receded in importance. It is less satisfactory in storage, more demanding in container choice, because generally more corrosive, and is in any case restricted to hydrolytically stable compounds. Probably, however, the strongest reason for manufacturers' preference for the oil concentrate is the greater certainty with which shelf life can be tested and assured. The product is a homogeneous solution in which only chemical changes are possible and these follow a simple pattern. "Accelerated" (high-temperature) storage tests can give a reliable indication. In the stock emulsion, on the other hand, much more complex and less predictable physical changes may also occur.

The oil in stock emulsions is broken down to small globules by violent mechanical action and the globules can be stabilized by macromolecular solutes — e.g. casein — which have little action at the air-water surface. The diluted product can therefore be non-spreading or even reflected from leaves.

Solution Concentrates

The simplest of all formulations is the solution concentrate, a homogeneous water-miscible liquid merely requiring dilution in the spray tank. An aqueous solution will be used where possible, but it is sometimes necessary to add a better, but water-miscible, solvent in order to reach an economically acceptable concentration of the active compound. For this purpose, ether-alcohols, such as butyl cellosolve (butoxyethanol) or diethylene glycol (2,2'-dihydroxydiethylether), are preferred to methanol or acetone as they have higher flash-points. It is important, where possible, that the concentrate should not incur the higher freight-charges imposed on flammable products.

The number of pesticides that can be formulated in this simple way is limited by two factors — solubility and hydrolytic stability. With the exception of the herbicide amitrol (and the insecticides octamethyl-pyrophosphoramide and dimefox which now have only very limited use), the solubility factor limits these formulations to salts of active acids or, in the case of diquat and paraquat, of active bases. The active acids, however, include 2,4-D, MCPA and other "hormone" herbicides which are the most important herbicides in terms of world tonnage used.

The inactive ion of the salt may have to be chosen for solubility as well as cheapness. In the case of MCPA an aqueous concentrate can be made containing up to 250 g/l as the sodium or potassium salts (or preferably a mixture), but, in the case of 2,4-D, only 2% can be achieved and an amine salt must be used. The ammonium salt itself is not soluble enough and dimethylamine or ethanolamines are mainly used as the neutralizing bases. Mixed bases give a higher solubility than single bases. Solubility advantage can therefore be secured along with economic advantage by the use of unfractionated bases. Since high solubility in the residual deposit assists leaf penetration, there is no conflict in this case between biological and packaging requirements.

In terms of inanimate chemistry all these compounds are very stable and there is no problem on this account in the storage of aqueous concentrates. The phenoxyaliphatic acids have all a rather limited life in fertile soil. There is generally no significant residue left in soil after three or four weeks in the summer. TBA, dicamba and picloram are much more persistent, but there is no dangerous residue, of the first two at least, 12 months after application of the dosage used in selective weed control. The decomposition in soil is entirely due to microbiological action.

A problem peculiar to the aqueous concentrate is the precipitation of tarry matter when the concentrate is diluted. Pesticides must be cheaply produced. An unnecessarily high degree of purification adds to the cost. Despite the saline nature of most concentrates, their organic content usually increases the solvent power of the product for other organic substances. It sometimes happens that some resinous by-product of manufacture is held in solution by the concentrate and not removed by filtration. On dilution, this by-product can come out of solution and lead to filter- or nozzle-blockage. Tests for filterability after dilution should always be carried out in the formulation laboratory. The addition of a suspending agent or "protective colloid" is often adequate to avoid the tar problem, but further purification during manufacture of the pesticide itself may be necessary.

An aqueous concentrate need not contain surfactants. The diluted emulsifiable oil or wettable powder has always at least moderate wetting properties due to the content of emulsifiers and wetting agents necessary for suspension. The diluted aqueous concentrate may have good or poor wetting power according to whether surfactants are added specially for this purpose. It is possible, therefore, to meet a wider range of biological specifications. In the formulation of dinoseb for spraying the pea crop, for example, minimal wetting is desirable since undamaged pea leaves then reflect the spray and reduce risk of chemical injury to the crop.

At the manufacturer's end, water-based concentrates have limitations which are clear and easily established. At the user's end, they would seem to be the simplest of all formulations, but their very apparent simplicity has often led to trouble. The user expects to have to cream a powder or otherwise coax it through a filter basket. He expects to have to stir an emulsifiable oil. Because the aqueous concentrate is water-miscible, he is inclined to hope that it will mix itself. It is only miscible in the sense that there is no phase boundary between the concentrate and the water. If a heavy concentrate is just poured into a tank full of water it will sink, only partly diluted, to the bottom. Trundling the machine over a rough farm track is surprisingly ineffective as a means of gross mixing of the contents of a full tank. A heavy over-dosing of the first part of a field and inadequate dosing of the rest has often resulted. The concentrate should always be poured into a half-full tank and the rest of the water then added quickly. The tank agitator, if there is one, should be used. If there is no agitator, a minute's work with a stick is a small price to pay for a good harvest and a cheap insurance against serious damage and ineffective weed control.

Chemical Formulation

When the pesticide is an active acid or base which can be prepared in the form of a salt and used in water solution, the formulator has some choice, determined largely by solubility and economic considerations, but there may be influence on biological effects. The form of the residue left on the leaf after evaporation may range from a viscous solution, probably super-saturated, to a cluster of crystals of low solubility giving very different opportunity for leaf penetration or pick-up by insects. A more fundamental change in the case of an active acid, is to replace the salt by an oil-soluble ester. This will generally increase penetration of the leaf cuticle but hydrolysis may be necessary for the pesticidal biochemical action, and if hydrolysis is slow other chemical action or evaporative loss may reduce activity. Thus esters of 2,4-D are generally more active but rather less selective than salts while esters of 2,3,6-TBA are almost inactive on the target, but, evaporating before hydrolysis, can extend some effect beyond the target. Esters of the corresponding benzyl alcohol are more active, although oxidation is necessary.

The ester formulations can have economic or convenience advantages. For instance, the alkali metal salts of 2,4-D have too low solubility to be useful: an amine salt is necessary; mixed ethanolamines or dimethylamine are preferred. It may be cheaper to esterify with a moderately high-boiling alcohol than to neutralize with a more expensive amine. Both types of formulation are, in fact, available, supplying local preferences for different crops. An unexpected economic advantage of an ester was realized when trichloroacetic acid was used extensively for grass control from the air. The sodium salt is, of course, much cheaper than the methyl ester, but, on account of the rapid hydrolysis of the salt to bicarbonate and chloroform, it had to be supplied in solid form. A concentrated solution was necessary for economy in application from the air but took much too long to make up in the field, mixing tanks without heating becoming coated outside with ice.

These are examples of what is often called "chemical formulation". Other examples have appeared in the specialized chemical text of reactions which alter the physical properties without destroying the toxicity; sometimes even enhancing or creating it. Thioethers are oxidized *in vivo* to the more water-favourable sulphones, H_2S is released from chlorthiamid to give diclobenil, HCl is lost from trichlorphon and isomerization to dichlorvos follows, phosphorothionates can isomerize to phosphorthiolates or oxidize to phosphates. Many such reactions have appeared incidentally, it being first thought that the applied compound was the effective pesticide, but once established by biochemical examination, the reactions have been deliberately used as devices of chemical formulation. Others will follow. Systemic behaviour in plants requires the compound to be water-favourable but many good insecticides are highly oil-favourable. There is room therefore for more examination of reactions like the hydrolysis of half esters or amides of dibasic acids. Direct decarboxylation is much used in living processes to enable water-insoluble oils and fats to be synthesized in aqueous media, but no such reaction has yet been exploited in pesticide chemistry.

Corrosion

Corrosion of containers must always be considered in the choice of formulations and is generally a greater risk with aqueous concentrates than with anhydrous formulations. Even in this respect the aqueous concentrates of salts of "hormone" acids are satisfactory. They are generally made slightly alkaline and do not attack mild steel when the container is kept closed. A combination that must be avoided is excess ammonia and zinc-containing metals. Galvanized containers should always be avoided for pesticide storage, and hydrogen evolution is exceptionally rapid when aqueous ammonia is kept in them. Even the diluted product will attack brass filter gauze very rapidly. It is worth mentioning that metal pesticide containers are very often corroded from the *outside*. They should obviously be stored away from foodstuffs and this often means that they are kept on a damp floor, which may well have had fertilizer spilt on it. Even the acids from organic manures can be very aggressive. The containers should always stand on a clean, dry floor.

Dusts

The mineral bulk of a dust should be composed of rather coarser particles than are necessary in a wettable powder. Ideally they should also be more uniform in size. Too fine grinding or too wide a range of particle size results in a "claggy" product which does not flow well through the regulating gate of the dusting machine. When an over-fine powder is dispersed in an air blast, the wind-borne particles are mainly aggregates of the ultimate ones and often larger than are produced from a more free-flowing, coarser dust.

Ideally the smaller particles of the active pesticides should adhere to the coarser particles of the dust base so that the operator will know that, wherever the dust is visible, there will also be pesticide. This is not, however, as important in practice as might be expected; there is not much tendency, if all particles are below about 20 μ diameter, for significant "winnowing" according to particle size to occur. In perfectly still air, of course, differential settling would occur, but the free rate of fall is less than 2 cm/sec and, except under extreme inversion conditions, the turbulence of the air frequently lifts all particles up or brings them all down much more rapidly. Any small air volume does not deposit its contents until it has become very stagnant close to the ground or within the crop and then all particles are deposited.

The ideal dust is certainly not often produced. A dust must be much more dilute than the wettable powder because dusting machinery cannot generally discharge evenly less than about 10 or 20 kg to the hectare. Two to five per cent of active ingredient is usual. High transport costs dictate that some locally available mineral base be used and, as dust is sold in a cheap market, the cost of this base is often more important than its quality. Both the final formulation of the dust and the means of applying it are subject to much improvization. Many a peasant farmer has dusted his crop with a mixture of wettable powder and road dust mixed on the floor and shaken out through his wife's discarded — or not discarded — stocking.

There are, however, many efficient dusting machines available and a large area can be quickly and cheaply treated. A very common practice is for local formulating companies to blend a wettable powder with some local inert dust. The wetting agents present in the wettable powder serve no useful purpose in this case but they are not detrimental and there is convenience and economy in using the one product of the pesticide manufacturer for both final products of the local formulator.

Aerosol and other Automatic Dispensers

A very fine spray can be produced by discharging through a small orifice a liquid which is contained in a pressure vessel above its boiling point. The issuing liquid is shattered more completely than in a normal spray nozzle operated under pressure, by a combination of three factors: (1) a small discharge orifice and thin issuing stream; (2) a liquid of very low viscosity; (3) the actual boiling of the liquid immediately the jet enters the air.

The method is expensive. Only small packages are feasible as they must withstand high pressure in storage. Moreover the need for an issuing stream of small cross-section limits their use to small spaces or areas. The jet is under control of a finger-button. The packages are non-returnable. They are suitable only for use in domestic premises, aircraft cabins, amateur glasshouses and small gardens where their great convenience and "instant" availability outweigh their high cost. Usually the cost of the active compound is only a small fraction of that of the total package.

The droplets are in the 10–50 μm diameter range, which can be obtained in large-scale operation only by an air-blast machine or a very high-speed rotating distributor. This range is particularly effective against flying insects. It can also yield a good deposit after penetrating fairly dense foliage, but is controllable only in still air conditions.

The aerosol insecticide dispenser has followed the development of similar packages for other uses — dispensers of disinfectants, deodorants, hair-lacquers, cleaning and polishing products. The manufacture and filling of containers is, in fact, normally carried out in factories specializing in these packages. The self-contained automatic dispenser can be adapted, as with the other above-mentioned products, to discharge other forms than sprays. A common alternative is a foam. A lower pressure and larger orifice are used and the liquid product is made much more viscous and has foam stabilizing agents incorporated. The dissolved — or emulsified — propellant expands when the pressure is released, giving a very visible and voluminous foam.

Foam products are made for dispensing cleaning materials and shaving soap. The method has been applied to herbicides for small garden use. A "spot" treatment of herbicide can be quickly given to rosette weeds in lawns or, with more care, to troublesome perennials such as bindweed in herbaceous borders. The advantage of the foam is that it "bulks out" the very low dosage necessary of a high concentration product so that the deposit is clearly visible and the operator knows what weeds he has already dealt with. It is desirable in this case that the foam should collapse after a few minutes in order to improve contact and minimize blowing in wind.

Because automatic pressurized dispensers must have a very small orifice in a nozzle system which cannot be dismantled, the fillings must be scrupulously free from suspended impurities. This necessitates a special standard of stability in storage and of freedom from corrosion. Often a specially purified active ingredient may be necessary.

Fluoroalkanes such as dichlorodifluoromethane (b.p. -28°C) and 1,1- and 1,2-dichlorotetrafluorethanes (b.p. $-2°$ to $+4°$) have been widely used as propellants for domestic dispensers, having the advantages of only slight odour, low toxicity and non-flammability. They have, however, come under suspicion of serious disturbance of the composition of the upper atmosphere. This is not due to their fluorine content directly but to their very great stability which could permit their slow upward escape into the ionosphere where chlorine could be liberated by photochemical reactions and lead to reduction of the ozone content which protects the earth's surface from very damaging radiation in the far ultra-violet. This possibility is difficult to prove or disprove and is a subject of active research, but meanwhile these compounds are being replaced in most countries by butane with the addition of a better solvent, or by methylchloride, which requires the use of a protective coating on the inside of the metal container, or in some cases, by carbon dioxide.

Smoke Generators

Smokes may be conveniently produced from specially fabricated smoke generators. These are available in various sizes. They are set into operation by ignition and are provided with a delay composition so that the house can be evacuated before the smoke composition itself comes into action. Generators of this type were first developed during World War II for military remote signalling purposes for which it was desired to have smoke plumes of different colours. It was found possible to make such smokes from quite complex organic dyestuffs. Indeed, rather unstable compounds can, surprisingly, survive treatment in a well-designed generator. Even the highly inflammable dinitro-ortho-cresol can be produced in smoked form, but is not (on grounds of toxic hazard) in commercial use.

In the self-contained smoke generator the compound to be vaporized and condensed is mixed with an oxidant and combustible material capable of generating a large amount of hot gas of non-oxidizing balance. Sodium chlorate and a solid carbohydrate is the most common mixture, the hot gas consisting of water vapour and carbon dioxide with a small proportion of carbon monoxide. Thus a mixture approximating to $2C_6H_{10}O_5 + 7NaClO_3$

giving $10H_2O + 9CO_2 + 3CO + 7NaCl$ is preferable to the mixture $2C_6H_{10}O_5 + 10NaClO_3$ giving $10H_2 + 12CO_2 + 3O_2 + 10NaCl$, but excessive CO can lead to ignition of the escaping gas.

The insecticide is protected from destructive oxidation (a) by the fact that sugars are exceptionally reactive with chlorate; (b) by the use of a slight deficiency, as above, in the amount of chlorate necessary for complete oxidation of the carbohydrate; and (c), if necessary, by the intimate mixture of chlorate and carbohydrate being formed into a coarser powder which is then mixed with the insecticide.

The design and filling of such smoke generators has to be carefully worked out by experience and accurately controlled. To avoid explosion the discharge orifice must not be too small. Rate of burning and danger of ignition of the issuing gas on contact with the air can be controlled by the degree of compression of the filling and incorporation in it of retarding agents such as ammonium chloride.

Dilution of the vapour with air before condensation, so that a fine smoke is produced, is achieved automatically by the turbulence set up by the high velocity of the jet of hot gas.

Azobenzene for mite control, lindane and parathion for general insect control, DDT, several of the bridged diphenyl acaricides, captan and dinocap fungicides and various proprietary mixtures are obtainable in smoke generators. Even pyrethrins can be put into smoke form without undue loss, when incorporated into the slow-burning coils used traditionally to distribute incense.

Granules

Granules can be made by several methods. Most dusts will aggregate to coarser particles in a fairly uniform way if tumbled in an oblique rotating drum — a concrete mixer, or the more refined pill-coating machine — while a liquid, preferably containing an adhesive substance, is sprayed in at intervals. The process is more reliable if the initial mixture contains a proportion of coarser particles to act as nuclei. Pastes, if rubbed through a sieve before drying, especially if they contain a self-setting component such as plaster of Paris, are easily broken down into fairly uniform granules after drying.

These methods, which require experience and "know how" for success, are well adapted to the manufacture of granules in which the active pesticide is incorporated at the start and present throughout the bulk of the finished granule. Most pesticide granules, however, are made by impregnation of dissolved pesticide into preformed, porous, inert granules or by sticking the powdered pesticide on to the outside of preformed inert granules, which, in this case, need not be porous. The last method is the most common and requires least research to bring into operation with a new pesticide. Suitable base material is sieved ground mineral matter — usually limestone or brick waste. Sieved crushed nutshell or corn-cob chips are also much used. Walnut shell base is already industrially available in the right size range as an abrasive for air-blast cleaning of internal combustion engines. The coating is accomplished by tumbling the base granules in a rotor, together with a suitable admixture of powdered pesticide and mineral dust, during addition of a water solution of a gum, a soluble cellulose derivative, high molecular weight polyethylene oxide or other adhesive.

There has recently been some production of "microgranules" with particle sizes in the 100–300 μm range. These can almost be considered as a coarse dust and they are usually distributed with air-flow assistance in a special machine, although the product is much more free-flowing than most dusts. Absence of very much smaller particles is the main reason for "clagginess" and bridging of orifices with ordinary dust formulations and this fine component must be eliminated from microgranules since the advantage claimed is reduction of drift hazard.

In this respect microgranules are a parallel and alternative development to controlled drop application (CDA) made possible by the development of spinning disc applicators. In both developments the object is to put the maximum proportion of the applied active ingredient in the most effective particle size. A much narrower particle-size spectrum can be obtained than with hydraulic spray nozzles and there is therefore greatly reduced wastage in unnecessarily large drops in order to avoid drift of undesirable small ones. Both developments are now being tested under different conditions against different targets and some results appear to be conflicting but there is little doubt that both will find a useful place in the near future.

Capture on impact, spreading and adhesion are very different between solid and liquid particles. Spherical solid particles, such as are produced by evaporation in flight of droplets with a heavy load of wettable powder, have very poor adhesion to dry foliage. Microgranules required to contaminate foliage must be non-spherical, perferably flat and, if possible, become sticky on exposure. Preparation of microgranules by the methods used for the normal size range is expensive but the small size permits methods based on air flotation to be used and with considerable economy.

Instant coffee, dried milk and other convenience food products have long been prepared by drying a spray in free fall through hot dry air. The method is more easily applied to pesticides since the starting liquid is factory-made and without food-value restrictions. If sufficient volume reduction occurs during drying and the liquid contains a film-forming solute, the droplet must collapse like a partly filled bag. Addition of hygroscopic solutes, such as the sugars in dried milk, can make the granules become sticky in moist air as is well demonstrated by instant coffee. This improvement in adhesion of microgranules carries the danger of clogging of distributing machinery unless special steps are taken to keep the product out of contact with moist air until it is dispersed or to ensure, by addition of agents, such as silica gel or anhydrous sodium sulphate, which can take up the first few per cent of water while remaining mechanically dry.

According to the method of manufacture and the solubility of the pesticide there is scope for variation of the rate of release of the pesticide from the granule. Obviously, if the pesticide has very low solubility in water and is contained within a very close-packed mineral matrix, it may take a long time to diffuse out, even if the granules are shaken in free water. Equally obviously, if the pesticide has a high solubility and forms only a thin envelope around the granule base, it will disperse in free water almost immediately. In moist soil, however, on to which most granules are distributed, the difference in action may be very much less. In one sense the pesticide in the second case is "available" immediately to any organism touching the granule. If, however, it is necessary that the pesticide should diffuse away from the location of the granule, this process is so much slower than that occurring within normal granules that the latter has little influence. If the formulator is to exploit logically the potential variation he can introduce, he must be well guided by the biologist about where, and how well distributed, the pesticide should be.

Delayed release has been successfully exploited to secure prolonged treatment of flowing water. Here the external resistance is low and mixing efficient so that very large "granules" can be used, which simplifies the technical problem. A more extreme form is the thick plastic strip for slow release of a volatile insecticide (usually dichlorvos) into the air of a room or store.

Generally any homogeneous body containing pesticide, filler and thermoplastic material will release its volatile or soluble content at a rate decreasing with exposure time. If the resistance is provided mainly by a surface layer or skin this tendency is reduced. Various other devices are being explored to make release rate more uniform including the chemical binding of some pesticides to functional groups in polymer chains. Release then depends on breakage of the bonds, usually by hydrolysis, but, of course, this method is only possible with some pesticides. Controlled release has achieved much more success and technical refinement in the pharmaceutical field than in agriculture for two very powerful reasons — a much higher cost per unit is acceptable and the product carries out its function in an aqueous environment at constant temperature and pH.

Baits

Baits may consist of palatable granules widely scattered in high dosage as, for example, in the control of immature "hopper" locusts, or used in a much more localized manner. Local baits may incorporate attractant substances or be shaped or coloured in a manner found to be attractive to the pest. In such applications the behaviour of each pest must be exploited. It is not possible to deal with this subject in a general way from the point of view of formulation. It is hoped that enough has been said to illustrate the forms in which the pesticide itself can be used and the problems likely to be encountered in meeting the particular requirements of the biologist — or rather of the pest as interpreted by the biologist. As always, storage tests for continued efficacy are an important feature of the formulator's work. The more complex the formulation and the more it must meet specific requirements not fully understood, the more must reliance be placed on actual performance against the pest in question, after realistic periods of storage under practical conditions.

Use Problems

The manufacturer cannot anticipate all the problems which the user of his product may meet. He can help the user avoid some mistakes by adequate and clear instructions. There is need for more general instruction in some basic rules of use of pesticides. It is well known that instructions are often not read. The formulator should try to make his product serviceable even if not used quite in the way intended, but in doing so he may have to make it fall short of the best performance if used correctly.

Formulations are often blamed for faults which lie in inadequate maintenance of distributing machinery. The commonest faults of this kind are:

1 Excessive frothing in the spray tank. It is difficult to use wetting agents, which may be essential for good biological effect, without to some extent stabilizing foam, but to create the foam, air must have been introduced into the liquid. Only the wettable powder can itself introduce air. The commonest way in which unwanted air gets into the tank contents is through a leak on the suction side of a pump used for return-to-tank agitation.It is more profitable to tighten a gland than to blame the formulation.

2 Filter or nozzle blockage. A bad formulation can cause this trouble. More often it is caused by a dirty water supply or a machine brought out of haphazard winter storage and not cleaned out. Water may be fit to drink but not fit to spray. The clear waters of the trout stream — which does not often flow through agricultural land — may contain insect parts, ribbon diatoms, and seedhairs which species of willow scatter in abundance in the cereal-spraying season. The proportion is not high but it builds up on the

wire mesh to form a closer mesh which eventually filters out the formulation powder and blocks flow completely.

3 Inadequate mixing of concentrate and dilution water. Mixing of emulsifiable concentrates or wettable powders is often done with needless energy, but the stirring of a solution concentrate is often neglected. To invert the tank of a knapsack sprayer two or three times is quite adequate, but it is quite essential.

4 Inadequate washing out. Corrosion products and dried formulations can produce filter-blocking scale in pipework. The time to wash out a sprayer is immediately after use, particularly if a formulation of insoluble pesticide has been used. One should not blame the next formulation used if this elementary precaution is not taken.

Further Reading

Advances in Chemistry Series, No. 86, Pesticide Formulation Research, Amer. Chem. Soc., Washington D.C., 1975.

Agricultural Publishing Centre, *Proc. 4th International Aviation Congress*, Wageningen, 1971.

Deutsch, A. E. and Poole A. P. *Manual of Pesticide Application Equipment*, Oregon State University, 1972.

Hartley, G. S. and Graham-Bryce, I. J. *Physical Principles of Pesticide Behaviour*, 2 vols, esp. Chapters 4 and 14, Academic Press, London, 1980.

Kanmer, B., Reid, W. G. and Petersen, H. Synthesis and properties of siloxcene-polyether copolymer surfactants, *I. & E. C. Res. & Dev.* (1967) **6**, 89.

Maas, W. *ULV Application and Formulation Techniques*, N. V. Philips-Duphar, Amsterdam, 1971. Monograph No. 18, *Granular Pesticides*, British Crop Protection Council, 1976.

Matthews, G. A., *Pesticide Application Methods*, Longmans, London, 1979.

Society of Chemical Industry, Monographs 21 and 29, London, 1966 and 1968.

Tahori, A. S. (ed.) *Herbicide and Fungicide Formulation Chemistry*, Gordon & Breach, New York, 1972.

United Nations Industrial Development Organization, *Formulation of Pesticides in Developing Countries*, New York, 1983.

Van Walkenburg, W. *Pesticide Formulations* Marcel Dekker, New York, 1973.

23

Fumigants

Fumigation

In practical pest control the word "fumigation" is restricted to operations where a special method of application is required or permitted because of the high volatility of the toxicant employed. There are numerous special situations in which fumigation is used, e.g. hydrogen cyanide against rabbits, moles and wasps, but the major operations are four: (1) the treatment of empty transport containers, grain stores, warehouses, glasshouses, etc., to clean up residual pest populations between storage or cropping uses; (2) the treatment of grain or other harvested products prior to or during storage; (3) the treatment of soil to destroy pests, particularly nematodes difficult to control by other methods, and (4) disinfection of animal skins, etc. by quarantine authorities.

These different situations call for different properties in the chemical. The first calls for no selectivity. Ideally the building should be sterilized completely, but it is important that there should be, after an acceptable period of ventilation, no corrosive, toxic or tainting residue. The third might be highly demanding in selectivity if, for instance, it is desired to kill nematodes in the soil under a growing crop. Only to a very limited extent, with dibromochloropropane in citrus, has this yet been found possible. For the most part soil fumigation is done in the absence of a crop. Complete sterilization (including the killing of weed seeds) is therefore sought, but the toxic effect must, of course, be of limited duration.

A very important area nowadays for fumigation is aircraft. Cargo and passenger planes move continually from one part of the world to another in very short times and offer opportunities on a scale never approached in the past for transport of viable insect pests from one region to another. "Disinsection" of aircraft is now standard practice.

In practice, therefore, the first and third situations call for similar biological effects. In respect of physicochemical properties, however, they are very different. All parts of the empty warehouse are freely accessible to the main air space and distribution is assisted by stirring fans. The air space of the soil, however, is in close contact with an enormous area of adsorbing and chemically active surfaces: agitation is generally impracticable and molecular diffusion must be relied on for distribution of the toxicant.

The second situation is the one where choice of chemical is most restricted by the demand for no residual toxicity, no detectable residual taint and no effect on viability of seed. Physically, this situation is intermediate between the other two. A large surface is involved but it is smaller than in the soil case and there is no free water. Diffusion is often relied on but it is practicable in suitably designed storage bins to use forced air circulation. In fact numerous such bins are in use for the drying of grain freshly threshed from the standing crop.

All fumigation operations depend for their success on rapid diffusion or mixing of the toxic vapour into all parts of the air-space to be treated. It is a necessary corollary that the space to be treated must be sealed off from the outside air. Advantage is taken of sites which are naturally nearly closed, such as rabbit burrows and wasps' nests and of the fact that grain stores, being designed to prevent ingress of birds, mice, etc., are also closed habitats. Many buildings which are desirably disinfested by fumigation are, however, much less easily sealed and it should be mentioned that the use of fumigants has in recent years been greatly helped by another branch of the chemical industry — the plastics industry. Field clamps of stored vegetables, piled sacks of grain in arid regions, houses and even food factories have been completely covered by polyethylene or polyvinylchloride (PVC) sheeting to permit successful fumigation. Sheets laid on the soil surface, held down by a ploughed slice of soil around the edge, make practicable the use of methyl bromide sterilization. This compound diffuses very rapidly in soil and uneconomic dosage would be required if free escape were permitted.

Since most fumigants are gases at room temperature or liquids which can rapidly build up a high pressure of heavy vapour there is considerable possibility of layering of concentration. With care and experience this tendency can be relied on to assist mixing, since deep but localized penetration can be allowed to occur by convection before forced mixing is commenced. Even in soil, when using methyl bromide, it is found that deeper penetration occurs when the application is made in spots than when made in lines. Least penetration occurs from a surface application where there is rapid initial spread under the sheet. The extent of convective penetration increases with the vapour density. It is much greater with methyl bromide than with the much less volatile ethylene dibromide. It does not occur with hydrogen cyanide (mol wt 27) nor significantly with formaldehyde (mol wt 30) as even the pure gases differ very little in density from air. The former is the only lighter-than-air fumigant in use.

The fumigation of stored products, although having to meet more exacting standards, can be carried out by more sophisticated methods than fumigation of soil. The high value of the products allows more expenditure and their generally dry nature simplifies handling and permits less stable products to be used than in soil.

Methods of filling large plastic containers have been evolved in which the product is completely sealed, containing only its interstitial air which is rather less than half the total volume. If no external air can gain access, there is only enough oxygen to oxidize about 0.4% of the carbohydrate of the grain to carbon dioxide. It is evident that pest insects will be completely asphyxiated before much of the grain is attacked. There may be problems of taint, varying according to the product stored, and seed grain slowly loses its viability under anoxic storage, but the method is cheap once the plastic containers are obtained.

Much grain is treated with insecticide before it is put into storage. Forced air fumigation in the drying towers is one method. Spraying on a conveyor belt with an insecticide of acceptably low toxicity and not necessarily volatile — pyrethrum or malathion — is another. Two devices can improve the efficiency of transient fumigation treatment and, since they reduce the amount of toxic substance used, they help to achieve an acceptably low residue. The first is the introduction of carbon dioxide, up to about 5% of the air content, along with the toxic vapour. The increased efficiency is probably due to increased respiration. The second is the reduction of pressure of the whole air content. If a completely filled container is used, there is no need for strong walls, the compressive strength of the bulk grain being sufficient to resist distortion. There is some doubt about the mechanism of the improvement by "vacuum" treatment and it is not uniformly effective with all pests and toxicants. When a pile of grain sacks or cotton bales has the air partially removed before fumigant is introduced and pressure is then restored, the fumigant is driven into the interior of the units more effectively than if diffusion alone is relied on.

Grain, as might well be expected, is more vulnerable if stored at a high moisture content, particularly to initial fungus damage which can then create "hot spots" attractive to insects. Moisture content is particularly important for direct effect of the chemical on viability of the seed. The dry seed is relatively resistant but the chemical must be removed by ventilation before the seed is sown. A moisture content of around 12–16%, depending on the kind of grain, is critical.

Fumigation of viable plants for quarantine purposes makes the most difficult demands on selectivity. The plants should be in a dormant phase, so maintained by low temperature (but not frozen) and in as dry a condition as is consistent with their survival. Excess soil should be removed to make the pests as accessible as possible to the fumigant. Hydrogen cyanide or methyl bromide are the chief agents used. The plants should be washed after exposure to cyanide but maintained dry and freely ventilated after exposure to methyl bromide.

Fumigants

Probably because all the fumigants have small molecules gaining access via the tissues adapted to gas exchange, they show little biochemical selectivity. They are used in high concentration and their use has therefore special danger. The operators must have special training and equipment. The problems of use will be illustrated with special reference to the two most widely used compounds — hydrogen cyanide and methyl bromide — and a summary of the important properties of other commercially used compounds follows.

Hydrogen cyanide is the most effective fumigant for empty buildings or containers, being the most rapidly and generally lethal of all readily available, very volatile substances. It is very soluble in water and easily adsorbed on protein and cellulosic fibres and reacts rapidly in the adsorbed state. It has therefore poor penetrating properties and finds little use in the treatment of stored grain and none in the treatment of soil.

The high chemical reactivity of hydrogen cyanide ensures satisfactorily low residues, the hydrolysis product, ammonium formate, easily oxidized to the carbonate, being quite harmless at practical levels. Safety with regard to residue is helped also by the behaviour of hydrogen cyanide itself as a toxicant. It is the classic example of a very potent but essentially acute poison since long-term, low-level intake has no toxic effects.

It will be seen that the danger of cyanide lies in its very rapid effect at high concentration. Handling the concentrate therefore requires proper equipment and training. It should never be undertaken by untrained workers and it is of special importance that no operator with the concentrate should be alone. A man overcome by cyanide can recover completely if he is at once dragged away from the source.

Anhydrous hydrogen cyanide boils at 26°C and is therefore supplied in pressure cylinders. It is an endothermic compound and can explode by a chain reaction initiated from an alkaline source which may be a metal oxide contamination in the container. For this reason it is always supplied containing about 0.2% of anhydrous oxalic acid in solution, but, even so, should not be stored in a hot place. It is sometimes supplied adsorbed on to discs of solid adsorbent. It can also be generated on site by dropping the sodium salt, which is indefinitely stable and without explosive hazard if stored dry, into excess of fairly strong sulphuric acid (if the sodium salt solution is only partly acidified, a black polymer is precipitated, from a reaction between the free acid and its anion).

Methyl bromide (b.p. 4.5°) is easily vaporized but can be packaged in light-wall pressure vessels. It is recommended for empty buildings at about 40 g/m^3, which is about five times the dose of hydrogen cyanide, but it is effective in both stored grain and soil at a comparable overall concentration.

Chief Other Fumigants

Compound and b.p.	Partition Water/Air 20°	Reactions	Chief use	Special remarks
Sulphur dioxide gas	80	Oxidized on surfaces	Empty buildings	Residue corrosive
Ethylene oxide 14°	200	Addition to $-OH_2-NH_2$ etc	Stored grain	Not seed grain. Explosive hazard
Methyl formate 31°	300	Hydrolysis	Furs and skins	—
Methyl isothiocyanate 35°	300	Hydrolysis and oxidation	Soils	Generated in situ from sodium N-methyl dithiocarbamate
Formaldehyde gas	500	Oxidation	Surface soil against "damping off"	—
Carbon tetrachloride 80°	1	Stable	Assists penetration of grain	Suspected carcinogen Inhibits explosion of carbon disulphide
Chloropicrin 112°	18	Hydrolysis	Soils	Added to cyanide or methyl bromide as sensory warning
Carbon disulphide 46°	1	Oxidation	Soils, esp. against fungi	Danger of explosion: wide concentration limits
Phosphine gas	—	Oxidation	Stored grain	Generated in situ by moisture on aluminium phosphide
Ethylene dibromide 131°	45	Stable	Soil, harvested fruit and vegetables	Suspected carcinogen
Ethylene dichloride 84°	30	Stable	Grain, in mixtures	—
Dichloropropene mixtures 78°	ca 20	Stable	Soils esp v nematodes	—
Dibromochloropropane	ca 50	Stable	Soils esp v nematodes	Now banned in U.S.A. except on Pineapples in Hawaii.

It owes this advantage to its much lower affinity for polar substances. The volumetric partition ratio between water and air is only 4:1 at 20°C compared with *ca* 300:1 for hydrogen cyanide. In consequence a lower proportion is removed from the diffusible continuous vapour phase and held back in discrete phases. It is, moreover, less reactive, undergoing rapid hydrolysis only in media more alkaline than are met in stored vegetable products or soil. In dilute solution in water, buffered at pH 7, its half life is about three weeks at 20°C. A lower rate of decomposition therefore occurs during a more rapid transport process and a higher proportion reaches remote sites. It must disappear from buildings and soil by diffusion and ventilation. It tends, of course, to be retained in fatty substances and sufficient time must therefore be allowed for oily seeds to lose the toxicant before they are allowed to take up moisture for germination.

Methyl bromide has the disadvantage that its toxic action is more insidious than that of hydrogen cyanide. Its maximum permissible concentration is only twice as great and it is undetectable by smell at a concentration which can produce serious effects after a few hours' exposure. For these reasons it is normally supplied containing a few percent of chloropicrin as a warning agent.

While ethylene dibromide (b.p. 131°) is used in open agriculture by simple injection into soil, methyl bromide is introduced under temporary impermeable sheets since it would otherwise escape too quickly. This is not because its vapour concentration is hundred times as great, since normal rates of both evaporate completely in the soil air space (5 cm depth of air over an acre would accommodate 20 kg of EDB as vapour). In dry sand the loss would be determined only by rate of gas diffusion which does not greatly differ between compounds. The greater retention is due to greater partition in favour of water (45:1 compared with 4:1) and greater adsorption on soil solids.

Further Reading

Hough, W. S. and Mason, A. F. *Spraying, Dusting and Fumigating Plants*, Macmillan, New York, 1951
Monro, H. A. U. *Manual of Fumigation for Insect Control*, Agricultural Studies, No. 56, FAO, Rome, 1961.

24

Pest Resistance

Resistance of Insects and Mites

In any species of a living organism individual susceptibility to poisonous substances will vary considerably. So, in large populations of insects and mites, there will always be a proportion of individuals who are naturally resistant to a particular pesticide and who will survive doses of it which are lethal to the rest of the population. If generation time is short and treatment with the same pesticide is repeated frequently the resistant strain survives and increases in numbers and eventually comprises the bulk of the population. Resistance can develop very rapidly if a steady and drastic selection pressure is exerted. Resistance is, however, less likely to develop when the kill achieved by each spraying is poor, treatment is intermittent and generation time is long.

Some species will be effectively resistant when they first encounter a particular pesticide. Resistance may be naturally present in one strain of a species even though all other strains are susceptible. More generally, resistant strains arise when the whole population has been selected by killing off the susceptible individuals. In all these situations the organism has an intrinsic potential to develop a genotype which can cope successfully with the toxicant. It matters little whether the genes necessary for resistance already exist in high frequency or low frequency or whether they are developed by mutation during exposure to the toxicant. The ultimate result in every case is a population which can withstand the toxicant more effectively.

At one time biologists believed that resistance genes were extremely rare in wild populations which had never been exposed to pesticides. Now, however, the general view is that most natural populations of any pest have sufficient genetic diversity to develop resistance to any pesticide, and that whether this happens, and the speed at which it happens are determined by the ecology of the pest, by the nature of the selection pressure, and by the genetic nature of the system confering resistance. Very little is in fact known about the factors which govern the development of resistance in the field and this is an area of knowledge in which much more information is needed if pesticides are to be used in the safest and most effective manner.

The first example of a pest species developing resistance appeared in California in the 1920s. It had become the practice to control a scale insect in citrus orchards by enveloping the individual trees in mobile tents into which gaseous hydrogen cyanide was introduced. After some years it was no longer possible to control the pest without so greatly increasing concentration or exposure time that the trees were directly damaged. About the same time in Queensland strains of cattle ticks evolved which were no longer controlled by the arsenical dips which had been in use for many years.

Despite these known examples, DDT was at first hailed, during World War II, as the miracle insecticide which would solve all insect pest problems and it came as a new surprise to many people when resistant bodylice appeared in Korea, resistant mosquitoes in India and resistant houseflies in many parts of the world. Resistance is now very widespread. Nearly all established insecticides have induced resistance somewhere in some of the 200 and more species about which there are clear records. At least 104 species of insects of public health importance are now resistant to one or more pesticides. In many localities wild strains now fail to respond to applications of quantities even a hundred or more times greater than were previously adequate.

Mites, because of their short generation period, are particularly prone to develop resistance rapidly. During the period 1952–1973, 20 different acaricides were recommended for use in apple orchards by the U.S. Agricultural Extension Service. Of these, 15 have now been discontinued because of development of resistance. In Australia, the cattle tick has become resistant to practically all the chemical control agents which have been introduced during the past 20 years.

Resistant insects are sometimes compared to the fabled human opium or arsenic eaters, capable of handling heroic doses of these poisons. There is the very important difference that the insect *population* becomes resistant by selective breeding, whereas the habituated human has adapted himself as an *individual* by slowly increased intake. There is no known adaptation of the individual insect to pesticides. The pest insect is normally short-lived in an environment made hostile by many factors other than the pesticide. It will either survive its single contact with an insecticide, be killed by it, or be so incapacitated that it will succumb to some other enemy.

Resistance is now closely studied in many laboratories. Not only is it desirable to know the performance of a new insecticide against strains already resistant to established insecticides, but also how quickly a new strain, resistant to the new insecticide, can be developed. Resistant strains are produced by breeding under what is called high insecticide pressure. The environment of the breeding stock is contaminated in some standard way which kills the majority of the insects before they reach the breeding stage. The progeny of the survivors have usually rather greater chance of survival and the degree of contamination is increased for each successive generation. In this way special stocks have been bred which are, in some instances, several thousand times more resistant than the original.

The mechanism of resistance can be morphological, behavioural or biochemical. By morphological is meant the development of some structure in the insect which reduces the dose transferred to the vital site. For example the cuticle may become considerably thickened or the legs become less hairy and so have less tendency to retain contaminating particles. By behavioural is meant a change in the behaviour of the insect which brings it less into contact with the insecticide. For example insecticides are often applied to internal wall surfaces and kill flies and mosquitoes by contact. Contact is made most efficiently by walking, less efficiently by resting on the surface and not at all in flight. Therefore a change from restless walking activity to an alternation between flight and rest makes the insecticide less effective.

Such modifications have undoubtedly arisen and are rather general in their effects. The physical properties of the insecticide, particularly melting point, crystal shape and vapour pressure, are more important for morphological or behavioural resistance than are differences in chemical reactions. Morphological or behavioural changes rarely give rise to a very high degree of resistance.

Resistance could also arise if the insecticide fails to reach the site of biochemical action, or does so at a slower rate. This could happen as a result of (a) failure to penetrate the cuticle in sufficient amount; (b) an increase in the rate of excretion of the pesticide; (c) storage of the pesticide in inert fat deposits. It has been shown that movement of some insecticides into and through the cuticle of susceptible strains of houseflies is two to five times more rapid than for resistant strains. There is some evidence that DDT-resistant larvae of tobacco budworm may have higher sclerotin levels in the cuticle than susceptible larvae and that this may bind a higher proportion of the applied DDT. A number of instances of diazinon resistance have been correlated with binding to tissues. BHC-resistance in one strain of housefly has been associated with a threefold increase in cuticular absorption.

The above effects are essentially biophysical. However, very high degrees of specific resistance are almost always the result of additional biochemical effects, in particular, an increase in the ability of the insect or mite to detoxify the pesticide by means of some enzymatic reaction. It appears that enzyme systems capable of detoxifying most insecticides exist naturally in insects but generally at too low a level to be an effective protection to the organism. Those individuals which appear to possess a high degree of natural resistance merely possess the detoxifying enzyme systems at a higher level of activity. This is determined by particular genes and so it can be seen why a severe selection pressure may rapidly increase the genetic purity of the resistant strains.

Study of the genetics of insect resistance reveals a complex situation. When insecticidal pressure is removed, an isolated laboratory colony becomes generally more sensitive again through succeeding generations, but resistance is much more persistent in some strains than others. If allowed, in the absence of insecticide, to interbreed with the original stock, the colony loses resistance more quickly but some resistant individuals may be found after many generations. The resistance is usually a dominant characteristic but may be associated with other characteristics less favourable to survival in an environment free from insecticide. Under field conditions, where associated undersirable characteristics would be more important, one would expect reversion to type to be more rapid.

Generally a strain selected under pressure from one insecticide will show resistance, as would be expected, to a closely related compound (e.g. DDT and methoxychlor), but not to unrelated compounds. In this respect the cyclodiene compounds behave as closely related to one another, but distinct from DDT, with BHC usually coming into the cyclodiene group. Resistance to organochlorine insecticides does not usually confer resistance to organophosphorus insecticides, but resistance to organophosphorus insecticides often gives a very pronounced cross-resistance to organochlorine insecticides. The reason for this is not known. Resistance to organophosphorus insecticides also often confers resistance to carbamate insecticides but this is not surprising as they both have the same toxic mechanism, namely, inhibition of cholinesterase. Multiple resistance — i.e. simultaneous resistance to a number of unrelated insecticides — can be induced in strains subjected to pressure from all these insecticides, but it can also appear when pressure has apparently been from one insecticide only. However, in such cases, it often happens that the resistance is not of a very high order and that a small increase in dosage of the insecticide can produce an acceptable level of kill. Such resistance is, therefore, most probably morphological or behavioural in origin.

However, cross resistance is a very complicated problem because insects with a high degree of resistance induced by pressure from one specific insecticide and almost certainly biochemical in origin are often found to be resistant to unrelated insecticides.

An example is the pattern of resistance found by exposure of houseflies to DDT, γ-BHC or dilan (= DDT with the three aliphatic Cl atoms replaced by H, NO_2 and CH_3 or C_2H_5). In strain 1, DDT resistance was associated with cross-resistance not only to methoxychlor but also to the quite unrelated pyrethrins. This strain remained susceptible to γ-BHC, dieldrin and thanite. Strain 2, almost completely resistant to γ-BHC, displayed slight cross-resistance to DDT only. Strain 3, resistant to dilan, was resistant also to DDT and, slightly, both to dieldrin and γ-BHC.

By interbreeding strains of houseflies resistant to organochlorine and organophosphorus insecticides it has been possible to study the genes that confer resistance to them. These genes are situated on chromosomes 2,3,4 and 5. Some are dominant, some are recessive and others intermediate. All appear to exist as alleles; the different members of the allelic groups confer resistance of different intensities. Three major genes appear to control resistance to organochlorine insecticides: *Deh* a dominant on chromosome 2, *kdr* and *kdr-o* recessive genes on chromosome 3 and *md* an intermediate dominant on chromosome 5. *Deh* controls dehydrochlorination and confers resistance to those organochlorines that are readily dehydrochlorinated. *kdr* and *kdr-o* confer resistance to knockdown by DDT and are thought to diminish nervous sensitivity. Several genes are known to confer resistance to organophosphorus insecticides. Houseflies can resist insecticides from most chemical groups by means of more than one breakdown mechanism. Often several such mechanisms can coexist within the same insect. Individual mechanisms can prolong (a) protection against most insecticides of a given group, e.g. most of the chlorinated insecticides; (b) protection against a limited number of compounds within a group, e.g. only against DDT and TDE; (c) activation against insecticides of different groups, e.g. diazinon and DDT; or (d) act as modifiers that manifest themselves only when other mechanisms are present. The mechanism delaying penetration of insecticides controlled by the dominant gene *Pen* is an example of (d). Synergists may be too specific and so increase rather than decrease resistance, e.g. sesamex acts as a synergist to organophosphorus compounds degraded by oxidases but with genes which control a modified carboxyesterase and gene *gst* which controls glutathione-S-transferase, sesamex acts as an antagonist and confers increased resistance.

Much chemical and testing effort is devoted not only to the search for insecticides which will defeat existing resistance, but in the hope that some will be found much less prone to induce resistance. That this may be possible has been shown in a manner extremely interesting to the chemist, but probably without commercial future, by the finding that as small a change as the substitution by deuterium (D) of the lone H atom in the centre of the DDT molecule produces a compound fully effective against DDT-resistant strains of *Musca* and *Aedes*. In the case of *Aedes*, many generations under laboratory pressure from deutero-DDT have increased the resistance by a much smaller factor than in parallel experiments with normal DDT. Resistance is due to the existence of an enzyme called DDT-dehydrochlorinase which is specifically active in dehydrochlorinating the molecule. It would seem that the activation energy for removal of DCl is just sufficiently greater than that for removal of HCl to put the reaction out of reach. More practical, but not very potent, compounds which have shown no tendency, in laboratory rearing programmes, to induce resistance are the bromo-acetic esters referred to below, particularly the 2,4,6-trichlorophenyl ester.

Cross-resistance is the exception rather than the rule, but it has usually been found in laboratory tests that a strain already resistant to one insecticide can develop resistance, under pressure from a second insecticide, more quickly than the original strain. It almost seems that insects can "get into the habit" of breeding resistance. The opposite phenomenon to cross-resistance is, however, known. A strain of *Drosophila* highly resistant to DDT was found to be more sensitive than the normal strain to bromoacetic esters. Similarly, it has been shown that BHC resistant flies are more susceptible to knockdown by halohydrocarbon narcotics such as chloroform than are non-resistant flies. This is a predictable effect based on biophysical considerations. It is possible that alternate use of insecticides negatively correlated with regard to resistance could help to ameliorate the resistance problem.

Resistance in Relation to Manner of Use

Until compounds have been discovered to which insects cannot develop resistance and which are also economic, increasing attention must be given to the strategy and tactics of use of existing insecticides. It is evident that certain general conditions are necessary to induce resistance. *If* it could be arranged that the individuals in a wild population were *either* subjected to so high a dose that they had no chance of survival *or* were not subjected to the insecticide at all, no selection could occur. Even were the dose in the first group not adequate, selection would be improbable were there a sufficiently well-mixed population of individuals not exposed, because interbreeding would eliminate the resistant characteristic, if associated, as is generally the case, with some characteristic disadvantageous in a normal environment. Resistance development is most favoured by subjection of all the individuals in an island population to a significant, but not always lethal, exposure. A population is effectively an island one if it occupies an area so large, in relation to the mobility of the species, that interbreeding with an outside population is unimportant. Widespread use of an insecticide leaving a persistent deposit, active by contact, provides the most suitable environment for the development of resistance.

This is why this phenomenon became of such great importance after the introduction of the stable organochlorine compounds. Persistence must not, however, be overemphasised, since the earliest resistant strains were induced by treatment with the most transient of poisons, hydrogen cyanide.

It is widespread use throughout an island community that is particularly likely to create resistance. The extremely persistent organochlorine compounds have been the most effective inducers of resistance, not so much directly because of their persistence, but because this property assists their distribution throughout the environment. Their low cost and apparent safety to mammals also, of course, promoted carelessly extensive application in the early days, which greatly aggravated the problem.

There are several modifications of strategy which have been advocated to avoid the development of resistance. The first is moderation, to the point of apparent inefficiency, in the use of the insecticide. If, instead of aiming to control the pest on all the land carrying the particular crop in a selected area, there were left a well-distributed pattern of untreated pockets, interbreeding of the survivors from the treated areas with the untreated population might prevent resistance developing. The pest would be less well controlled at first and the competing companies in the chemical industry would not find it desirable to advise the apparently inefficient use of their products. Government legislation would be essential. If it were necessary to sacrifice not only pockets of crop on one holding but complete holdings in a peasant community, a political problem would at once arise. It should be emphasized that, for success of this plan, some areas should receive at least the full dosage and others none. A reduced dosage throughout the area is more likely to aggravate resistance build-up.

Another plan is to arrange for alternation in the pesticide used — say an organochlorine for two years, then an organophosphorus for two, and so on. The plan would be most likely to succeed were the compounds known to show no tendency to cross-resistance but rather the reverse — the strains resistant to one being more sensitive to the other — as in an example, unfortunately using one rather feeble insecticide, quoted above. Such an arrangement would be difficult to enforce in a community of separate farmers. Obviously, trade in insecticides can be more easily controlled by government than can their use in the field. If both insecticides had a rather short storage life, control of supplies might be adequate.

A third plan, or perhaps more a combination of details, in which education and propaganda would be the chief activity of government, is the more cautious and selective use of pesticides. This would include the discouragement of widespread prophylactic use of insecticides leaving a persistent residue, an improved system of warning of potential pest build-up and the encouragement of localized application rather than overall spraying.

Together with all these measures a greater use of biological control and conservation of predators and parasites is desirable. The aim should be a total system of pest management involving the wise use of selective pesticides with full consideration, as far as knowledge permits, of the interactions of species.

Effects on Predators, Parasites and Population Balance

Apart from differences in individual susceptibility to a particular pesticide within a species, there may be gross differences in susceptibility between one species and another. In the extreme, some species may be totally unaffected by the dose applied. If this is so, then application of the pesticide may remove the predators and parasites which normally hold the resistant species in check. Even if the species has no predators or parasites the effect of removing competition for food, light, water, etc. may be sufficient to allow the resistant species to become dominant. The total effect of using the pesticide may, therefore, be to create conditions in which a previously minor pest can flourish. A notorious example of this is the red spider mite on fruit trees. Prior to the introduction of DDT this had been only a minor pest because it was held in check by predators and by competition. It was not affected by DDT, which killed practically all the fruit tree insects, including some mite predators. As a result of widespread and injudicious use of DDT in orchards red spider mite became, and still is, a major pest to fruit growers.

It might appear from this that the desirable aim is always to discover insecticides which attack only the specific target pest and nothing else. This is a good aim if you can be quite sure that the target pest is the only species which is, or could be, a pest to that particular crop. In commercial glasshouses biological control methods using introduced predators of the pest insect have been widely investigated. This method of control is highly specific to the particular pest but this specificity can, in practice, be a disadvantage if some minor pests are present which can become major pests themselves if competition from the original major pests is removed. In such circumstances, better overall results can be achieved by using a general insecticide which kills major and minor pests alike.

Nevertheless where a pest is mainly kept in check by predators or parasites any reduction in populations or activities of these predators or parasites could lead to an enormous increase in a pest problem. Long-term effects on population numbers may completely outweigh any short-term advantage gained by application of insecticides.

The above discussion illustrates the need to consider pest management as a total problem and not just to use insecticides in isolation. The correct choice of pesticide and of its method and timing of application demands an extensive knowledge of the ecology of the pest and of its relationships with other species.

Agricultural pest insects are necessarily herbivorous, that is, they feed on plant tissue although, in the case of some sucking insects they do far more damage by transmission of virus than by direct consumption of the crop. The predators and parasites of agricultural pest insects are carnivorous. The ideal agricultural insecticide might be one that could make this very broad distinction. The biochemical processes of herbivorous and carnivorous insects may have some characteristic differences dependent on the biochemical differences between the two sorts of feed. So far no selectivity based on this difference is known, nor, in the writers' knowledge, deliberately sought. The difference is obscured by several factors. Insects of many families, while structurally closely related, have adapted themselves to very different feeding situations. For example, the family Syrphidae, of the order Diptera (flies) includes some of the small hoverflies characteristically predators of aphids, but also feeders on the tissues of growing plants and fungi and scavengers of decaying organic matter. Habits of feeding and movement do not therefore follow genetic relationships. Biochemical processes tend to be more closely coupled with genetic relationships than with feeding habits.

The differences between pest and beneficial insects most likely to influence their response to insecticides arise therefore from the habits themselves and the different opportunities they create for exposure to the insecticide. Most herbivorous insects are (in the feeding stage) slow-moving and hidden, either because they burrow into the crevices between leaves, form tunnels within leaves or stems, or produce leaf-curling or gall-formation. While parasites are also hidden, they need to be more mobile than their hosts in the egg-laying adult stage because they have to seek out a smaller food source. Predators are necessarily more mobile because they must seek out small prey to devour in numbers.

A spray directed generally into the air, regardless of season, would therefore be likely to hit a higher proportion of parasites and predators than of pests. A persistent surface deposit active by contact with walking insects is, by and large, more effective against beneficial than against pest insects. That it often serves, in fact, a very useful crop-protective function depends a great deal on timing and placement. No matter how chemically stable the compound, it is bound to be most active on crop foliage during and shortly after spraying. During spraying, accessible insects can be directly hit. After some days there will be some loss by physical factors of weathering and dilution of the overall surface concentration of deposit by growth of the crop.

The success of a persistent general insecticide applied at the right time is usually achieved despite reduction of the parasites and predators. A low dosage of some very selective insecticide can reduce the pest population to a level which can be held in check by the remaining parasites and predators. A non-selective insecticide can achieve a more complete clean-up but has had to brush aside the help it might have had from beneficial insects. As these decline and as resistance in the pest perhaps develops, higher dosages are found necessary. In any plan of integrated control, the moderate dosage of selective insecticide will always be preferred.

The systemic insecticides show a high degree of selectivity by automatic correct placement, quickly retreating within the plant tissue and becoming directly available only to leaf-eating or sucking insects. If parasites or predators are killed, it is because they consume already poisoned pests. Three factors safeguard them to some extent. A sucking pest already affected is less attractive than a healthy one. Some decomposition of the insecticide occurs in the body of the pest. Finally, and most important, the first water-soluble systemic compounds were intrinsically more toxic to aphids and spider mites than to most other insects. This was, of course, a disadvantage when the pest is a leaf-eating or stem-boring one, and was not planned. Effective systemics of a wider spectrum of action are now appearing and may make the safety of beneficials less secure.

The generally greater mobility of beneficial predators and parasites than of pests has another important effect on the balance as affected by insecticides. If the beneficials are eliminated, and the pests reduced, in a local treated area, the beneficials from the surrounding untreated area can invade the treated area and clean up the residual pest. It therefore pays to leave pockets or strips untreated or to treat these strips at different times. Similar strip-harvesting of a crop suitable for this method — e.g. alfalfa (lucerne) in California — is another practice recommended by the protagonists of integrated control, in order to conserve the mobile beneficials.

An advantage claimed for insecticidal control measures moderated in some way to leave predators and parasites in action is that the development of resistant strains is made less likely. Although the residual population of pest may contain a higher proportion of resistant individuals, the parasite or predator will kill these off. There is some dispute whether this statistical argument is valid without some factor of discrimination. It is, for instance, likely that a resistant individual, being more healthy than its neighbours after ingestion of insecticide, would be sought out by a parasite, but clear experimental evidence is hard to obtain.

If it seems unreasonable that a species can develop resistance to an insecticide but not to a predator or parasite, it should be remembered that the insecticide is new but the natural enemy very old. Evolution has been going on many million times longer than exposure to insecticides. Doubtless many parasites have long ago become extinct because their hosts successfully developed resistance. Many species were preyed upon to extinction by a too successful predator. There are now left the species which have achieved a precarious balance in a world of ancient hostilities. Insecticides are a new factor in selection. After they have been used for many million years and most have been discarded, the situation may become much more stable.

Resistance and Predator Suppression

It may now be apparent why resistance and effect on natural enemies have been included in the same chapter. In the field it is often difficult to distinguish which has produced an observed decline in the effectiveness of an insecticide. The biologist must make laboratory observations on a pest population brought in from the field and tested in isolation before he can say with certainty that resistance has appeared. The effects tend also to be induced by the same defects in chemical properties or mode of application — excessive persistence and too widespread application.

The history of the cabbage-root-fly (*Erioischia brassicae*) in the U.K. provides an interesting example of resistance and predator suppression. It seemed easy to attack with a stable soil-applied insecticide. It could do considerable damage to the crop and could not be effectively controlled once the damage (plants wilting due to root destruction) was evident. General soil treatment in advance of planting was adopted. The practice brought about increase in the population of the fly through slaughter of its beetle predators. Damage in fields where no insecticide was used increased but good control could still be obtained by soil incorporation of dieldrin. There then appeared, in some areas of intensive *Brassica* cropping, strains of fly which were no longer controlled by this insecticide. Other compounds, such as diazinon, intrinsically less effective against the original strain, are holding the pest at present, but the grower is on balance in a worse position than before the first use of insecticides. Some authorities contend that had treatment been confined from the beginning to seasons when a bad outbreak was expected and had the treatment been localized by dipping, drenching or granule application to individual plants this undesirable development could have been avoided.

Resistance in insects and other arthropods is not necessarily detrimental to man's interests. It is most strikingly evident in rapidly breeding flies, aphids and mites, but parasitic and predatory flies, wasps and mites have also been shown to be capable of developing resistance. One of the problems of biological control is that, while it is very cheap and successful against some pests, it may have made no progress against other pests of the same crop. If insecticides are called in to deal with the latter, they upset the biological control of the former. The chemist may be able to produce an insecticide harmless to the parasite or predator. Alternatively the biologist may be able to breed a strain of parasite or predator sufficiently resistant to an established insecticide. As mentioned in Chapter 2, at least one example of this is already known and the search for more will be intensified.

The biological situation is immensely complex. There is no space in this book to deal with it more adequately, nor would the writers be competent to do so. They may already, in the interests of brevity, have made generalizations unacceptable to the expert. Their object has been to show that the use of insecticides is necessarily a subject of increasing complexity. The search for new insecticides is therefore one of increasing difficulty but also a stimulating challenge. The future research chemist in this field will meet endless frustrations if he is not prepared to let his biological colleagues teach him some of their problems. He must be prepared to give advice as well as take it and will then find that the pesticide field is so full of interest that the frustration is less important.

Whatever the future, the world of agricultural pests no longer lies at the feet of the chemist with the powerful, stable, general insecticide and the engineer with the long spray boom. The fact that agriculture in many of the developing countries employs much more hand labour than in the highly mechanized countries may make them better able, with adequate study of the problems, to use pesticides more intelligently. They have more need of them and can secure higher yields if the pest problems are surmounted. They are in a position to profit well from the mistakes made in the U.S.A. and northern Europe.

Resistance of Fungi

In general, a high degree of resistance to "conventional" protective agricultural fungicides, which do not penetrate to any significant extent into plant tissue, has been seldom observed in the field. Even when attempts were made to induce resistance in the laboratory by successive transfers of fungal mycelium to agar medium containing increasing concentrations of the fungicide, there has been little success. Resistance has, from time to time, been reported to chlorinated nitrobenzenes, dicloran, hexachlorobenzene, dodine and organomercurials. These examples of resistance are very limited and when one considers the long period during which protective fungicides have been used commercially the number of cases in which resistance has become a problem for practical disease control is very low and is restricted mainly to fungicides used on a limited scale for special purposes. In all cases the acquired resistance disappeared after transfer of the fungus to a medium free from the fungicide.

The situation is quite different with regard to systemic fungicides which penetrate and move about in the plant tissue. Very soon after compounds of this type were put into commercial use there were dramatic examples of acquired resistance. In 1968, dimethirimol was introduced to control cucumber mildew but, by 1969, resistance had developed. Even though use of dimethirimol was discontinued, resistance to it was still widespread in 1971.

A similar example was use of benomyl at 0.5 ppm to control heart-rot in cyclamen. Very rapidly a resistant strain emerged which was not killed by 1000 ppm of the fungicide. Emergence of resistant strains took place very quickly in these two examples because of the artificial, confined environment of the glasshouses. Resistance to systemic fungicides in the field has taken longer to develop but reports are now increasing rapidly and concern practically every systemic fungicide which has been introduced commercially.

It is not yet clear how large a problem this is going to be in practice because little is known yet about the epidemiology of resistant strains and their competitive ability. It is probable that populations will become fully resistant only in those cases where the resistant strains have a large and continuous selective advantage over the susceptible strains.

However, to reduce the emergence of resistance, it is desirable that more than one systemic fungicide, with different biochemical mechanisms of action, should be applied either together or alternately. The use of such fungicides should be restricted as much as possible and methods of application should be chosen to reduce selection pressures to a minimum. The possibility should be borne in mind that a systemic fungicide may upset the total balance of micro-organisms in the soil or on the plants and that competing fungi or even fungi which produce antibiotics effective against the pathogen may be inhibited. This, as with insecticides, could cause new disease problems to arise.

The interesting question why resistance has developed rapidly to systemic fungicides but not to protective fungicides is probably answered by the fact that protective fungicides all act by interfering with the general energy processes and protein synthesis of the fungus, which are not determined by single genes, whereas most systemic fungicides act by inhibiting specific enzyme reactions which are often carried on a single gene. Plant breeders produce strains of crop plants which are resistant to various fungi but, invariably, new strains of fungi emerge which overcome this resistance. One of the most notorious examples is the wheat rust (*Puccinia graminis*) which has produced successive new strains which have successively rendered dozens of new wheat varieties, which were initially resistant, susceptible. This suggests that "natural" resistance also depends on the production within the plant of natural antifungal agents which act like systemic fungicides by inhibiting specific enzyme systems in the fungi but which are, because of this fact, prone to induce resistance. The occurrence of such natural antifungal agents — the phytoalexins — has been demonstrated and some have been isolated. More knowledge about "natural" resistance would assist understanding the problems of acquired resistance.

Resistance of Weeds

The agronomist concerned with weeds is interested in a whole population of species competing with one another and with the crop, rather than, as in the case of insects or fungi, with some particular species directly damaging to the crop plant. Consequently, when he refers to "resistant weeds" he usually means species which have always been resistant to a given herbicide rather than species in which selection of more resistant variants has raised the level of resistance.

A natural population of weeds will, of course, change towards a population mainly of resistant species if reliance is placed over a long period on control by a single chemical. In this way wireweed becomes dominant on the orchard floor when paraquat has been relied on exclusively for control and has removed the competition of most other species. A great increase in wild oat as a problem weed in wheat and barley after many years' use of 2,4-D and MCPA has had a less direct cause. These herbicides enabled the farmer in cereal-favourable areas to concentrate on these more profitable crops and pull out of labour-costly mixed farming. Wild oat prospered not because of less competition by other weeds but because its palatable foliage was no longer eaten by grazing cattle before it could seed.

Compared to insects and fungi, plants have long generation times and their seeds are mobile or stay in a dormant state in soil for long periods. Evolution of plants is thus a comparatively slow process and even if genes carrying resistance were produced by herbicide application they would be continuously diluted by non-resistant individuals. For these reasons, acquired resistance of plants to herbicides has been slow to develop.

It was first clearly shown in an annual weed *Erechtites hieracifolia*, which can no longer be controlled by 2,4-D. Groundsel was later reported to show increased resistance to simazine and atrazine and now a strain of fathen has evolved with greatly increased resistance to these herbicides. Some reports of increased resistance may have been confused with another phenomenon — accelerated degradation of some soil-applied herbicides by increased population of adapted strains of some species of microflora. This leads to a general decrease of the effectiveness of a long-used herbicide but, of course, this decrease may be more evident on some species than on others. The herbicide EPTC used in maize began to fail in fields which had been treated with it for several years. Its effectiveness was restored by addition of a bactericide to the spray. This phenomenon is unlikely to arise except with pesticides applied to the soil.

There is obviously need for integration of chemical usage with other factors of management, as has now become important with insect pests. "Ringing the changes" on herbicides will clearly sometimes be desirable. There obviously is a potential for induction of resistance to herbicides into plants, and weed scientists are alive to this possibility. If resistance could be induced artificially by pressure from successively increasing doses of herbicide this could be made very positive use of to produce strains of major crop plants which were more resistant to herbicides and thus improve the margin of safety of selective herbicides.

Resistance of Vertebrates

The most important example in terms of its practical consequences has been the development of resistance to warfarin in rats and mice. Resistance to warfarin is known to occur in four species, the Norway rat, the roof rat, the mouse, and man. In man, transmission of resistance is by a single autosomal dominant gene, but, in rats and mice, more than one gene may be involved. It is interesting to note that resistance can be observed in species such as man which have relatively small populations and relatively slow reproduction rates and long generation times.

Other examples of resistance in vertebrates include pine mice which have acquired resistance to the organochlorine insecticide, endrin, as a result of increased rate of excretion of hydrophilic metabolites, and two strains of mosquito fish from the Mississippi which are resistant to the organochlorine insecticides aldrin and dieldrin. Resistance to organochlorine insecticides has also been found in three species of frog. DDT-resistant mice have been artificially produced in the laboratory, and it appears that this resistance is due to preferential deposit of DDT in the fatty tissues and consequent reduction of levels in sensitive tissues.

Further Reading

Brown, A. W. A. *Insecticide Resistance in Arthropodes*, W. H. O., Geneva, 1958.

Dekker, J. The development of resistance to fungicides, in *Progress in Pesticide Biochemistry*, Hutson, D. H. and Roberts, T. R., (Eds), Vol. 4 (Wiley, 1985).

Hoy, M. A., Westigard, P. H. and Hoyt, S. C. Laboratory strain of predacious mites resistant to permethrin and O'Ps, *Jean Ent.* 1972).

Insecticide Resistance and Vector Control, Tech. Report Series No. 443, W. H. O., Geneva, 1970.

25

Safety of Pesticides

Introduction

Pest control chemicals must be toxic to some living organisms to fulfil their useful purpose. There is a unity between all forms of life, so accidental ingestion of pesticides by humans or animals might produce adverse effects. In this case, there would be a possibility of health risks to the operatives who are actually engaged in handling and spraying them. There is the possibility of hazard to children, when the carelessness of adults permits them access to such chemicals, and the possibility of their being deliberately used for suicide or murder. Since the chemicals are applied to plants which will produce edible crops and, in some cases, to the crops themselves, there is the possibility that small residues might remain in the crop until it is eaten by the consumer and that, if this happens, it might be deleterious to the consumer's health either acutely or in the long term. There is the possibility that they may drift on the wind and that small concentrations may build up in the atmosphere at large. Chemicals might be hazardous to beneficial insects such as bees, to wild animals and birds which feed in the crop, and to creatures which live within the crop or in the soil beneath it and, thus, indirectly to wildlife which feeds on those creatures. Chemicals which fall on to the soil can be washed down into it by rain and eventually find their way into lakes and rivers and thence into estuaries and harbours, where they might adversely affect fish and other aquatic life. All these are possibilities, the risks of which have to be weighed against the benefits which the pesticides produce. What is clear is that it is as unthinkable for the community to do without modern pesticides as to do without modern medicines. Present-day agriculture in developed countries is dependent on chemicals as much as it is on the internal combustion engine. No one would want to return to the hunger, malnutrition, disease and discomfort of a primitive existence. However, our goal must be to employ chemicals in agriculture, horticulture, public health and amenity and recreational areas as part of the total management of the environment for the long-term benefit and survival of mankind, and to minimize any possible risks arising from their use.

Right from its start in the 1940s the modern pesticides industry has been aware that there were risks and has taken steps to eliminate or minimize them. In the early days, farmers were not made sufficiently aware of the possible dangers of pesticides and sometimes used them indiscriminately and not too wisely, but the standard of knowledge has risen greatly in recent years. However, there was always the possibility that unscrupulous manufacturers might not give sufficient consideration to the safety of their products or that careless growers might handle and use them in an unsafe way, and it was to prevent situations like these that governments had to act by means of legislation and regulatory controls to protect the consumer and the community as a whole.

A major responsibility of the government of any country is to try to ensure that adequate supplies of nutritious and wholesome food are available at reasonable prices to its inhabitants, and it must encourage and promote any technology which can help to achieve this aim. At the same time, it has the responsibility for trying to ensure that application of the technology does not present unacceptable or unreasonable risks to the community or to the quality of lives. It is inevitable that introduction of any new technology must bring with it the possibility of some new risks, and the aim of government must be to enact legislation which will minimize these risks without seriously detracting from the benefits.

Until recently, the U.K. adopted voluntary rather than legislative control based on the Agricultural Chemicals Approval Scheme and the Pesticides Safety Precautions Scheme. The Approval Scheme was concerned mainly with establishing that the product was efficacious for the purpose for which it was intended. Government representatives had access to trial plots and records of a manufacturer who sought approval for a new product, and might arrange for independent trials to be carried out in government experimental stations. Approval was for a particular use or set of uses and entitled the manufacturer to use the official approval mark on his labels, the wording of which had to be agreed.

The Safety Precautions Scheme agreed conditions of use to ensure that hazards to users, consumers and to wildlife were reduced to an acceptably low level. It was administered by the Ministry of Agriculture, Fisheries and Food, acting in association with other government departments and calling on various expert committees for advice.

Substantially the same mechanisms of investigation continue but the decisions of the Ministry are now mandatory, bringing the U.K. into line with the majority of European countries.

In the U.S.A. control over pesticides began with the Federal Insecticide Act of 1910 which laid down certain labelling requirements designed to ensure that the products were both effective and safe. These requirements were greatly extended for all pesticides by the Federal Insecticide, Fungicide and Rodenticide Act of 1947 which required that all pesticides should be registered and could not be used in any application without obtaining a "label" specifically for that use. Such a label has to carry adequate instructions for use and warning statements about possible injury to men, animals and plants. The scope of the Act was increased by the Federal Environmental Pesticides Control Act of 1972 which lays down that a pesticide shall be registered only if (a) its composition is such as to warrant the proposed claims for it; (b) its labelling and other material required to be submitted comply with the requirements of the Act; (c) it will perform its intended function without unreasonable adverse effects on the environment; (d) when used in accordance with widespread and commonly recognized practices it will not generally cause unreasonable adverse effects on the environment.

The administration of the Act is in the hands of the Enviromental Protection Agency set up in 1970, which has an Office of Pesticide Programs specifically to deal with crop protection and pest control. They are required to make an analysis of the risks and benefits before making any decision on registration of a new pesticide or amendment or withdrawal of the registration of an established product. That is, they are required (a) to make inferences about future impact of the pesticide which are justified by existing scientific knowledge; (b) to determine possible harmful risks and to estimate their magnitude and to compare these with the benefits to society which may result from use of the pesticide.

The Environmental Protection Agency has control not only over registration and use of pesticides but also of biological methods of crop protection and pest control such as release of predators or use of pathogenic micro-organisms. Also they may consider whether new varieties of plants produced by the plant breeders might contain naturally occurring chemical substances which might have harmful short-term or long-term effects on men or animals. In particular, where varieties have been bred to be resistant to a particularly disease and it is believed that this resistance is due to increased production of natural fungitoxic substances, then the effects of these on man and animals need to be studied.

Registration requirements are strict and apply not only to new pesticides but also to established pesticides which can be called to account and have their registrations amended or cancelled if new evidence comes to light of possible risk in their use. The procedure then is for E.P.A. to issue a "rebuttable presumption" that the registration should be cancelled, and the manufacturer then has six months in which to bring evidence to convince E.P.A. otherwise. At the moment "rebuttable presumptions" have been made against 47 established pesticides.

An amendment to the Federal Environmental Pesticides Control Act in 1978 directed E.P.A. to re-register all pesticides as expeditiously as possible using as their criteria the data which would be required for registration if they were submitted for the first time now not just the data on which the original registration was granted. Any company that wishes to continue to sell a pesticide first registered before 1977 must apply for re-registration of that pesticide.

E.P.A. are slowly issuing "registration standards" for all such pesticides. These review all the information that is known about a particular pesticide and identify the "data gaps", that is, information which would be required now for registration but which was not submitted (because it was not required) when the original application for registration was made, or information which was submitted at that time but is now considered inadequate. A condition for re-registration is that these "data gaps" shall be filled to the satisfaction of E.P.A. by the applicant within a specified time. If a number of companies have registrations for the same pesticide they can be required to share the costs but the individual companies may also be required to provide data on any impurities present in their active ingredients and on their formulations and formulating materials.

The registration standard also contains a statement of the regulatory position of E.P.A. with respect to the pesticide. At the extreme they may conclude that it is too hazardous to permit continued use and will issue a "rebuttable presumption". Or they might decide that the registration should be suspended until the data gaps have been filled. More usually they will permit sale and use to continue provided that the data gaps are filled within the specified time. At the same time, however, they may require the registrant immediately to modify product labels to provide additional percautionary statements, to restrict use to certified applicators, to establish re-entry intervals, to modify or discontinue certain formulations and certain uses, to specify certain packaging limitations and to satisfy any other requirements which E.P.A. think are necessary to ensure that proper use of the pesticide will not result in unreasonable adverse effects on humans, animals or the environment.

One consequence of this is that pesticide companies are having to spend a greater proportion of their research and development budgets — currently estimated at about 25% — just to protect their existing products, which reduces the effort available to develop better and safer new products. The evidence which must now be provided makes a very impressive list entirely contradicting a rather common popular picture of the pesticide industry irresponsibly scattering untested substances over the population.

The cost of providing the necessary evidence of safety for a new pesticide may be anything from £500,000 to £15 million and falls entirely on the company which wishes to market it. It would be difficult to give a precise figure in any one case even if the company concerned were willing to disclose its full accounts, because some of this cost is incidental to other research costs. The total cost of discovery and development of a new pesticide may exceed £50 million when the cost of extensive field trials and of the "wasted" basic work on unsuccessful compounds is included. One unfortunate result of this high cost is that it has become increasingly unprofitable for the manufacturer to develop a compound for a restricted and specialized market. It is obvious, however, that compounds with a specialized action or use are, on the whole, those least likely to give rise to side-effect problems. Also, because of their multiplicity and diversity, they are less likely to create real cumulative risk to the consumer than a few very widely used compounds. One effect of present safety legislation is to force the manufacturer to develop only those compounds which have a wide spectrum of activity and a large market, and this may, ironically, be the least safe state of affairs.

With regard to control of use, rather than manufacture, of pesticides the Federal Environmental Pesticide Control Act of 1972 provided that pesticides shall be classified for "general use" or "restricted use", and chemicals in the latter category can be applied only by or under supervision of a certified applicator.

The National Environmental Policy Act requires a full statement of environmental impact for every major federal activity which may "significantly affect the quality of the human environment". Obviously any crop protection or pest control programme which was planned over a whole region or area rather than just on an individual farm would come into this category.

Safety to Wildlife

In 1963 a U.S. journalist, Rachel Carson, published a book, "Silent Spring" in which she dramatized certain errors which were made in the early years of modern crop protection because farmers were inadequately warned about the inherent hazards of distributing highly biologically active compounds over wide areas. Nearly all the evidence of lasting damage from pesticides to wildlife relates to one group of pesticides, namely, the organochlorine insecticides. This is not to say that other pesticides could not, if misused, have damaging effects on wildlife, and it is essential that a constant watch be kept to detect early warnings of any such damage and thus to avert it. This is done in the U.S.A., for example, by the National Pesticide Monitoring Program. There is no evidence that any such damage has occurred, and the extent of ecological and environmental information which nowadays has to be supplied to regulatory and registration authorities makes it very unlikely that it would occur.

It is important to emphasize here a difference about which there is a great deal of confusion in the minds of the public, namely between damage to individuals in a species and damage to a species as a whole. Individuals in a species are constantly prone to death from many natural causes, including hunting by humans, but the species as a whole survives. Accidental isolated emissions of pesticides into the environment have resulted in death of many individuals in some species but have given no reason to believe that any permanent harm has been done to those species. Even the large-scale misuse of certain pesticides described in "Silent Spring" has had no permanent effects on any species. Silent Spring has turned out, in fact, to be Noisy Fall — the birds sing in greater numbers and there is no evidence of harm to the health of the population who are more healthy and better-fed as a result of crop protection and pest control.

The safety precautions to ensure no hazard to wildlife have already been outlined and comprise extensive ecological and environmental testing and toxicological studies on non-target species, coupled with continual monitoring. A particular region in which great care needs to be exercised is water. In all developed countries there are legislative controls over the discharge of chemicals in effluents, such as the Federal Water Pollution Control Act Amendment of 1972 in the U.S.A. Factory effluents have, without doubt, been a source of contamination of the environment with pesticides over a protracted period in the past. There is, however, at present no legislative control over possible run-off of pesticides from land into watercourses, rivers or lakes except that given by common law which provides for redress if actual damage is caused to person or property.

The extensive environmental and ecological work which now has to be carried out on any new pesticide makes it very unlikely that incidents involving widespread destruction of wildlife could occur again unless a user grossly disregarded all of the manufacturer's instructions. The safeguard against such misuse — which is mainly caused by ignorance — is the increasing education of farmers in safe and effective ways to apply crop protection treatments. The only safeguard against misuse from lack of concern is the legislative sanctions which are applied to anybody who commits an anti-social act, and laws against misuse of pesticides should be stringent. This should apply not only to people who cause excessive damage to wildlife by flagrant misuse but also to people who discard unwashed pesticide containers or leave pesticides in unlabelled and improper containers within reach of children.

The danger of large-scale episodes of wildlife destruction has, therefore, been largely removed. It is doubtful whether such incidents had any permanent long-term effects on wildlife populations and, in most cases, recovery has been much more rapid than ecologists anticipated. It remains to examine the question whether pesticides could have any more subtle effects on wildlife which could have lasting effects on populations of mammals, birds and beneficial insects.

The situation with regard to pesticides and effects on wildlife can, therefore, be summarized as follows. Because of ill-considered application, a number of incidents of destruction of wildlife occurred in the early days of use of organochlorine compounds — although not in the U.K. — but there is no evidence that these incidents have had permanent long-term effects on population numbers. Because the organochlorine insecticides are very persistent and tend to accumulate in biological food chains, the reproductive capacities of some predatory birds have been affected. There is no evidence that any other pesticides have produced long-term effects on wildlife populations.

A rational attitude based on these conclusions would be to continue to require adequate environmental and ecological studies as a necessary part of registration requirements, to keep a constant watch for any adverse effects on wildlife, to supervise carefully any application of pesticides over large areas, particularly from the air, and to avoid the use of highly persistent pesticides when some acceptable alternative is available. This last point is prompted by the impossibility of ever conclusively proving a negative. Although there is no evidence that persistent pesticides are doing harm through their low-level presence in the environment we cannot be sure that no harm, however small, is occurring nor that they will never be concentrated to harmful levels by some living organisms, so that, when use of persistent compounds can reasonably be avoided, it should be. The decision must, in each case, be made on a cost-benefit assessment. If use of a particular persistent pesticide is essential for protection of a particular crop and there is no effective alternative it may be that a certain amount of risk of environmental damage may have to be accepted by society as the price it pays for the benefits it receives. It has been said that "the perfect is the enemy of the merely good". To refuse to use pesticides which are of overall benefit to mankind because they have some shortcomings would not be sensible if it led to food shortages while the search for the perfect pesticide was in progress.

A great difficulty is the complexity and uncertainty of environmental and ecological work. A vast amount of data has been collected, and is being collected, on the concentration of pesticide residues present in various parts of the environment using highly sensitive analytical techniques which are often capable of detecting as little as one part of pesticide per million million, equivalent to 1 gram distributed through 1 million tonnes. The concentrations of pesticides found are generally very small, but there is no method at present available by which this vast amount of data can be interpreted in terms of a quantitative risk to any species of wildlife. A practical answer may be to maintain constant ecological watch for any detectable effects of wildlife populations and, in the absence of these, to assume that any risk is hypothetical.

Safety to the Consumer

The consumer wants food which is pure and wholesome, of high quality and attractive appearance, in as great a variety as possible, at reasonable prices and in good supply. The general increase in affluence of people in developed countries over the past 30 years has made it possible for them to get what they want since they can afford to pay for it. Apart from any of the other requirements mentioned above, the matter of purity and wholesomeness is one on which the consumer is very sensitive, as the fear of mysterious and secret poisons in the food he eats is a very deeply-rooted and atavistic one which prompts an exaggerated response if any suggestion of contamination is made. In previous centuries, widespread adulteration of foodstuffs was common commercial practice, but legislation and public inspection in developed countries have steadily brought this under control, so that any gross adulteration of food is now very rare. Legislation and general education in food handling and hygiene have reduced the likelihood of bacterial contamination of food, although there is still room for improvement in this area as local instances of food poisoning are still much too common. Nevertheless, public fears of gross adulteration or bacterial contamination of foodstuffs have been largely allayed. In recent years, however, the consumer has been made aware of what is to him a more insidious threat of the possibility of residues of pesticides in his foodstuff which he thinks might make him acutely ill or, more alarmingly, have long term effects on his health.

Government authorities responsible for registration of pesticides have, very properly and rightly, made provision of sufficient acceptable data on residues an essential requirement for permission to sell. With increasing public concern, tests have been made more and more comprehensive, so that nowadays a new pesticide is subjected to an extensive and searching toxicological testing programme. This programme includes study of acute toxic effects from doses of various sizes: 90-day and two-year continuous feeding to dogs and rats — after which the animals are humanely killed and every organ of their bodies closely examined histologically for any departures from normal; studies of reproduction over three generations of rats to ensure no effects on embryos and no transmitted effects to offspring, and studies of general toxicities to birds, fish and shellfish.

At the same time it is a requirement for registration that analytical methods for a new pesticide shall be developed, capable of detecting and measuring 0.1 parts per million in meat, 0.01 parts per million in food crops and 0.005 parts per million in milk. Determinations then have to be made of residues present after harvest in all crops to which the pesticides may be applied and, in the case of animal feeding stuffs, of any residues in the meat or milk.

There has been a certain amount of confusion in the minds of consumers about residues. This is partly because the layman does not always appreciate that there are no poisonous or non-poisonous substances, only poisonous or non-poisonous amounts. The enormous increase in the senitivity of analytical methods has increased this confusion. If the only analytical method available for a particular pesticide could not detect more than 1000 parts per million, then a sample containing 900 parts per million would be designated by the analyst as "non-detectable", and the consumer would feel reassured. If then a method was developed for detecting 0.01 parts per million, a sample containing 0.03 parts per million would show up positive even though this is 30,000 times less than the amount in the previous "non-detectable" sample. The consumer then feels uneasy on a general principle that "if it is there at all, it must be doing some harm".

This illustrates the crux of the pesticide residue problem. Everybody agrees that harmful residues should not be present, but what amounts should be specified as the maximum allowable for safety? We are up against the impossibility of proving a negative and of being able to say for certain that a particular amount of residue might not cause some harm to somebody, somewhere, sometime. Likewise, it it not realistic to specify that no residues should be present, because this can likewise never be proved, as the most that can be said is that the substance is "not detectable" by the most sensitive analytical methods available. Registration authorities are forced therefore, into specifying amounts, that is, laying down finite limits for residues. The 64 thousand dollar question is, "What is a safe amount?" To specify "non-detectable" by the most sensitive analytical methods is unrealistic because modern analytical methods are so sensitive that the amounts involved are fantastically small — 0.01 parts per million is equivalent to one teaspoonful in a rail tanker wagon. From an overall cost-benefit view, the banning of a pesticide, because it could not achieve such low limits, might have large economic repercussions on the production of one type of food, without any compensating benefit, since this action may have been taken against a non-existent danger. What then is a reasonable amount of residue to specify which will not expose the consumer to an unreasonable risk? What is an unreasonable risk?

A generally accepted basis is that the maximum permitted amount of residual pesticide in a foodstuff is determined from three factors: (1) the smallest dose, expressed in parts per million, which produces detectable harmful effects in experimental animals; (2) a safety factor which is usually 100, but may be less if a great deal is known about the physiological and pharmacological effects of the pesticide; (3) a food factor based on the proportion of the particular foodstuff is an average diet. Thus if the minimum harmful dose is 10 parts per million, the safety factor 100 and the food factor 0.2, the permitted residue level will be 10 divided by (100×0.2), that is 0.5 parts per million. The safety factor is intended to be large enough to compensate for any differences between man and test animals, for any variations in susceptibility due to age, health or personal idiosyncrasies, and for any differences in eating habits such as the person who eats an inordinate amount of a particular food.

The problem of determining safety is a problem of interpreting data obtained on experimental animals under laboratory conditions in terms of an actual hazard to people in practical use. Nobody is sure how to do this. Is there, in fact, any evidence of harm caused by pesticide residues in practice? In developed countries regular "market-basket" surveys are made in which government analysts purchase various foodstuffs in the normal way in shops and supermarkets and analyze them for pesticide residues. Such surveys invariably show that most samples contain well below the acceptable levels of residues. For instance, the government analyst in the U.K. has reported that residues were, in general, of the order of a few parts per thousand million in the various foodstuffs. These findings are confirmed by the extensive monitoring programmes of the U.S. Bureau of Foods. In the few cases where abnormal levels of pesticide residue could be detected, these were traced either to human error or human greed. For instance, a recent case in the southern United States in which millions of broiler chickens had to be destroyed because they contained more than the acceptable amount of an organochlorine insecticide, resulted from the fact that seed treated with this substance had been improperly obtained and sold as animal feed by unscrupulous operators.

The very low levels of pesticide residues found in practice are not surprising when it is realized that the acceptable residue levels are not the amounts which normally occur, but the maximum amounts which could result from use of the pesticides in a proper way. They serve, therefore, as a means of detecting improper use of pesticides. Instructions for use and application are drawn up by the manufacturers so that, if these are followed, there is no danger of undesirably high residue levels.

There remains the question whether ingestion of, or exposure to, very minute amounts of pesticides over a long period might increase the risk of an individual developing malignant tumours. Cancer is a very emotive word and both the public and regulatory authorities have given this possibility a great deal of attention. It involves all the difficulties of conclusively proving a negative.

There are some chemicals which have been shown unequivocally to increase the risk of cancer in humans — the most notable are the chemicals in cigarette smoke — but none of these is used as a commercial pesticide. However, a large number of chemicals, including some pesticides, when fed to laboratory animals such as rats or mice in very large amounts over nearly their whole lifetimes, produce statistically significant increases in the numbers of tumours which develop. What is being demonstrated is an increase since many animals, like humans, develop carcinomas as part of the ageing process. The problem is what significance results obtained by feeding large amounts of a chemical to a small number of animals have with respect to the possibility that ingestion of minute amounts by a large population of humans might increase the risk of cancer.

A cardinal principle of toxicology has always been that there are no poisonous substances but only poisonous amounts and that, for any chemical, it is possible to determine a "no effect" level of dosage, that is, an amount which, if fed daily over a long period, produces no detectable adverse effects on the animals. This is the basis on which permitted residue levels are set as described above. It is apparently true for carcinogens since a dosage level can always be found for laboratory animals at which any significant increase in tumour formation is no longer detected. But there is a school of thought that believes that there is no true "no effect" level for a carcinogen and that even just one molecule, if it arrives at a sensitive site of action within a cell, can trigger off the chain of intracellular events which leads eventually to development of a tumour. This leads to suggestions, for example, that, if a dose of 1 g per day of a pesticide produces a 10% increase in the number of tumours in 100 laboratory animals, then exposure of the whole population of the U.S.A. (about 250 million) to a dose of 1 microgram per day would result in 25 extra cases of cancer. Some very much more sophisticated and complex methods of extrapolation have been proposed but they all are based on the assumption that there is no "no effect" level for a carcinogen. The situation has been complicated in recent years by the development of tests involving the effects of a chemical on mutation of bacteria and on DNA integrity in cell division in isolated cell cultures. These purport to show whether a chemical should be regarded as a potential carcinogen and subjected to further tests but a positive result in these tests has been taken by some people as an indication that the substance is actually a carcinogen in the whole animals. Once again, interpretation of results of these tests in terms of a risk to the population at large is a matter of controversy. One great difficulty in all extrapolations is the near impossibility of determining quantitatively the exposure of individuals to a particular pesticide. It is difficult to get even approximate figures for exposure of workers actually spraying pesticides. The amounts of a particular pesticide to which individuals in the population at large are exposed during their lifetimes are imponderable.

This is a very complex and controversial subject which cannot be dealt with at length in this book. Regulatory authorities tend to "play safe". If there is any suspicion that a pesticide might be a carcinogen and there is some other pesticide which is not suspect which will do the job as well they will be inclined to withdraw registration on the grounds that there is no reason to accept any risk, no matter how remote, if a safe alternative is available. If the suspect pesticide is one which is essential to a particular crop or region or for which there is no satisfactory alternative for a particular pest control or crop protection problem the regulatory authorities will carry out a risk:benefit analysis. This will generally result in a request to the manufacturer for more data. In the U.S.A. nearly all the rebuttable presumptions against re-registration that have been issued are based on suspected carcinogenicity. A large proportion of the "data gaps" identified by the E.P.A. in the registration standards which they are compiling for all pesticides first registered before 1977 and which they are requiring the manufacturers to fill before re-registration concern possible carcinogenic, mutagenic or terato-genic (deformation of unborn embryos) effects of the pesticides and their metabolites, and very extensive experimental investigations are being called for. Until much more is known about the events within a cell that lead eventually to the development of tumours and the precise effects of chemicals on these processes the regulatory authorities will continue to be very cautious. It is worth noting, however, that a careful study in the U.S.A, over the past 40 years of mortality data for the nation as a whole and for farm workers and contract spray operators in particular, has shown no alterations in mortality which could be attributed to the use of pesticides.

It is obviously desirable for growers to use pesticides which, on the basis of toxicological investigations on animals, are of as low toxicity as possible so that the safety margin is wide and, preferably, they should not be persistent but be broken down rapidly in practical conditions to harmless substances. These requirements are more than ever being taken into account in development of new crop protection chemicals.

Dead insects, parts of insects and insect excrement are aesthetically objectionable in produce from the market, particularly if the produce is packed ready to use in transparent plastic. Some insect remains may come from useful predators but some may represent a health hazard. So may weeds seeds in grain. An example is contamination of processed green peas by like-sized green berries of black nightshade, a weed for this reason particularly undesirable in the pea crop.

A more serious problem is that the by-products of some fungi are very toxic. In particular, the substance aflatoxin produced by some fungi is one of the most potent cancer-producing agents known. It has been reported that a toxin produced by potato blight may cause birth abnormalities in children.

Ergot, attacking the seed head of rye, is highly toxic though used under control medicinally, and for long made inhabitants of the sandy areas of north central Europe, where rye was the most productive cereal, envious of farmers in the heavier wheat lands. The risks to health which might arise from using pesticides therefore have to be weighed against the risks to health of not using them. Many consumers in the affluent world have a bias in favour of the natural hazard against the artificial one — until the caterpillar crawls out of the salad at the dining table! Our attitudes are too much conditioned by what can easily be seen and what ill-understood results of research are dramatized by the news media. The balance must be weighed objectively and on a not too delicate instrument. Worry about flies' legs or traces of chemical may be worse for health than the presence of either.

Safety of Farm Workers

In the early days of modern pesticides some deaths of spraying operators occurred because some substances used at that time, particularly DNOC, were much more highly toxic than most pesticides used nowadays, and their dangers had not been communicated to the personnel concerned. As a result, the Agriculture (Poisonous Substances) Act of 1952 was introduced in the U.K. and provides for provision, use and maintenance of protective clothing and equipment and for the keeping and inspection of records. Special regulations are made with respect to certain specified pesticides. The Act is enforced by inspectors of the Ministry of Agriculture, Fisheries and Food, and both employer and employee must comply with its provisions. As a result the safety record of pesticide use on farms in the U.K. has been excellent and there have been no fatal accidents to spray operators since the Act came into force. The Act applies only to "employees", so a farmer or other self-employed person could conceivably use pesticides without taking suitable precautions, but it is unlikely that they would do so.

Similar protection of workers is provided by legislation in most developed countries, for example, by the Occupational Safety and Health Act in the U.S.A. It is estimated that about 12 deaths per year occur in the U.S.A. from occupational exposure to pesticides. Aerial application of pesticides poses particular safety problems not only for pilots flying through spray but also for "markers" on the ground. In the U.S.A. in 1970 there were about 275 accidents during aerial spraying of pesticides involving about 30 deaths. In that country aerial application is regulated by the Federal Aviation Administration.

Safety of Industrial Workers

The workers in the chemical industry are protected from hazards inherent in the processes which they are operating by a complex mass of legislation. In the U.K. these comprise all the various Factory Acts which lay down requirements for safe design of plants, safe methods of working, availability and supply of adequate protective clothing and safety training. Factory inspectors, with unlimited powers of access, ensure that the provisions of these Acts are carried out and the trade unions keep a constant watchful eye on safety. Most far-reaching of all, the recent Health and Safety at Work Legislation in the U.K., requires that the toxicological hazards, both from acute exposure and from exposure to very small amounts over a period of years, of any chemical substances with which industrial workers might come into contact shall be established and communicated to the workers and that adequate precautions shall be taken to guard against them. Similar legislation exists, or is being introduced, in most developed countries, such as the

Occupational Safety and Health Act in the U.S.A. The possibility of workers being harmed as a result of their own negligence or carelessness can be minimized only by constant safety training and competent supervision. All large manufacturers of chemicals now regard the safety of their workers as a top priority and safety training and control is an essential part of their operations. Before any new plant is put into operation extensive hazard studies are made to visualize any accident which might happen and how it could be prevented.

The possibility of harm not only to workers in a factory but also to people resident in the neighbourhood from accidental failure of chemical plant and resultant dissemination of toxic substances into the air can be reduced to a minimum only by ensuring that chemical plant is adequately designed for the job, with built-in "belt and braces" safety precautions, and operated properly. One or two incidents in recent years suggest that there is still room for improvement in this respect by some manufacturers.

Safety in Transport and Distribution

Safety in transport and distribution is covered by a multiplicity of Acts which regulate the carriage, transport and storage of dangerous substances. The important matter of labelling and of adequate packaging are dealt with in the U.K. by the Farm and Garden Chemicals Act of 1967 and by the Pharmacy and Poisons Act of 1933 and all the various rules made under it subsequently. The latter Act also restricts the classes of people to whom certain pesticides may be sold.

In the U.S.A. transport and storage of pesticides are regulated by the Federal Environmental Pesticide Control Act, the Poison Prevention Packaging Act, the Hazardous Materials Transportation Control Act and various other Acts administered by the Department of Transportation. All incidents in which a pesticide is unintentionally released during transport or storage have to be reported to the Office of Hazardous Materials. In 1973 it was estimated that about 200 such incidents occurred, 35 of which caused injury to humans but no deaths. Since about 1.3 million tonnes of formulated pesticides were transported 517 million tonne-miles this would seem to be an adequate safety record. But all accidents should be prevented if possible and the Environmental Protection Agency has now set up a Pesticide Accident Surveillance System to investigate accidents involving pesticides more thoroughly.

Responsibility of Manufacturers and Farmers to the Public

If, despite the various regulations covering their manufacture and use, pesticides are allowed to escape from a factory or drift during a spraying operation and, as a result, cause harm to any person or to his property, then the remedy lies in common law. The principle in the U.K. was laid down by Blackburn and approved by the House of Lords, as follows: "The true rule of law is that the person who for his own purposes brings on his lands and collects and keeps there anything likely to do mischief if it escapes, must keep it at his peril, and if he does not do so, is prima facie answerable for all damage which is the natural consequence of its escape". There is no need to prove negligence, the fact that injury has occurred is sufficient. This is just the same principle which applies if you allow a bonfire in your garden to set light to your neighbour's house. The principle that the person who has a pesticide in his possession is to be held responsible for any damage it causes applies not only to manufacturers and farmers but also to distributors, wholesalers, retailers, transport organizations and anyone else who may handle and keep a pesticide, including the householder who keeps pesticides in his garden shed. Of course, prevention of harm is far better than provision of recompense if harm occurs, but this can be achieved only by widespread and thorough instruction of all who handle pesticides in the possible damage they might cause if misused and in ways to prevent this. The possibility that accidents may occasionally happen no matter how much care is taken can be insured against by all who handle pesticides and this should be a legal requirement to ensure that any person harmed does receive financial compensation.

A particular hazard to the public is discarded pesticide containers which have not been decontaminated properly. This is, in fact, the largest source of injury from pesticides in the U.K., unfortunately, mostly to children. It is an offence under the Dangerous Litter Act of 1971 but it is often not easy to pin-point the culprit. The related hazard of adults putting pesticides into unintended containers such as lemonade bottles and leaving them within reach of children is totally reprehensible and can be stopped only by education and safety propaganda.

The suggestion is often heard nowadays that the pesticide manufacturer should be held responsible for all harm caused by pesticides no matter how it is caused or who causes it. This is as ridiculous as requiring the car manufacturer to pay for damage caused by a drunken driver or for a cutlery manufacturer to pay compensation to a victim stabbed by a maniac with a table-knife. The common law principle would seem to be the sensible one and extends not only to actual harm to person or property but also through common law to torts such as negligence and nuisance.

Safety in the Third World

The dangers of pesticides to humans in the "Third World" have been much greater than in Western industrialized nations. There have been many fatalities, mainly among users rather than consumers. Some estimates have put the figure as high as 10,000 per year. Several pesticides made by Western industry but banned for use in their home countries, are still exported for use by peasants engaged in subsistence agriculture. This is considered by many critics to be very blameworthy, but the horrifying facts must be put in perspective. Third World peasants can afford only the cheapest pesticides and, unfortunately, these are often the most toxic, which is why they are banned in developed countries. The obstacles to providing the Third World with safer pesticides are economic and political. But accidents could be reduced if more consideration was given to safe packaging and comprehensible labelling and, above all to education in safe handling and safe use. A great deal is already being done in this respect by the large international pesticide manufacturers, by agencies of U.N.O. and of various governments and by the World Bank. A vital need is to augment the pitifully small numbers of agricultural extension workers and advisers in many Third World countries. The high estimate of pesticide death rate represents only about 1 in 4,000 of total deaths. Deaths from consumption of natural poisons, from malnutrition and associated diseases and from outright starvation are much higher and would be higher still were pesticides not available.

Several factors contribute to the much higher incidence of acute poisoning in the Third World: the high cost of protective clothing and its intolerable discomfort in tropical heat; poor communication due to language barriers; desperation about loss of a crop which is vital to a family's survival; carelessness, ignorance and suicide.

There is room for a great deal of improvement, most of all in education, needing co-operation of industry and governments. The most likely successful direction of improvement is perhaps in the development of more small-scale applicators adapted to the needs of peasant farming. In one respect at least the peasant farmer has the possibility to use pesticides more wisely. He works on a smaller scale. He is close to the land. He observes in a more detailed way than the driver of a tractor hauling a wide spray-boom can ever do. Schumacher's conclusions in "Small is Beautiful" are worth much more attention.

We mentioned, under "Safety of Industrial Workers" that there have been incidents involving accidental release of toxic materials from factories and there is still need, in industrial countries, for further improvement of safety procedures. Since this was written for the second edition such an incident causing 2,500 fatalities and many more injuries occurred around a factory in Bhopal in India. It is appropriate to mention here because one factor in this enormous catastrophe was the existence of a crowded shanty town around the factory — a juxtaposition which should always be avoided, as should the storage of large amounts of a volatile, reactive, toxic intermediate if an alternative continuous process is economic and practicable under local conditions. In this case water somehow gained access to a large tank of methylisocyanate to be used for manufacture of carbaryl. It is important to appreciate that neither the explosion nor the deaths were caused by this approved insecticide. But it is vital that companies who choose to operate processes involving dangerous intermediates in developing countries where the quality of labour and supervision may be poor take every conceivable precaution to ensure safe operation of their factories. Some large multi-national manufacturers are tackling this problem by setting corporate standards for safety and establishing manufacturing technology centres to establish integrated management networks to ensure that these standards are complied with and the safest technology used on a global scale. This is a precedent which should be widely followed.

Further Reading

Baxter, W. F. *People or Penguins*, Columbia University Press, London and New York, 1974.

Biros, F. J. *Pesticides Identification at the Residue Level*, American Chemical Society, Washington, D.C., 1970.

British Agrochemical Association, *Pesticides: A Code of Conduct*, London, 1968).

Busvine, J. *Insects and Hygiene*, 3rd ed, Chapman & Hall, 1980.

Edwards, C. A. *Environmental Pollution by Pesticides*, Plenum Press, London and New York, 1973.

Faust, J. D. *Fate of Organic Pesticides in the Aqueous Environment*, American Chemical Society, Washington, D.C., 1976.

Goring, C. A. I. and Hamaker, J. W. *Organic Chemicals in the Soil Evironment*, Vol. I & IV, Marcel Dekker, New York, 1972.

Green, M. B. *Pesticides: Boon or Bane?* Elek Books, London, 1976.

Gunn, D. L. and Stevens, J. G. R. (eds.) *Pesticides and Human Welfare*, Oxford University Press, Oxford, 1976.

National Academy of Sciences, *Contemporary Pest Control Practices and Prospects*, Washington, D.C., 1975.

Rosen, A. A. and Kraybill, H. F. *Organic Pesticides in the Environment*, American Chemical Society, Washington, D. C. 1976.

Schumacher, E. F. *Small is Beautiful*, Abacus, 1976.

Tahori, A. S. *Pesticide Terminal Residues*, Butterworths, London, 1971.

26

The Future?

Inevitably, this chapter is made up mainly of questions. We can only hope to have set out most of the material for argument.

Human populations have increased steadily and are likely to go on increasing, but the amount of arable land available in each country remains the same, or actually decreases as cities and towns expand to accommodate increased numbers, as agricultural land is taken for motorways, airports, shopping plazas, parking lots and the like, and as affluent societies demand that more land be reserved for their amenity and recreation. If these populations are to continue to be provided with their present variety and quantity of food-stuffs at reasonable prices and if they are not to be faced with the need to spend much higher proportions of their incomes on food than they do at present then yields per hectare will have to be increased still more and, to achieve this, use of crop protection technology will have to be intensified, not restricted. With growing populations the human race simply cannot afford to allow substantial proportions of the food they grow to feed insects or nourish micro-organisms nor can they permit unwanted plants to compete with essential crops for growing space, nutrients and water.

It may be argued by some that modern agricultural technology has become too efficient and has resulted in over-production of certain foodstuffs, e.g. wheat in the U.S.A. and dairy products in the E.E.C. Nevertheless it is undeniable that, on a world scale, the pressures of increasing populations on food supplies are becoming a serious problem. According to W.H.O. figures, 1 billion people, about a quarter of the world's population, live in a state of chronic undernourishment. The technology to feed these people from the land that is available exists: the reasons why it is not applied in those countries where the need is greatest and why food produced in the developed countries in excess of their own requirements cannot be used to feed the hungry in the developing countries have to do with politics, economics, religion, the international monetary system, human self-interest and greed, the exploitation of poor nations by rich nations and, within those nations, of poor people by rich people. It is not appropriate to discuss these matters in a book about chemicals, nor are the authors qualified to do so. What is certain is that the solution to hunger in the developing countries and over-production in the developed countries is not to reduce the efficiency of agriculture. If ways cannot be found to use excess production in the developed countries to feed hungry people in the developing countries then a plausible solution may be to reduce the amount of land in cultivation in the developed countries as has been done in the U.S.A. and is being considered in the E.E.C., although the political and social obstacles to such a policy may be formidable. There is no way in which farmers in developed countries will discard their tractors for horses, substitute hand-weeding for herbicides, or tolerate stoically the ravages of fungi and insects, particularly if it is uneconomical for them to do so, nor will the modern consumer accept the fungi-blotched, insect-infested fruit and vegetables which were not uncommon 50 years ago, particularly if they cost more? But, even if such moves were thought desirable, they are impracticable because the effect of modern agricultural technology in the developed countries, including the use of pesticides, has been not only to increase yield per hectare but also to reduce greatly the demands for labour with consequent reductions in production costs in developed countries where labour costs are high. The result has been that one agricultural worker in the U.S.A. now produces enough food for himself and 37 other people whereas fifty years ago he produced only enough for himself and nine other people, and a peasant in Africa produces only enough for himself and three other people. Urban workers are unlikely to return to the land in large numbers, particularly if farmers could afford to pay them only meagre wages.

There will be a continuing need for improved agricultural machinery, better crop varieties and more specific and safer pesticides but, as has been explained above, the major problems which need solution on a world scale are not technological but political, social and economic. Within the context of this book we are going to consider in this chapter only the future of crop improvement and pest management. The need to control arthropod pests, fungi and weeds is now generally recognized and accepted. For the foreseeable future, pesticide will remain the main weapons in the farmer's armoury of defences against pests and diseases, but there is considerable public controversy about the significance of unwanted or hazardous side-effects which they might produce. This matter has already been discussed in Chapter 25 and the various arguments will not be repeated here. It appears inevitable that, no matter what the validity may be of these arguments and of the accusations made against pesticides, public opinion, spurred on by the mass media, will demand tighter controls over the registration of pesticides and greater restrictions on their use, and that politicians will respond to these demands.

Affluent societies may be willing and able to pay the increased food prices which will inevitably result in order to feel a greater sense of security against possible or imagined risks. If, however, controls and restrictions reached a point where they resulted in actual food shortages, then public opinion might undergo a sharp reaction, as it probably would also if insect-borne diseases such as malaria once again became prevalent in areas such as the southern states of U.S.A. where they were originally indigenous. Even if controls and restrictions did not result in actual food shortages, they might reduce the amount of foodstuffs which major exporting countries such as the U.S.A. had available for sale abroad, and this could have economic, political and international consequences which would be unwelcome to the governments of those countries.

There is considerable future scope for us to learn how to use existing pesticides so as to produce maximum benefit with minimum of risk. This will require much greater understanding than we at present possess of the ecology and population dynamics of pests and diseases so that reliable "early warning" systems can be instituted to permit optimum timing of crop protection operations and to avoid unnecessary or excessive applications of pesticides. In this respect, improvements in formulations and in application methods and equipment have an important part to play.

However, all this knowledge will be useless unless it can be imparted as practical advice to farmers and to those who actually carry out the crop protection and pest control operations. For pesticides, as for most technologies, the risks lie not so much in the intrinsic nature of the technology but in the way it is applied, and the greatest problem is how to deal with human ignorance, apathy, carelessness, stupidity or greed. There is a massive task of education to be undertaken, the burden of which will fall largely on government agricultural advisory and extension services and the costs of which will have to be met from public revenue.

The "user pays" principle, currently popular in Western governments, could have very detrimental long-term effect on future food production in a healthy environment which we all "use".

All knowledgeable and informed people who are concerned with crop protection and pest control are now agreed that we should move towards the concept of "pest management". This requires that we develop as extensive a range as possible of chemical and non-chemical weapons for the continual battle against pests and diseases, acquire the biological knowledge required to decide how each may best be used and then provide the farmer with the information on their relative utilities and limitations and with expert advice to help him select the best combination for each situation. If this aim can be achieved the farmer will have a range of options of which use of pesticides is only one, albeit the most effective and generally applicable one, but which are not mutually exclusive and which may, according to circumstances, be used singly, in combination or successively.

Pest Management

The proposition that the strategy for dealing with any crop protection and pest control problem should be selected from all the methods available in such a way as to produce maximum benefit at minimum cost would appear to be self-evident. (The term cost in this context and in the expression cost: benefit includes not only monetary expenditure but also all social and environmental effects). The major difficulty has been, and still is, a wide variance of opinions on the relative importance of the various benefits and the various costs and a tendency to emphasize some and underestimate others which has made it impossible to achieve a general concensus on what is the optimum strategy in any particular situation.

Nevertheless, there is a general trend towards the view that control of pest and disease populations by a multiplicity of methods may be preferable to reliance on any one method and that maximum use should be made of natural regulatory forces inherent in the ecosystem. This would reduce the chances of evolutionary adaptation to the control method by the target pest and would avoid waste of human resources.

There are, however, considerable additional difficulties in the way of optimizing crop protection and pest control strategies. Some of these have already been referred to in the previous chapters. The first is that we do not have nearly enough basic knowledge and understanding to do it. If it is to be done in the future, a vast amount of information will have to be obtained on population dynamics of pests and of their natural predators, of the ecology and economics of crop systems and of the complex inter-relationships of all life-forms in the general environment. The questions of where sufficient scientific resources are to be found to do this work, and who is to pay for it, have yet to be answered. Yet, without adequate understanding of the behaviour of the crop/pest/environment system which you are attempting to affect, cost:benefit comparisons of alternative strategies are impossible.

The second difficulty is that, even if sufficient knowledge were available to optimize crop protection or pest control strategies, it would be necessary to impart sufficient of this knowledge to farmers to enable them to make the right decisions or to make available to them instant expert advice. This is one aspect of the general problem of what is nowadays called "technology transfer". It is inconceivable that farmers could, or would be willing to, acquire all the relevant knowledge. Propagation of the concepts of pest management calls for a great increase in specialist advisers. Agricultural advisory and extension services would have to be greatly expanded with consequent greatly increased costs to public revenue to pay not only for their employment but also for their training. A subsidiary problem is how and where they are to be trained in sufficient numbers. Advice might be provided by private consultants or private advisory firms or by the pesticide industry extending its already large technical service to supply not just a product, but a crop protection service, to the farmer. In either case, this would involve extra costs to the farmer which would have to be met either by higher food prices or by direct government subsidy and, in either case, would have to be borne ultimately by the public at large.

This brings us to what is probably the key issue, namely, that farmers are not motivated by an altruistic wish to produce more food but by a desire to maximize their personal profits and increase their standards of living. If they are asked to alter their current methods of crop protection they will have to be convinced that it is financially advantageous for them to do so. Also, if they are offered apparently cheaper alternatives they will need to be convinced that these will really be effective. Farmers will always attempt to optimize their strategies of pest management on the basis of monetary costs and returns. If this optimization differs from the optimum for society as a whole determined on a total cost:benefit basis, then society will have to meet the extra costs to the farmer in one way or another such as by higher food prices or increased taxes in order to give him the required incentive to change. The only alternative is to force the farmer to comply by law, which would either necessitate the public meeting the same increased costs or, if it did not, but left the farmer to bear them, might provoke a political reaction which would be unwelcome in a democratic country.

A further difficulty in the way of optimization of pest management strategies is that some methods, particularly biological control methods, cannot be applied to an individual farm but must be instituted over a whole area or region. This is particularly true of a project to eradicate a pest rather than just to control it. Such a project is being considered in the U.S.A. to eradicate the boll-weevil. The cost has been estimated at $871 million. The question of who is to meet this cost and of how it can be compared with the costs to individual farmers of conventional control by pesticides has yet to be resolved. The technical feasibility of complete eradication of a pest is also in doubt. The idea that biological control methods, once the initial cost has been met, require no expenditure on maintenance is open to doubt. The so-called "eradication" of the screw-worm from the U.S.A. by biological means, which was initially apparently highly successful is currently costing $10 million per year to prevent re-infestation. Apart from the technical problems there are social and political implications to taking crop protection and pest control out of the hands of the farmer, as there are to such possible solutions to a crop protection problem as recommending that a particular crop be no longer grown in a particular region and that some other crop be substituted.

In the U.K. the growing of beet for sugar extraction is already controlled by the sole purchaser of the crop — the British Sugar Corporation — who supply seed and permit cropping only on approved fields in any season. The object is to control virus diseases and eelworm, and is generally successful. Also, as in many countries, peas for processing (drying, freezing or canning) are controlled by the processing companies with regard to date of sowing and pesticide operations. This control is necessary because minimum time must elapse between the combined operation of reaping and shelling ("vining") by large machines in the field and washing of the peas in the factory. There is certain to be extension of this type of control in the growing of green vegetables for processing.

Extension of Cultivated Area

In addition to meeting the challenge of current crop protection and pest control problems, agriculture may be faced with new problems as a hungry world explores all potential new sources of food. About one quarter of the total world area of land which is sufficiently flat and has enough soil for agriculture is at present infertile because of lack of water, but most of these are areas which receive the greatest amounts of sunshine and have, therefore, the greater potential for photosynthesis and crop growth. Irrigation of hitherto uncultivated land by schemes such as those to direct the rivers in the U.S.S.R. which flow into the Arctic Sea to water the arid regions of central Asia or to tow polar icebergs to arid tropical areas, as well as by schemes to desalinate sea-water on a massive scale by use of solar energy, could present new pest and disease problems in the land thus opened up for crop production.

At the other extreme, there are vast areas in the world which cannot be farmed during their very wet seasons because of difficulties of access. The possibility can be visualized of cultivating these areas entirely from the air by clearing the ground with herbicides, sowing seed and applying fertilizers and pesticides all from specially designed flying machines, leaving the only ground operation as harvesting of the final crop.

If any of these schemes come to fruition it will be necessary to obtain the highest possible yields of high value crops in order to justify the very large capital investment which will be needed so that pesticides will have a vital part to play.

Cultivation of food in the ocean as distinct from merely taking out what is there may assume greater importance as available terrestrial land becomes fully utilized. Chemical assistance will be required but will pose very difficult problems of selectivity and will demand extensive biological and ecological understanding of the marine environment.

If toxic chemicals or behaviour controlling chemicals are to make useful contribution to "mariculture" some very new problems must be faced. Water is a much better solvent for all existing pesticides than is air, i.e. the amount contained, at saturation, in a given volume of water is greater, usually very much greater, than in the same volume of air. This profoundly alters the main means of localization. For one very important reactant in living chemistry, the reverse applies: water dissolves only about 1/30th of its volume of air. Oxygen is rather more soluble than nitrogen but not enough to alter the important conclusion that since aerobic organisms must make contact with enough oxygen they must make far more contact with applied pesticides than their terrestrial counterparts. Operating partly against this major difference is the fact that large volumes of water are less turbulent than air so that a pesticide dissolved in one deep pocket or narrow bay will take longer to dissipate than a fumigant in air.

To secure localized action chemicals for use in water will have to be of much lower water solubility than any at present in use in land-based agriculture. One change in this direction has been to apply a herbicide to large colonies of weed in a gelatinous formulation which adheres to the leaves or to use an oil-favourable herbicide dissolved in an oil of very low solubility. In the matter of behaviour-controlling chemicals, the finding that colonization by barnacles is induced by a very thin film of insoluble protein may provide a clue. The guidance of salmon coming in from the sea to the river of their origin is certainly an olfactory response to dissolved chemicals and is parallel to the behaviour of insects to pheromones in air.

Food Sources

Extension of processing into farm management has produced changes and yet others, more fundamental, are likely to follow. The encroachment of margarine into the butter market, with disputed advantage to the health of the consumer when the fat source is polyunsaturated, is an example, decreasing the area of good pasture in favour of oil-seed crops.

As we said in the first edition of this book "all the staple foods eaten today have been cultivated for thousands of years. For as long a time, man has travelled with feet or wheels on the ground and boats on the water, yet, within the space of a human life-span, the internal combustion engine in successive forms has taken him into the air and out of it. It will be rash to assume that the enormous acceleration of modern technology will leave agriculture basically unchanged".

The choice of crops, a very limited choice among tens of thousands of species, has been made not only on success of cultivation in the local climate and soil, on palatability and non-toxicity (though one should note that Cassava is toxic before being processed into tapioca) but also on convenience of harvesting and, if necessary, processing. There is little value to us in a heavy crop if the valuable part of it cannot be gathered in. If the seeds are wanted, and they usually contain the major nutrient value, they must ripen together or at least remain attached till all are ripe and then be easily detached by threshing. Buckwheat, botanically quite unrelated to wheat, is a heavy cropper and the grain has good flavour and food value, but much of it is shed spontaneously over a long period. The crop has the side-advantage of being a good honey source and is grown largely for this reason in Russian. In America it is mainly a source of luxury flour for the farmer's wife and a good crop for pheasants who have time to gather grains individually. As a commercial grain crop on a large scale it is a non-starter.

Much of primary vegetable food production finds its way to our tables via animals. They have the ability to collect their primary food from pasture on hills which would be too steep for any arable farming except labour-intensive terrace cropping, but they are also used as converters of better quality vegetation, sometimes cut and sometimes further processed, in order to produce, as prime beef or pork, milk products or eggs, more concentrated and traditionally more acceptable foods. As chemical converters, however, animals are inefficient. Higher yields of edible fat and protein can be obtained by direct extraction from green crops. Textured vegetable protein, mainly from soybeans, is already available and almost indistinguishable from good quality meat in many products of good cuisine. The barriers to its more widespread adoption are only habit and tradition.

Vegetable protein need not come from soya although this has the advantages of a concentrated, easily harvested source with a long history of harmless consumption. Green crops can provide a greater yield per hectare but processing is more complex. The protein content, coagulated by heat from a wet extract, retains a great deal of water which must be removed but improvement should not be beyond the resources of chemical engineering. The best crop for the process may well be one not at present cultivated and therefore not bred for improvement. Species of amaranthus, also used by peasant farmers in South America for grain, are nutritious and edible, and species of chenopodium and some compositae are good yielders. High quality protein in high yield may in future come from plants such as redroot, fat hen and sowthistle, which at present feature only in the weed lists. They will avoid some pest problems and present others.

Some micro-organisms can produce good protein under factory conditions from a suitable carbon source together with phosphate, nitrate and minor elements and production as a component of cattle feed is already on a large scale. It has to date used mainly two carbon sources, methane (biogas) and the straight chain hydrocarbons of crude oil. The source is almost ironic. Straight paraffin chains are difficult and expensive to produce inanimately, but, with suitable "handles", they are valuable in the production of surface-active compounds and many surface coatings. They are widely dispersed in the products of living chemistry and yet their accumulation in fossil oil is an industrial nuisance in interfering with liquid flow. Living chemistry must be called on again to break down what was long ago built up. (Both build-up and destruction go on, of course, in Nature: otherwise all soil would have become intractable through accumulation of leaf waxes.) So-called "protein from oil" arose as a side-line of bacterial wax removal.

Oil is by no means the most suitable carbon source if factory managed bacteria are to be used to produce edible protein on a large scale. Methane is better. Sugars, the most widely used fuel of all living chemistry, much better still. At present the photochemical production of sugars is the only move in the carbon cycle in which the green plant, and therefore agriculture, has a monopoly. In the densely overpopulated world of the future (if the population does not extinguish itself catastrophically or learn to reduce itself harmoniously) we could devote the areas exposed to sunlight entirely to the production of sugar and make all our other food under factory conditions with the aid of "genetically engineered" bacteria or other proliferating cells.

The consumer may not like the prospect, but is he not being already conditioned to it? By free choice and under pressure of advertisement, pre-packaged convenience foods are making up a major portion of his diet. Many of these — "flavoured" cheeses, sausage, luncheon meat — are, in form and flavour, of unrecognizable origin. We are not saying that their origin is at present other than the labels indicate, but that, technically, the source could change and the label with it without detriment to the appetite or health of the consumer. At the same time there is a strong popular reaction in favour of "pure, natural, goodness". There is dilemma and conflict, but the impact of convenience packaging on the grower and his use of pesticides may in future be much greater than at present.

Effects on the Chemical Industry

A major future problem for the pesticides industry is that the costs of discovery, development and registration of new active compounds are becoming rapidly greater, as described in Chapter 4. At the same time, large market opportunities for a new product are becoming more rare because comparatively cheap, large tonnage, commodity pesticides can provide a degree of control of most pest and disease infestations which is acceptable to many farmers.

Future trends in crop protection and pest control are, as outlined earlier in this chapter, to evolve strategies which minimize the amount of pesticide which has to be used.

The consequence is that the number of companies in the world actually engaged in discovery and development of new pesticides is likely to decrease, and these will be the large international chemical companies with a diversity of interests and liquidity of assets sufficient to allow them to tie up large amounts of money for long periods without return and to buffer them against the costs of abortive development projects and sales which do not achieve expectations. Even such companies may be led to consider whether discovery and development of new pesticides is a justifiable investment compared with other ways in which they could use the money. The conclusion is that, in future years, there is likely to be less, rather than more, industrial research to produce new pesticides and what there is will most likely be targeted, for reasons of economy, towards products for use in major world crops such as small-grain cereals, corn, cotton, soya, sugarcane and sugarbeet.

There will be little incentive for a manufacturer to search specifically for a compound to deal with a pest problem in a minor crop or a minor pest problem in a major crop. It is true that discovery of new pesticides still depends almost entirely on empirical screening and that this is as likely to reveal a compound which is useful in artichokes as one which is useful in soya but, even if it does so, the company might not develop such a compound commercially because the costs of toxicological, residue and environmental studies are largely independent of the size of the ultimate market, and because production of small tonnages is relatively costly. There are already many compounds on manufacturers' shelves with demonstrated potential to deal with various minor crop or minor pest problems, but there they will stay. Even in the case of established pesticides, the small size of the market may make it uneconomical to meet the costs of obtaining a "label" for a minor crop use. This is an undesirable state of affairs, because the concept of "pest management" requires a wide range of active compounds so as to have as many options as possible, but it is not likely to be resolved unless it can be made adequately profitable for a manufacturer to develop and market the requisite pesticides. This might be done by allowing the price of minor crops to rise so that farmers could afford to pay more for crop protection, but the success of this tactic would depend on the willingness of the consumer to pay to maintain a wide variety of choice of foodstuffs. It might be done by national departments of agriculture, or possibly associations of growers, financing the work needed for registration, although this could create difficulties with respect to the originating company's exclusive rights.

The dilemma is that registration authorities want pesticides which are highly specific for one pest or disease whereas industry needs pesticides with a broad enough spectrum of activity to provide sufficient markets to give an adequate return on their investment. There is already considerable evidence that growers of minor crops are not getting pesticides which are adequately tailored to their particular needs and it must always be remembered that what is a minor crop on a national scale may be the main economic mainstay of a particular region and the main source of livelihood to its inhabitants.

Another future problem for the pesticides industry is at the research level. Any search for highly selective compounds poses problems in screening. Screening of candidate pesticides is normally carried out on a representative selection of pests or diseases in a selection of major crops. To detect high specificity the range of screening organisms and crops will have to be greatly increased. The more selectivity depends on biochemical discrimination the more difficult will the screening problem become, for example, in searching for compounds which interfere specifically with an aspect of insect behaviour.

The increase in screening and evaluation costs will exacerbate the financial difficulties already discussed.

It is likely that the main burden of screening for highly specific activities will need to be passed to crop-based organizations. Collaboration of these organizations with the pesticide industry has always been close but it will be neccessary to arrange a different basis for it in the future. The crucial problem is that patent protection, of vital importance to a research-intensive industry, will be more difficult to arrange since many unpatented compounds will go for test and the evidence of value of the few found to be active will not have been provided within the organization of the originating company and, therefore, not patentable by them. The present limitation of government initiative by the "user-pays" principle will not help.

Factory rearing of predatory species and of micro-organisms for control purposes will have to be developed on a vast scale using industrial mass-production methods. Since the customers for such products are the present customers of the pesticide industry it is logical that the pesticides industry should widen its scope to provide them by extending its activities on the one hand into biological production and on the other hand into machinery development. Many of the leading pesticide companies already have extensive interests in these areas and these will be extended in the future. For example, production of antibiotics for the pharmaceutical industry and, more recently, of protein from bacteria or yeasts grown on hydrocarbon feedstocks have given the chemical industry experience of handling micro-organisms on an industrial scale, and biochemical engineering is now a recognized offshoot of chemical engineering. The media for mass production of insects, either as predators or as hosts for viruses, is likely to be provided from industrial sources. It is unlikely that the chemical industry would wish to enter into conventional plant-breeding but research on genetic engineering is being carried out within the industry and may lead to methods for factory production of new varieties.

It is probable that pesticide producers will move towards providing a complete crop protection and pest control service for their customers. Most large companies which manufacture pesticides already operate an extensive technical advice service which would form the basis for such an extension of their operations. This would bring into the companies the full "added value" of the pesticide right up to its actual use, and this might make development and manufacture financially viable for some pesticides, such as those for minor crops or minor uses, which cannot, under present circumstances, justify the money which would have to be spent on them. The amounts of money at stake are not inconsiderable as the "mark up" in export markets is about two-and-a-half times, that is, the price to the farmer is about two-and-a-half times the price at the factory gate.

Since companies would be involved in the total "pest management" operation they would have the incentive to extend their activities to manufacture or production of the biological materials required and would have money available to finance the basic biological and ecological research required to make the ideas of "pest management" a practicable proposition. From the farmers' point of view it would be an advantage to be able to obtain all he required for crop protection and pest control from one source, conveniently from the commercial source with whom he already deals. The wide regional planning necessary in many management strategies makes it doubtful whether the best service can ever be given by competing companies. In the long-term interest of society as a whole, governments may have to resume some of the responsibilities they are abandoning in the encouragement of short-term "user-pays" policies.

It is certain that, whatever way food production develops, other species will continue to compete with man for sustenance. Whatever problems of crop protection and pest control arise, the ingenuity, adaptability and resources of the chemical industry will find solutions, always provided that the financial rewards for doing so are adequate.

Further Reading

Corbett, J. R. Future of pesticides and other methods of control, in Vol. 3 of *Advances in Applied Biology*, J. H. Coaker, (ed), Academic Press, London, 1975.

Elliott, M. *Insecticides for the Future, Needs and Prospects*. Wiley, 1977. National Academy of Sciences, *Pest Control Strategies for the Future*, Washington, D.C., 1972.

Hilton, J. L., (Ed.) *Agricultural Chemical, of the Future*, Rowman and Allanheld, Totowa, New Jersey, 1985 National Academy of Sciences, *Contemporary Pest Control Practices and Prospects*, Washington, D.C., 1975.

Ennis, W. B. (Ed.) *Introduction to Crop Protection*, American Society of Agronomy, Madison, Wisconsin, 1979.

Hilton, J. L. (Ed.) *Agricultural Chemicals of the Future*, Rowman and Allanheld, Totowa, New Jersey, 1985.

National Academy of Sciences, *Contemporary Pest Control Practices and Prospects*, Washington, D.C., 1975.

Glossary

Acaricide. A chemical used to kill mites. From *Acaridae*, the family of Arachnidae (spiders) which includes the phytophagous mites and the ticks parasitic on animals.

Alga *(pl.* **Algae).** Primitive green aquatic plants ranging from unicellular species to giant seaweeds.

Aphicide. An insecticide specially effective against sap-sucking plant-lice or aphids.

Apoplast. More or less gelatinous aqueous matter outside the cell walls of plants, forming a tortuous continuum in which diffusion of water-soluble substances can occur.

Arthropods. Members of the broad class of jointed-foot animals (*Arthropoda*) to which insects, spiders, crustaceans and millipedes belong.

Axil. The upper (usually acute) angle between a leaf-stalk and the stem from which it branches. Buds of new vegetative growth or flowers form in the axils. Adj. *axillary*.

Bioassay. Estimation of amount of toxicant in a sample by measurement of its effect on test organisms, usually estimation of amount necessary in a standard type of application to produce 50% kill.

Boom. A bar, held parallel to the ground during operation, on which are mounted, at regular spacing, the nozzles of a crop sprayer or duster. The boom is often hollow, serving also as a supply tube for the spray liquid.

Carnivore. An animal (or, rarely, a plant) which eats animal flesh. Adj. *carnivorous*.

Chloroplasts. The *organelles* (q.v.) inside plant leaf cells to which the chlorophyll is confined and in which the reactions of photosynthesis are carried out.

Chromosome. The small rod-like stainable elements in the nucleus of a cell responsible for transmission of genetic information.

Commodity product. An expression used in the trade to distinguish a patent-free substance from one over which a company exercises exclusive rights.

Cuticle. The outer protective envelope of any living organism. In the case of mammals or arthropods the alternative names "skin" or "integument" are often used, but "cuticle" invariably in respect of green plants. Plant cuticle is a macromolecular structure of predominantly paraffinic composition over-lying cellulose and pectin.

Cyst. Used here for a group of eggs contained within a tough protective envelope, the dormant stage of some species of nematode or eelworm. This cyst is actually a dead, swollen, female. Adj. *encysted*.

Cytoplasm. The fluid or gelatinous content of living cells as distinct from the reproductive nucleus.

Ecology. The study of an organism's mode of life and its relations to its surroundings.

Ecto-. A Greek-derived prefix meaning external. Used to qualify parasite, to distinguish, for example, fleas and ticks from *endo-* (internal) parasites such as lungworms and disease-producing micro-organisms.

Endo-. Opposite of *ecto-* (q.v.). An endogenous chemical is one produced naturally by a plant itself as distinct from one applied externally, which is called exogenous.

Gene. An individual unit of a chromosome which is responsible for transmission of some inherited characteristic.

Gerris. A genus of bugs (Hemiptera) with long legs, adapted to resting and moving upon the surface of water of normal surface tension. Water skaters.

Helminth. A member of the large group of primitive worms including *nematodes* (q.v.) and the worms parasitic in animal gut and tissues.

Herbicide. A chemical used to kill unwanted plants. A weed-killer.

Herbivore. An animal which eats plants. Adj. *herbivorous*.

Host. An animal or plant supporting a *parasite* (q.v.).

Hydrophilic. Describes a molecule or group of atoms having, usually because of hydrogen bonding, a strong affinity for water.

Hydrophobic. Used as opposite of *hydrophilic* (q.v.).

Inoculum. Incoming fungus spores or other agents of disease which initiate the development of a *parasite* (q.v.) within the host.

Instar. A stage of development of an insect between two moults of the hard exoskeleton, but excluding the egg. An adult butterfly is the sixth instar. The first four are caterpillars, of increasing size, followed by a pupa.

Integument. See **Cuticle**.

Inversion. Used in meteorology to describe the state of the lower atmosphere when the temperature is lowest near the ground. Frequent at night. The lower atmosphere is non-turbulent in inversion in contrast to its turbulent state under the opposite (lapse) condition when the ground is warmed by solar radiation.

In vitro. Strictly "in glass": refers to an experiment on living organisms, usually micro-organisms, carried out in an artificial laboratory environment — for example on parasitic fungi growing on an artificial culture medium.

In vivo. Refers to an experiment on living organisms growing in their natural environment — for example on parasitic fungi growing on their host. Contrast *in vitro* (q.v.).

Label (permissive). In the U.S.A. any agricultural chemical has to receive approval of the Environmental Protection Agency (EPA) for the purpose for which it is intended. Such purpose must be defined and limited by the wording of an agreed label. Hence the "granting of a label" has come to be of much more than verbal importance.

Label (radioactive). When a substance is made incorporating a radioactive isotope of one of its constituent atoms, in order to help trace the movement and chemical reactions of the substance, it is said to carry a (radioactive) label.

Larva. A non-flying but mobile immature stage (*instar*, q.v.) of most insects, wholly different, structurally, from the adult form. Compare *nymph* (q.v.).

Ley. The name given to an annual, or short-period perennial, grass crop, usually introduced into an otherwise arable *rotation* (q.v.).

Lipophilic. "Fat loving", used to describe a molecule or group of atoms tending to promote oil- rather than water-solubility. Contrast hydrophilic (q.v.).

Lipophobic. Used as opposite of lipophilic and therefore also of *hydrophobic* (q.v.).

Mesophyll. Refers to the tissue or cells in the interior of a plant leaf.

Metabolite. A product of some action of biological chemisty on a compound introduced into an organism. More generally the introduced compound is a food-constituent, but, in the context of this book, it is a toxicant.

Mutant. An individual having an abnormality of structure, properties of behaviour in which it differs distinctly from the type and which has internal (genetic) rather than environmental origin, so that there is probability of transmission to offspring.

Mycelium. The nutrient-seeking fibres of a fungus, equivalent to the roots of a green plant.

Myoneural junction. The site of transmission of an impulse from a nerve to a muscle.

Nematodes. Small unsegmented worms, many of which are parasites on plant roots.

Nymph. In insects, an immature stage (*instar*, q.v.) which is similar to the adult except for absence of functional wings and sexual organs. Distinct from *larva* (q.v.) of other insects, which is entirely different from the adult.

Obligate. Adj. used to qualify parasite, to distinguish those which cannot live outside their hosts. Most parasites are obligate in nature, and the word is sometimes restricted to those which cannot (yet) be cultured in the laboratory on special media.

Organelles. Organized microstructures inside cells to which certain biochemical processes are confined — e.g. mitochondria, *chloroplasts* (q.v.).

Ovicide. A chemical which kills eggs before they hatch or one so used. Almost restricted to action on eggs of phytophagous mites (red spider). The word is almost universally accepted in this sense, but the classical scholar insists that it should mean "sheep (Latin, *ovis*)-killer" and that an egg-killer should be "ovacide".

Ovipositor. The extensible tube on the abdomen of a female insect which she uses to place her eggs in suitable location. Often capable of remarkable drilling power. Hence oviposition — the act of egg-placing.

Parameter. Some varying factor which influences the nature of an observed effect.

Parasite. A plant or animal living on or in another plant or animal, which is called its *host* (q.v.). The host continues, for some time at least, to live and feed its parasite (contrast *predator* q.v.), but may eventually be killed by it. A parasite of one host may itself be a host to another parasite, so the terms are relative. A crop-eating insect could be called a parasite or a herbivore, but is not usually so-called. It is usually simply called a pest, which may be subject to parasites, themselves perhaps subject to "hyper-parasites". A fungus living on the crop is always called a parasite. Adj. *parasitic*.

Parthenocarpy. The development of the fleshy part of a fruit without fertilization of the contained seed.

Phloem. A system of interconnected elongated living cells in plants adapted to convey the products of photosynthesis, particularly sucrose, from the leaves to growing tissues.

Phytophagous. Greek form of Latin-based adj. herbivorous (q.v.).

Phytopharmacy. The treatment of diseases of plants.

Phytotoxic. *Toxic* (q.v.) to plants, usually restricted to higher (green) plants. Hence *phytotoxicity*, which is used generally to include the action of intentional herbicides but by some authors restricted to adverse side-effects on the crop of fungicides, insecticides or formulating agents.

Predator. An animal (or, rarely, a plant) which feeds upon other animals, called its prey. The prey is killed and consumed by its predator which generally devours many individuals during its life (contrast *parasite*, q.v.). There are borderline cases between predation and parasitism, e.g. species of wasp which inject a permanent paralysing drug into a caterpillar before laying eggs in it.

Pre-emergent. Adj. describing a (chemical) treatment of a fully cultivated field after sowing of the crop seed but before the crop has emerged. The weed seeds may have emerged, so that the treatment, if herbicidal, may be acting via leaves or roots. Sometimes loosely used in the sense of *presowing* (q.v.).

Presowing. Adj. describing a (chemical) treatment of a field before sowing the crop seed. A presowing treatment may include a cultivation operation to mix in the chemical, which, when the treatment has a herbicidal effect, must enter the plant from the soil. See also *pre-emergent* (q.v.)

Prey. An animal when fed upon by a *predator* (q.v.). A predator of one species can itself be prey to another.

Prophylactic. Adj. used to qualify a chemical or treatment used to prevent a disease-producing organism from invading the individual or crop so treated, as distinct from one used "curatively" on the individual or crop. "Eradicant" is often used in the sense of "curative" when describing the treatment of fungus diseases of crops. "Protectant" is sometimes used in the sense of prophylactic.

Post-emergent. Adj. describing a (chemical) treatment of a crop after it has emerged above the soil. Contrast *pre-emergent* (q.v.).

Resurgence. An increase of a (pest) population, after a period of decrease, to a level higher than its original one, especially when the decrease is caused by an intended control operation.

Rotation. Applied to cropping, the practice of growing different crops on the same land in a regular, recurring, sequence, Rotation is adopted because of complementary effects, or demands, on the soil or for convenience of spreading times of peak labour demand. The most important reason, however, is to hinder the development of weeds, pests or fungi to damaging population levels. Other means of pest control make the last reason for rotation less important.

Rotavator. A power-driven agricultural machine having an axle on which are mounted L-shaped blades and which rotates faster than the land wheels, so that the blades chop and stir the soil to a depth of a few inches. A rotary hoe. Hence *rotavation*, the treatment of soil with such implement, which provides the best means of mixing an applied substance into the surface soil.

Saprophyte. A plant (usually fungus) living on dead tissue. Adj. *saprophytic*.

Sarcophagous. Greek form of Latin-based adj. *carnivorous* (q.v.).

Spiracle. Small openings in the abdominal segments of insects connected to a system of internal tubes (trachea) through which oxygen and carbon dioxide are exchanged with the atmosphere.

Stoma (*pl. Stomata*). Small apertures in the surface of a leaf, opening or closing in response to light intensity, time of day and other factors, adapted to control exchange of carbon dioxide, oxygen and water vapour between active internal leaf cells and the atmosphere.

Stylet. A hollow tube-like organ, especially that possessed by aphids with which they probe the tissues of plants and through which the sugary contents of the *phloem* (q.v.) vessels are transmitted to the insect.

Synergism. An activity of two or more agents which is greater than would be expected from summation of their single actions. Hence *synergist*, which has come to mean a compound itself of low toxicity, which increases the action of a toxicant with economic advantage.

Systemic. Used of a chemical which enters a plant either by roots or leaves and is translocated (q.v.) within it. Thus, a systemic insecticide renders a plant toxic to insects feeding on it and a systemic fungicide attacks the fungal organism actually within the plant tissues.

Taxonomy. The science of classification and naming of species.

Toxic. Adj., having a poisonous action. Used here in general sense, requiring qualification if restricted to effect on mammals, insects, plants, etc. By some authors used in a sense restricted to higher animals. Hence, *toxicant*, a poison.

Translocation. The movement of chemical substances, either endogenous (q.v.) or applied, within a plant.

Vector. A carrier. In the present context it refers to small animals, usually insects, which can carry pathogenic (disease-producing) micro-organisms from a diseased to a healthy plant or animal.

Xylem. A system of more or less continuous channels in plants, formed of fused dead cells, which transport water and soluble minerals from roots to leaves.

General Index

This book is not a practical handbook of crop protection and pest control. Individual species of crop plants, fungi, insects and weeds are not indexed. For these, either the Weed Control Handbook (Fryer, J. & Makepeace, R., Blackwell, Oxford) or the Insecticide and Fungicide Handbook (Martin, H., Blackwell, Oxford) should be consulted.

Index of Active Chemicals and List of Properties

Page references are given in the last column of this index. Where the chemical is mentioned in discussion on several successive pages, only the first is listed. We have not distinguished the *major* reference because the choice will depend on the particular interest at the time of the reader.

The other columns list some useful properties.

(1) m.p. This is, of course, melting point. If the chemical is normally liquid a figure is replaced by L. An added d indicates decomposition. An added b indicates that the figure refers in this case to boiling point.

(2) Air. This gaves the saturation concentration at 20° in the vapour. If the chemical has a very low boiling point the concentration refers to that in a full normal atmospheric pressure, denoted by A.

(3) Water. This gives the solubility in water. The symbols S− and S+ following the figure indicate that the chemical is acidic or basic and may form more soluble salts as an anion or cation respectively. If an element symbol, e.g. Na, is added, the figure itself refers to the solubility of the salt. Replacement of a numerical value by VL or VS means very low or very soluble.

(4) LD50. The single dose, by mouth, known to be lethal to 50% of rats. It must be strongly emphasised that this is a less definite quantity than the physical ones and its significance is subject to many more qualifications. The object of including this list of acute toxicities to the most common experimental animal is to show their very wide range as a very rough guide to safety in use. Safety to consumers and the environment needs much more extended study and chemicals permitted for use in agriculture must be fully examined over a long period by methods outlined on pp. 326–330 of this book before they can be registered. In this column the symbol V indicates a special hazard by inhalation.

The units used are, for "air" $\log_{10}(\mu g/m^3)$, for "water" $\log_{10}(\mu g/litre)$, for LD50 $\log_{10}(\mu g/kg$ body weight). Use of logarithmic notation permits a very wide range to be covered by 2 digits and restriction to 2 digits means that we accept realistically, that 25% tolerance is all that most data justify or that most estimates require.

Name	m.p.	air	water	LD50	Pages
Absiscic acid	—	—	—S—	—	253, 254
Acephate	85	1.2	5.8	5.9	98
Acethion	—	—	—	—	96
Acetophos	—	—	—	—	95
Acrolein	L52b	8.8	8.3	4.7	142
Alachlor	40	2.4	5.4	6.0	39, 41, 239
Aldicarb	99	2.9	6.8	3.0	99, 140
Aldoxycarb	140	1.9	6.9	4.4	140
Aldrin	104	0.2	1.4	4.6	40, 76, 82, 272, 319
Allethrin	L	2.9	VL	6.0	108
Allidochlor	L	4.9	7.3	5.8	238
Alloxydim	180d	1.1	9.3Na	6.4	221
Ametryne	85	1.0	5.3	6.0	231
Aminocarb	93	—		4.5	99
Aminopyridine	158	5.0	VS	—	126, 150
Amiton	—	—	S+	VL	57
Amitraz	86	0.8	3.0	5.9	101
Ancymidol	110	—	—	6.6	252
Anthraquinone	285	1.7	2.8	5.3	150
Antu	198		5.8	6.7	146
Arsen-ates(-ites)	—	—	—	5.3	43, 207, 254
Asulam	142d	0.5	6.6S—	>6.6	241
Atrazine	175	0.5	4.5	6.3	39, 41, 47, 50, 53, 231, 318
Avermectins	—	—	—	—	140
Azamethiphos	89	1̲.8	6.0	6.1	95
Azauracil	—	—	—	—	203
Azidirachtin	—	—	—	—	119
Azinphos ethyl	53	0̲.6	6.7	4.1	96
Azinphos methyl	73	1̲.1	7.5	4.2	40, 95
Aziprotryne	95	1.4	7.7	6.6	232
Azobenzene	68	1.8	—	—	294
Azocyclotin	219	0.0	<3.0	5.0	165
Bacillus thuringiensis	—	—	—	—	14, 19
Barban	75	0.7	4.0	6.1	219
Benalaxyl	78	2̲.0	4.6	6.6	192
Benazolin	78	2̲.6	5.8S—	6.5	242
Bendiocarb	130	1.8	4.6	6.6	99
Benfluralin	66	3.9	<3.0	>7.0	236
Benodanil	137	2.9	4.3	6.8	193
Benomyl	d	—	3.3	>7.0	203
Benquinox	195	—	3.7	5.0	178
Bensulide	34	1.3	4.4	5.6	229
Bensultap	—	—	—	—	118
Bentazone	137	<3̲.0	5.7	6.0	242
Benzoximate	73	—	VL	6.7	138
Benzoylprop-ethyl	70	1̲.8	4.3	6.2	220, 239
Benzthiazuron	280d	0.8	4.1	6.1	230
BHC (see also lindane)	—	—	—	—	43, 307, 308
Bifenox	85	1.6	2.5	6.8	237
Bifonazole	—	—	—	—	180
Binapacryl	67	3.2	3.3	5.3	175
Bioallethrin	L	—	VL	6.0	108

Name	m.p.	air	water	LD50	Pages
Bioresmethrin	30	1.8	VL	6.9	109
Bitertanol	—	1.1	3.7	6.7	182
Blasticidin	250	—	S	4.6	187
Borates	—	—	—	6.7	207
Bordeaux mixture	—	—	—	—	157
Brodifacoum	230	<1.5	1	2.4	147
Bromacil	158	0.6	5.9	6.7	234
Bromadiolone	200	—	4.3	3.1	147
Bromfenvinphos	—	—	—	—	92
Bromophos	53	3.4	2.8	6.6	93
Bromoxynil	194	—	5.1S−	5.3	218
Bufencarb	26–39	2.4	5.8	5.0	40, 99
Bupirimate	50	0.9	4.3	6.6	197
Buprofenzin	104	2.1	2.8	6.3	102
Butachlor	L	1.9	4.4	6.3	238
Butam	L	—	VL	6.8	237
Bupyronoxyl	—	—	—	—	127
Butralin	60	2.2	3.0	7.1	236
Butrizol	L	—	8.7	5.0	203
Buturon	145	3.2	4.5	6.5	230
Butylate	L	4.1	4.7	6.5	39, 241
Cadmium succinate	—	—	—	—	159
Captafol	160	—	3.1	6.7	179
Captan	178	<2.2	4.5	6.9	40, 47, 179, 190, 294
Carbamorph	—	—	—	—	199
Carbaryl	142	4.7	5.1	5.9	14, 40, 47, 99, 252, 334
Carbendazim	310	<2.7	4.4	7.2	203
Carbetamide	119	—	6.5	7.1	
Carbofuran	150	2.4	5.8	3.0	40, 47, 99
Carbon disulphide	L46b	9.2	6.3	V	303
Carbon tetrachloride	L77b	9.0	5.5	3.7	303
Carbophenothion	L	2.1	<3.0	4.9	9.7
Carboxin	92	<6.1	5.2	6.6	200
Cartab	180	—	8.3	5.5	118
Cellocidin	—	—	—	4.9	187
Chloralose	137	—	6.6	5.5	146, 150
Chloramben	200	2.9	5.9S−	6.8	39, 41, 47, 216
Chloraniformethan	—	—	5.2	6.4	194
Chloranil	296	—	3.2	6.6	178
Chlorate	248	—	8.9Na	6.0	207
Chlorbicyclen	—	—	—	—	75
Chlorbromuron	96	0.8	4.5	<6.7	230
Chlorcamphene (see Toxaphene)					
Chlordane	L	2.3	2.0	5.7	75, 82
Chlordimeform	32	2.6	5.4	5.5	40, 101
Chlorfenac	156	3.3	5.3S−	5.8	217
Chlorfenethol	70	—	VL	6.0	136
Chlorfenprop-methyl	L	3.9	4.6	6.1	214
Chlorfenson	86	—	VL	6.3	136
Chlorfenvinphos	L	1.9	5.1	4.3	92
Chlorfluricol-methyl	—	2.9	4.3	>7.1	251
Chloridazon	205	<1.0	4.7	5.4	102
Chlormephos	82	5.9	4.8	3.8	97

Name	m.p.	air	water	LD50	Pages
Chlormequat chloride	240d	—	6.0	6.0	250, 258
Chlormethoxyfen	140	—	VL	4.7	237
Chlorobenzilate	36	1.2	VL	6.0	137
Chloromethiuron	175	1.0	4.7	5.4	102
Chloroneb	133	4.5	3.9	>7.1	192
Chloropicrin	L112b	8.3	6.4		303, 304
Chloroxuron	151	2.5	3.6	6.5	230
Chlorphacinone	—	—	—	—	147
Chlorphonium chloride	114	—	VS	5.3	252
Chlorphoxim	66	2.1	3.2	6.4	94
Chlorpropham	41	—	4.9	6.7	240
Chlorpyriphos-ethyl	43	2.4	3.3	5.2	40, 94
Chlorquinox	—	—	—	—	198
Chlorsulfuron	174	1.9	5.0	6.8	244
Chlorthalonil	250	—	2.8	7.0	177
Chlorthiamid	151	1.0	5.9	5.9	218, 290
Chlorthiophos	L	1.8	2.5	4.0	94
Chlortoluron	147	0.2	4.8	>7.0	230
Citronella oil	L206b	4.5	—	—	64
Clenpyrin	—	—	—	—	102
Climbazole	—	—	—	—	181
Clobenprop-methyl	—	—	—	—	221
Clobyralid	151	2.0	7.0S−	6.7	217
Clotrimazole	—	—	—	—	181
Copper salts	—	—	—	6.0	40, 43, 66, 142, 155, 158, 207, 280
Coumachlor	169	3.1	2.7	5.3	147
Coumafuryl	—	—	4.0	4.4	147
Coumatetryl	172	—	3.6	4.2	147
Creosote	—	—	—	—	65, 207
Cresyl acetate	L	6.4	—	—	173
Crimidine	187	—	7.0	3.1	146
Crotoxyphos	L	2.4	6.0	4.7	91
Cryolite	—	—	—	—	69
Cyanamide (Ca)	—	—	—	—	254
Cyanazine	167	2.3	5.2	5.3	241
Cyanide (H)	L26b	9.1A	misc	3.9V	145, 149, 300, 302, 306
Cyanophos	14	4.0	4.7	5.8	93
Cycloate	11	4.9	4.9	6.4	241
Cycloheximide	116	—	7.3	3.3	187
Cyfluthrin	—	—	3.3	5.6	111, 112
Cyhalothrin	L	—	<3.0	5.4	112
Cyhexatin	245	—	<3.0	5.7	165
Cymoxanil	160	0.8	6.0	6.0	191
Cypendazole	124	—	4.5	6.4	204
Cypermethrin	L	1.5	<3	6	110, 115
Cyperquat	—	—	—	—	226
2,4-D	140	0.7	5.8S−	5.6	28, 39, 41, 43, 46, 209, 250, 289, 317
Dalapon	185	—	VSNa	6.9	18, 39, 214, 219
Daminozide	154	<6.9	8.0	6.9	250, 257
2,4-DB	119	—	4.7S−	5.9	213

Name	m.p.	air	water	LD50	Pages
Dioxathion	L	—	VL	4.6	97
Diphacinone	145	3.3	4.2	3.4	147
Diphenylamine	53	4.9	5.5	—	253
Dipropalin	—	—	—	—	236
Dipropetryn	104	1.0	4.2	6.6	232
Diquat	—	—	8.8Br₂	5.3	47, 224, 254, 288
Disugran	—	—	—	—	258
Disulfoton	L	3.4	4.4	4.0	40, 96
Ditalimphos	83	1.4	5.1	6.7	190
Dithianon	225	0.9	2.7	5.8	178
Dithiocarbamates	—	—	—	—	169
Diuron	158	1.6	4.6	6.5	38, 49, 230, 233
DNOC	86	3.1	5.1S−	4.5	66, 194, 208, 225, 254
Dodemorph	72	1.7	LS+	6.3	198
Dodine	136	—	4.8S+	6.0	180
Drazoxolon	167	1.7	VL	5.1	184
DTA	—	—	—	—	134
Eau celeste	—	—	—	—	158
Edifenphos	L	—	VL	5.5	190
Edlinazime	228	0.4	5.5	>7	231
EPN	36	5.9	4.6	4.4	40, 90
EPTC	L	4.9	5.6	6.4	39, 241, 243, 318
Etacelasil	L	3.5	7.4	6.3	253
Ethalfluralin	55	1.1	2.3	>7	236
Ethephon	74	—	9.0	6.6	258
Ethidimuron	156	1.0	6.5	>6.7	230
Ethion	L	1.5	VL	5.3	40, 97
Ethiophencarb	33	0.1	7.3	5.6	99
Ethirimol	159	1.3	5.3S+	6.8	196, 316
Ethofumesate	70	0.9	5.0	>6.8	242
Ethoxyquinol	—	—	—	—	253
Ethylene dibromide	L	8.1	6.6	5.2	300
Ethylene dichloride	L	8.6	6.6	5.8	303
Ethylene oxide	L11b	9.2A	misc	V	303
Etrimfos	L	3.0	4.6	6.2	94
Farnesol					121
Fenaminosulf Na	>200	—	7.6	4.8	184
Fenamiphos	49	1.0	5.8	4.2	98, 140
Fenarimol	117	0.1	4.1	6.7	196
Fenfuram	109	0.2	5.0	7.1	194
Fenitrothion	140	2.3	4.1	5.9	93
Fenoprop	179	—	4.1S−	5.8	214
Fenoxaprop	84	3.4	2.9S−	6.4	221
Fenpropathrin	45	2.0	2.5	5.2	
Fenpropimorph	L	—	5.8	6.5	199
Fensulfothion	L	—	6.2	3.8	94
Fenthiaprop	57	2.9	2.9	6.0	221
Fenthion	L	2.7	3.3	5.3	93
Fentin acetate	121	1.7	4.0	5.3	164
Fenuron	133	2.3	6.6	6.8	230
Fenvalerate	L	3.7	<4	5.5	110, 115
Ferbam	—	—	5.1	>6.6	40, 47, 171
Flamprop-isopropyl	73	0.7	4.0	>6.6	220, 239

Name	m.p.	air	water	LD50	Pages
Fluarimol	—	—	—	—	196
Fluazifop-butyl	5	0.9	3.3	6.5	221
Fluchloralin	42	2.6	<3	6.8	236
Flucythrinate	L	1.3	2.6	4.9	112, 115
Flumetralin	101	<1.3	<2	>6.7	252
Fluoroacetate (Na)	200d	—	VS	3.0	5, 149
Fluorodifen	94	0.1	3.3	6.9	39, 236
Fluosilicate (NH$_4$)	—	—	—	—	69
Fluotrimazole	132	—	VL	>6.7	182
Flutolanil	102	2.4	4.0	>7	193
Fluvalinate	L	<0.4	<0.7	6.8	112
Folpet	177	2.0	6.0	>7	179
Fonofos	—	5.9	4.6	4.0	40, 90
Formaldehyde	G	9.1A	VS	5.1	300, 303
Formetanate	100	0.4	6.8	4.3	101
Formothion	L	1.1	6.4	5.6	96
Fosetyl-Al	>200d	—	8.1	6.8	190
Fospirate	—	—	—	—	91
Fthalide	—	—	—	—	177
Fuberidazole	280d	—	4.9	6.1	204
Furalaxyl	70	0.9	5.4	5.9	191
Furcarbanil	—	—	—	6.8	69
Gibberellic acd	223	—	6.7S−	>7	7, 257
Glufosinate	—	—	VS	6.3	218
Glyodin	—	—	8.5	6.8	180
Glyphosate	—	—	VS±	6.7	47, 61, 227, 265
Glyphosine	200d	<2.2	8.5S−	6.8	228, 258
Griseofulvin	—	—	—	5.6	187
Guazatine	—	—	VS+	5.4	180
Heptachlor	95	3.9	1.7	5.2	75, 82
Heptenophos	L	4.2	6.3	5.0	91
Hexazinone	115	3.4	7.5	6.2	242
Hydroprene	L	3.4	2.7	>7	121
Hymexazol	86	<3.7	3.9	6.6	199
IAA	168	—	S−	—	209, 248
IBA	128	—	S−	—	249
Imazalil	L	0.0	S+	5.5	200
Inezin	—	—	—	—	190
Idofenphos	76	1.3	<3.3	6.3	93
Ioxynil	209	—	4.7S−	5.0	218
Iprodione	136	<1.2	4.1	6.5	183
Isazophos	L	4.3	5.4	4.7	94
Isoxathion	—	—	—	—	94
Isobenzan	120	2.7	—	5.6	77
Isodrin	—	—	—	—	76
Isoprocarb	90	—	VL	5.7	99
Isopropalin	L	—	2.0	>6.7	236
Isoprothiolane	167	—	4.7	6.1	200
Isoproturon	155	1.4	4.7	6.3	230
Kadethrin	—	—	—	—	109
Karbutilate	176	4.8	5.5	6.5	230
Kasugamycin (HCl)	202	—	5.1	7.3	187
Kinetin	—	—	—	—	249

Name	m.p.	air	water	LD50	Pages
Kinoprene	L	2.0	3.7	6.7	121
Kitazin	—	—	6.0	5.4	188
K-orthrin	98	1.5	VL	5.1	109
Lead salts	—	—	—	—	33
Lethane	—	—	—	ca.4	69
Lime–sulphur	—	—	—	—	168
Lindane	112	2.2	2.1	5.6	55, 58, 74, 82, 142, 294
Linuron	93	2.3	4.9	6.6	39, 230, 233
Malathion (maldison)	L	2.7	5.2	6.4	40, 96, 267, 300
Maleic hydrazide	295	—	6.8S−	>6.6	251
Mancozeb	—	—	VL	6.9	172
Maneb	Sd	—	VL	6.8	40, 47, 172, 280
MCPA	118	1.2	3.9S−	5.9	28, 47, 50, 60, 210, 317
MCPB	100	—	4.6S−	5.9	60, 213
Mebenil	—	—	—	—	193
Mecarbam	L	—	L	4.6	97
Mecarbenzid	—	—	4.5	6.4	204
Mecoprop	94	—	5.8S−	5.9	214
Mephosfolan	L	—	4.8	3.6	98
Mepiquat chloride	285	—	>9	6.2	252
Metalaxyl	72	1.5	6.9	5.8	183
Metaldehyde	246	—	5.3	5.8	141
Metalkamate	—	—	—	—	40, 99
Methabenzthiazuron	119	1.1	4.8	6.4	230
Methacriphos	L	4.2	5.6	5.8	93
Methamidophos	44	3.2	>9	4.5	98
Metham-sodium	d	—	8.9	6.3	171
Methiocarb	117	2.3	4.5	5.0	99, 126, 141, 150
Methomyl	78	2.5	7.8	4.2	40, 99
Methoprene	L	2.5	3.1	>9	121
Methoprotryne	68	0.6	5.5	>9	232
Methoxychlor	77	—	2.0	6.8	40, 308
Methylbromide		9.6A	6.7A		56, 145, 300, 302
Methyl eugenol	L	5.7	VL	—	130, 133
Methyl formate	31b	9.2	8.5	V	303
Methyl isothiocyanate	35	7.9	6.9	V	171, 303
Methyl parathion	35	2.1	4.8	4.1	40, 47
Metiram	140d	—	VL	>7	173
Metobromuron	95	1.6	5.5	6.4	230
Metolachlor	L	2.3	5.6	6.5	39, 238
Metoxuron	126	2.6	5.8	6.5	230
Metribuzin	126	<2.0	6.1	6.3	242
Mevinphos	L	3.2	misc	3.7	91, 93
Mirex	480	—	—	5.5	76
Monalide	87	1.4	4.3	>6.6	237
Monocrotophos	54	1.4	9.0	4.2	91
Monolinuron	80	1.8	5.9	6.3	230
Monuron	174	0.6	5.4	6.6	230
MTMC	76	—	6.4	5.4	99
Myristicin	L	5.4	VL	—	2, 3
NAA	134	—	5.6	6.3	248, 252
Nabam	Sd	—	8.3	5.6	171
Naled	L	4.6	VL	5.6	91, 130

Name	m.p.	air	water	LD50	Pages
Napropamide	75	—	4.9	>6.7	237, 238
Naptalam	185	—	5.3S−	6.9	39, 238, 252
Neburon	102	—	3.7	>7	230
Nereisotoxin	—	—	—	—	3
Nickel salts	—	—	—	—	160
Niclosamide	230	<2.1	3.8	6.7	142
Nicotine	L	5.6	misc	4.7	2, 33
Nitralin	151	1̄.4	2.8	>6.3	39, 235, 236
Nitrofen	70	1.7	3.0	5.8	236
Norflurazon	174	1̄.5	4.4	>6.9	227
Noruron	—	—	—	—	39
Nuarimol	126	1̄.6	4.4	6.1	196
Ofurace	145	—	3.3	6.4	191
Omethoate	L	2.5	misc	4.7	95
Oryzalin	141	—	3.4	>7	236
Oxadiazon	90	1.1	2.8	>6.9	242
Oxamyl	100	3.3	8.5	3.7	140
Oxine	75	—	3.7	—	174
Oxycarboxin	127	—	6.0	6.3	210
Oxydemeton-S-methyl	L	2.6	misc	4.8	95
Oxydeprophos	L	1.8	5	5.0	93
Oxydisulfoton	—	—	—	—	96
Oxyphorate	—	—	—	—	96
Paraoxon	L	—	—	3.8	85, 92
Paraquat (dichloride)	300d	—	VS	5.2	52, 60, 224, 254, 258, 288, 317
Parinol	169	—	4.4	6.7	195
Paris green	—	—	—	—	68
PCP	191	4.6	4.3S−	5.3	60, 65, 142, 173
Pebulate	L	2.5	4.8	—	241
Penicillin	—	—	—	—	187
Pencycuron	132	—	2.6	>6.7	184
Pendimethalin	55	5.4	2.5	6.0	236
Pentanochlor	85	—	3.9	>7	237
Permethrin	L	1.0	2.3	6.0	110
Phenazine oxide	—	—	—	—	184
Phencycloate	—	—	—	—	111
Phenmedipham	143	—	3.7	>6.9	240
Phenothrin	L	1.4	3.3	—	110
Phenthoate	17	2.4	5.3	5.5	96
Phenyl imidazole	—	—	—	—	102
Phenyl isothiocyanate	L	5.1	L	—	3
Phenyl mercury salts	—	—	—	—	163
2-Phenyl phenol	57	4.4	5.8	6.4	174
Phorate	L	3.9	4.7	3.3	40, 96
Phosalone	48	—	4.0	5.2	97
Phosazetim	104	—	3.7	3.8	148
Phosfolan	40	—	8.8	4.0	98
Phosmet	72	3.6	4.3	5.0	96
Phosphamidon	L	2.6	misc	4.2	91
Phosphine	G	6.2A	5.6	4.5	303
Phoxim	5	—	3.8	6.3	94
Picloram	215d	0.9	5.6S−	6.9	216

Name	m.p.	air	water	LD50	Pages
Piericidin	—	—	—	—	3
Pindone	108	—	4.3S−	4.7	147
Piperalin	—	—	—	—	184
Piperonyl butoxide	L	3.4	—	6.9	107
Pirimicarb	90	2.4	6.4	5.2	99
Polygodial	—	—	—	—	134
Potassium carbonate	891	—	9.2	—	255
Probendazole	138	—	5.2	6.4	205
Procymidone	166	3.1	3.7	6.8	183
Profluralin	32	8.4	2.0	7.0	236
Proglinazine	110	1.4	5.9	>6.9	231
Promecarb	88	2.4	5.0	4.9	99, 240
Prometone	91	1.5	5.8	6.5	231
Prometryne	118	1.1	4.7	6.7	231
Propachlor	77		5.8	6.3	39, 41, 47, 239
Propanil	92	2.4	5.3	6.1	39, 47, 237
Proparthrim	—	—	—	—	109
Propazine	212	1̄.6	3.7	>6.9	231
Propetamphos	L	2.3	4.0	5.1	98
Propham	87	—	4.7	5.3	240
Propineb	160d	—	VL	6.9	171
Propoxur	85	3.0	6.3	5.0	99
Propylphosphonic acid	—	—	—	—	257
Prothoate	28	2.8	6.4	3.9	97
Prothrin	—	—	—	—	109
Pyracarbolid	110	0.1	5.7	>7	195
Pyrazophos	50	0.9	3.6	5.3	189
Pyrethrin	L	—	VL	5.8	109
Pyridinitril	—	—	—	—	184
Pyriminil	—	—	—	—	148
Pyrimiphos	L	3.0	3.7	6.3	94
Quintozene	146	5.3	VL	>7	177
Red squill (see Scilliroside)					
Resmethrin	45	1̄.1	<3.0	>6.4	109
Reineckate (NH₄)	—	—	—	—	69
Rotenone	163	—	VL	5.3	2
Ryanodine	220d	—	S	5.9	2, 3
Sabadilla	—	—	—	—	2
Salicylanilide	135	—	L	—	173
Schradan	L	4.2	misc	3.9	57
Scilliroside	170d	—	4.7	2.8	148
Secbumeton	86	1.9	5.8	6.4	230
Selenium	—	—	—	—	57
Sethoxydim	L	—	4.4	6.5	222
Siduron	135	—	4.3	>6.9	231
Silatrane	—	—	—	—	148
Silicofluorides	—	—	—	—	69
Simazine	225	2̄.8	3.7	>6.7	23, 231, 318
Simetryne	82	—	5.6	6.3	231
Sodium fluoride	980	—	7.6	6.7	146
Streptomycin	203	2.9	4.0	>6.7	204
Strychnine	270d	—	5.2	3.0	145
Sulfometuron	203	2.9	4.0	>6.7	244

Name	m.p.	air	water	LD50	Pages
Sulfotep	L	3.5	4.4	3.7	86
Sulphur	90	0.6	VL	—	33, 40, 155, 167, 273, 280
Sulphur dioxide	G	9.4A	8.3	V	145
Sulphuric acid	L	VL	misc	—	207, 254
Swep	—	—	—	—	240
Soap	—	—	—	—	64
2,4,5-T	153	2.9	5.2S−	>5.5	43, 47, 60, 212, 330
TBA	90	2.7	6.9S−	6.2	60, 214, 218, 290
TCA	56	6.3	miscS−	5.6	219
TDE	—	—	—	—	40, 73, 309
Tebuthiuron	161	2.3	6.4	5.8	230
Tecnazene	99	7.1	VL	≫4.7	177
Tenuidine	—	—	—	—	119
TEPP	L	3.4	misc	4.0	43, 58, 86
Terbacil	175	0.5	5.9	>6.7	234
Terbucarb	—	—	—	—	240
Terbufos	L	3.5	4.1	3.2	40, 96
Terbumeton	123	1.4	5.1	5.7	231
Terbuthylazine	178	1.1	3.9	6.3	231
Terbutryne	104	1.1	5.4	6.3	231
Tetcyclasis	—	—	—	—	252
Tetrachlorvinphos	95	0.0	4.0	6.6	91
Tetramethrin	60	2.0	3.7	>6.7	109
Tetronic acid	—	—	—	—	7
Thanite	—	—	—	—	70
Thiabendazole	304	—	7.0	6.5	204
Thiazafluron	136	1.4	6.3	5.4	230
Thiocarboxime	—	—	—	—	99, 141
Thiocyclam	125d	1.8	7.9	5.5	118
Thiometon	L	3.4	5.3	5.1	97
Thiophanate	195d	—	VL	>72	193
Thiophanox	—	—	—	—	99
Thioxamil	—	—	—	—	99
Thiram	146	—	5.5	5.9	170
Tiocarbazil	130	3.4	3.4	>7	241
Tolclofos-methyl	80	3.8	2.5	6.7	189
Tolylfluanid	96	0.3	6.6	60	179
Toxaphene	70	—	3.5	4.9	40, 47, 78
Treviasine	—	—	—	—	119
Triadimefon	82	<1.1	5.4	5.5	201
Triadimenol	121	<2.0	4.9	5.9	201
Tributylphosphoro-trithiolate	L	—	VL	5.6	254
Tributyltin oxide	—	—	—	—	164
Tricamba	—	—	—	—	215
Trichloronate	L	3.7	5.6	4.4	90
Trichlorphon	83	2.0	8.2	5.8	91, 290
Triclopyr	148	1.2	5.6S−	5.8	217
Tricyclazole	187	0.2	6.2	5.4	202
Tridemorph	L	3.7	misc	5.9	198
Trietazine	100	—	4.3	6.5	231
Trifluralin	49	2.1	<3.0	>7	39, 47, 50, 67, 235, 236

Name	m.p.	air	water	LD50	Pages
Triforine	155	0.5	3.8	>7	197
Triiodobenzoic acid	—	—	S–	—	214
Triprene	—	—	—	—	121
Valone	67	—	4.3	4.3	147
Vamidothion	47	—	9.6	4.8	95
Vernolate	L	4.9	4.9	6.2	241
Vivithrin	—	—	—	—	111
Warfarin	159	—	4.5	3.7	146, 318
Xylylcarb	72	3.7	5.8	5.6	99
Zeatin	—	—	—	—	249
Zinc chromate	—	—	VL	4.5	159
Zinc phosphide	420	—	dec.	4.7	145
Zineb	d	—	4.0	>6.7	172, 280
Zirem	240	—	4.8	6.1	171